THE KINETICS OF
CHEMICAL CHANGE

THE KINETICS OF
CHEMICAL CHANGE

BY

C. N. HINSHELWOOD, M.A., Sc.D., F.R.S.

DR. LEE'S PROFESSOR OF CHEMISTRY IN THE
UNIVERSITY OF OXFORD

OXFORD
AT THE CLARENDON PRESS

Oxford University Press, Amen House, London E.C.4

EDINBURGH GLASGOW NEW YORK TORONTO MELBOURNE
WELLINGTON BOMBAY CALCUTTA MADRAS CAPE TOWN

Geoffrey Cumberlege, Publisher to the University

Reprinted photographically in Great Britain at the University Press, Oxford,
from sheets of the first edition 1942, 1945, 1947

PREFACE

THE first edition of the *Kinetics of Chemical Change in Gaseous Systems* appeared in 1926, and was at the time a fairly complete monograph of at least part of the field. The second and third editions were progressively larger and less complete. To-day a fourth edition which attempted any kind of comprehensiveness would have to be an encyclopaedic volume of formidable dimensions. It is no mere taste for paradox which leads one to doubt whether progress in a subject is reflected only in the increasing size of the books written about it. Encyclopaedias are very valuable works, but in some ways the ideal would be that successive editions of a book should get smaller and smaller. A lot depends upon whom the book is written for, and to cut the Gordian knot I decided instead of a fourth edition to produce a new book which, without very great detail, should give as simple and balanced account as possible of the general principles of chemical kinetics. It is, of course, written for any one who cares to read it, but primarily for those who are interested in the wider aspects of physical chemistry and who want to know, as serious students though not as experts, what the general landscape of a particular part of the country is like. If the treatment is in places impressionistic, I hope it is so in the better sense which would allow a painting to be not less true than a photograph. At any rate I believe that the shortcomings are in the execution rather than in the method.

The examples discussed are no longer drawn exclusively from reactions in the gaseous state—though these predominate. Convenience rather than abstract justice has dictated their selection, and, indeed, lest the author index be regarded as a minor temple of fame in which representation has been granted or withheld with too arbitrary a hand, I have omitted it. Just as in the third edition of the former book I included a section which developed the wave mechanics needed in the later discussions, so in the present book I have included a chapter on elementary statistical mechanics, in which most of the kinetic and statistical theory used in the rest of the treatment is specially worked out for the purpose. This seems worth while for clearness and simplicity, and indeed for abstract uniformity, since kinetic and statistical theory is the very stuff of which chemical kinetics is made.

I am indebted to my colleagues and especially Mr. E. J. Bowen, F.R.S., and Mr. J. H. Wolfenden for help in a number of ways and, as always, to the Clarendon Press.

The manuscript was ready at the end of July 1939. It might have been revised in various ways, but went to press as it stood in the autumn of the same year.

C. N. H.

OXFORD
January 1940

CONTENTS

I

INTRODUCTION

THAT everything changes is an unescapable fact which from time immemorial has moved poets, exercised metaphysicians, and excited the curiosity of natural philosophers. Slow chemical transformations, pursuing their hidden ways, are responsible for corrosion and decay, for development, growth, and life. And their inner mechanisms are mysteries into which it is fascinating to inquire.

A chemical change is a rearrangement of the atoms of which molecules are built up: in other words, a change of pattern. The whole world is made of patterns of different kinds or orders. The so-called ultimate particles are arranged in patterns which constitute nuclei and atoms, and the atoms in their turn in designs of a different order which constitute molecules. These may aggregate themselves into extended systems constituting liquids and solids, or remain flying freely in the state of gas. The pattern formation is the result of interaction between the units which tends to make them set themselves into groupings with a minimum of potential energy. The tendency, however, is not unopposed. All matter is endowed with motion. Even at the absolute zero the order established is a compromise between the interaction and the zero-point energy, and at higher temperatures thermal motions tend to destroy the groupings. Patterns or groupings of a given kind cease to exist in appreciable number at temperatures where the average energy of thermal motion becomes great enough to overcome the interactions which hold them together. Solids melt, liquids vaporize: at high temperatures molecules are resolved into their atoms, and, at higher ones still, atoms into their own constituent particles. In a certain relatively restricted range of temperature molecules are able to exist, and yet are not so stable as to be incapable of rearrangement when subjected to disturbance. This is the familiar range in part of which, by definition almost, we live, and where chemistry is possible.

The rate at which a chemical change takes place is not simply an affair of the appropriate molecular encounters. The rearrangements expressed by the equation $2H_2 + O_2 = 2H_2O$ may, according to the temperature and other conditions, require minutes, days, or years. At ordinary temperatures they are immeasurably slow. On the other hand, the formally analogous reaction $2NO + O_2 = 2NO_2$ is extremely rapid at the melting-point of ice.

If we consider such changes as the slow decomposition of nitrogen pentoxide, the question arises why the molecules do not decompose all at once or not at all. The answer must be that the molecules are not all in the same state. Now all matter is in a condition of chaotic motion: and the state of motion of individual particles changes according to the way in which they collide with or interact with others. The solution of the problem of slow chemical transformations, therefore, is obviously connected with the details of the kinetic theory.

THE KINETIC THEORY OF GASES

In gases, the kinetic theory gives precise information about the following matters:

The mean speed of the molecules.

The distribution of the speeds about the most probable value. We know, for example, what proportion of the molecules have speeds more than double the mean speed, less than half the mean speed, and so on.

The types of motion executed by molecules of different kinds.

The mean free path of the molecules, from which, when the velocity is known, the number of collisions taking place in unit time may be calculated.

It will be useful first to deal with these matters in order.

1. *The Root Mean Square Velocity.*

This is obtained from the well-known expression for the pressure of a gas $pv = \frac{1}{3}mn\bar{u}^2$, where p = pressure, v = volume, m = mass of a molecule, n = number of molecules in the volume v, and $\bar{u}$ = root mean square velocity.

If v is the molecular volume, n = Avogadro's number N and $pv = RT$; therefore $\frac{1}{3}mN\bar{u}^2 = RT$.

Since
$$\frac{mn}{v} = \rho, \quad \bar{u} = \sqrt{\frac{3p}{\rho}}.$$

One of the most useful applications of this formula is in the calculation of the number of molecules striking unit area of a surface in a given time. This calculation is of importance in connexion with the interaction of a gas with a solid substance, or in problems relating to contact catalysis, where we may require to know how many molecules strike the solid catalyst in each second. Suppose we have a solid surface of unit area exposed to the bombardment of gas molecules. Approximately one-sixth of the total number of molecules may be regarded as moving in the direction of the surface with the average velocity. In one second all those within distance $\bar{u}$ could reach and strike the surface, unless turned back by a collision with another molecule, but for every one so turned back, another, originally leaving the surface, is sent back to it. Thus the number of molecules striking the surface in a second is equal to one-sixth of the number contained in a prism of unit base and height $\bar{u}$. This number is $\frac{1}{6}\bar{u}n'$, n' being the number of molecules in 1 c.c. Thus the mass of gas impinging on the surface per second is

$$\tfrac{1}{6}\bar{u}n'm = \tfrac{1}{6}\bar{u}\rho.$$

A more precise investigation allowing for the unequal speeds of different molecules shows that the factor $\frac{1}{6}$ should really be $\frac{3}{13}$. We therefore arrive at the result

mass of gas striking an area A in one second $= \frac{3}{13}\bar{u}\rho A$.

As an example of the use of this result we may consider Strutt's work on the reaction between silver oxide and ozone. The paper in which this is described* is one of the first in which the importance of considering chemical reactions from the point of view of molecular statistics is emphasized.

Silver oxide reacts with and destroys ozone, and the question may be asked, what fraction of the total number of ozone molecules which hit the silver oxide is destroyed? Or otherwise, how many times, on the average, must an ozone molecule hit the solid before it is decomposed? The answer to this question was found in the following manner. If a current of air at low pressure is drawn through a tube where an electric discharge is taking place, the issuing gas shows a yellowish glow, the cause of which can be traced to the interaction of nitric oxide and ozone. The glow is extinguished when the gas is passed through oxidized silver gauze, and the disappearance of the glow must be due to the destruction of the ozone, since if more ozone is introduced into the stream after the silver gauze is passed the glow reappears. Strutt caused a rapid stream of air at low pressure to pass first through a discharge tube and then through a piece of oxidized silver gauze, the total area of which was known. The rate of flow was adjusted until the glow was just destroyed by the passage of the gas over the gauze. If v is the actual volume of ozone streaming by in a second, then a mass ρv passes the gauze, and if A is the total area of the gauze, the mass

* Proc. Roy. Soc., 1912, A, **87**, 302.

hitting it is $\frac{3}{13}\bar{u}\rho A$. Thus the ratio of the number of molecules of ozone striking the gauze to the number passing is

$$\frac{\frac{3}{13}\rho\bar{u}A}{\rho v} = \frac{3\bar{u}A}{13v}.$$

Since the experiment is so arranged that all the ozone is just destroyed in passing, this gives the number of times each molecule strikes the silver oxide before it is decomposed. The glow was found just to be extinguished when the rate of streaming was 200 c.c. per second at a pressure of 3 mm., the total area of the oxidized silver gauze being 0·037 square centimetres.

$$\bar{u} = 3\cdot75\times10^4.$$

Therefore $\qquad \dfrac{3\bar{u}A}{13v} = \dfrac{3\times3\cdot75\times10^4\times0\cdot037}{13\times200} = 1\cdot6.$

Thus there are, on the average, only 1·6 molecular impacts on the solid for every molecule of ozone decomposed. This shows that practically every molecule of ozone which strikes the silver oxide is destroyed.

This calculation illustrates the fundamental importance of quantitative investigation of the behaviour of individual molecules in chemical changes. The application of analogous calculations to problems connected with the passage of gas streams over solid catalysts in technical processes is obvious.

Langmuir made a number of studies of the interaction of various gases at low pressures with heated metal filaments;[*] these illustrate in a very interesting manner similar principles. The action of oxygen at pressures below 0·02 millimetre on a heated tungsten wire was among the examples investigated. The rate at which the oxygen came in contact with the filament was calculated. This gives the maximum possible rate of reaction. The ratio of the observed rate of reaction to this maximum possible rate was found to range from 0·0011 at 1,270° abs. to 0·15 at 2,770° abs. In this case, therefore, only exceptional molecules of oxygen are able to react with the wire.

2. *The Distribution of Speeds among the Molecules.*

As a result of collisions in a gas the speeds of the individual molecules are continually changing. A given molecule may be brought momentarily almost to rest, or, on the other hand, after several successive collisions of a suitable kind it may acquire a velocity much above the average. Theories of chemical change are often concerned

[*] *J. Amer. Chem. Soc.*, 1913, **35**, 105, 931; 1919, **41**, 167.

with molecules of exceptionally high energy. The chance that a molecule emerges from the hazards of several successive encounters with kinetic energy much above the mean is small, and, as the excess of kinetic energy over the average which it has to acquire increases, so the chance diminishes very rapidly. The number of molecules out of a total number N, the speeds of which lie between c and $c+dc$, is given by Maxwell's law

$$\frac{\Delta N}{N} = \frac{4}{\sqrt{\pi}\left(\frac{2kT}{m}\right)^{\frac{3}{2}}} c^2 e^{-\frac{mc^2}{2kT}} dc.$$

The derivation is given on page 26.

A much simpler expression is obtained by considering the distribution of velocities in two dimensions instead of three. The distribution law so obtained cannot give numerical results very different from those yielded by the three-dimensional law, and, as it reduces to a very simple algebraic form, it is sometimes a convenient approximation to use instead of the true distribution law.

The proportion of the molecules for which the kinetic energy exceeds E is accordingly given by

$$\frac{N_1}{N} = e^{-E/RT}.$$

At this stage we will only consider one very important qualitative deduction, which relates to the effect of temperature on the number of molecules possessing kinetic energy in excess of some specified value. It is convenient to make calculations in terms of gram molecules, the statement that a certain proportion of the molecules have energies greater than, for example, 30,000 calories per gram molecule meaning simply that the individuals among them have energies greater than 30,000 divided by Avogadro's number. At an absolute temperature T the average kinetic energy of translation is $\frac{3}{2}RT$. From the two-dimensional formula, the proportion of molecules which possess kinetic energies greater than E is $e^{-E/RT}$. This is a very small fraction when E is several times greater than RT. For some fixed value of E the fraction increases very quickly with increase in T. Let us consider as an example what proportion of the molecules of a gas at 1,000° abs. possess, according to this formula, kinetic energies of translation corresponding to 20,000 calories per gram molecule. The fraction is

$$e^{-\frac{20000}{2\times1000}} = 0\cdot000045, \quad \text{or} \quad 0\cdot0045\%.$$

At an absolute temperature of 2,000°, where the average energy of the molecules is just doubled, the fraction with energies exceeding 20,000 calories becomes

$$e^{-\frac{20000}{2 \times 2000}} = 0.0067, \quad \text{or} \quad 0.67\%.$$

It appears, therefore, that an increase of temperature just sufficient to double the average energy causes the proportion of molecules with energies greater than 20,000 calories to increase considerably more than a hundred times.

The result, that the proportion of molecules with energies of exceptionally large value increases with temperature at a very much more rapid rate than corresponds to the simple linear increase of the mean energy, is of great importance in connexion with the influence of temperature on the rate of chemical reactions.

3. *The Types of Motion executed by the Molecules of a Gas.*

Detailed information about the motion of gas molecules is obtained from the study of specific heats, and to some extent from the study of absorption spectra.

The total translational energy of an ideal monatomic gas is $\frac{1}{2}M\bar{u}^2$ per gram molecule, where M is the molecular weight, and, since $pv = RT = \frac{1}{3}M\bar{u}^2$, the kinetic energy is $\frac{3}{2}RT$. The increase of kinetic energy of translation per degree is therefore $\frac{3}{2}R$, or 2·97 calories. Since this agrees exactly with the observed atomic heat it may be concluded that monatomic gases possess no energy other than kinetic energy of translation. The atoms therefore are not in rotation.

The principle of the equipartition of energy states that each mechanical degree of freedom possesses the same amount of kinetic energy when statistical equilibrium is established among a large number of bodies, such as gas molecules, which are capable of exchanging energy. The energy associated with the three degrees of freedom of a monatomic gas is $\frac{3}{2}RT$ calories per gram molecule, that is to say, $\frac{1}{2}RT$ for each degree of freedom. From the equipartition principle, therefore, it follows that each degree of freedom of a gas molecule should contribute $\frac{1}{2}RT$ calories to the total energy of the gas, and therefore $\frac{1}{2}R$ or 1 calorie to the molecular heat at constant volume.

Diatomic gases such as oxygen, hydrogen, and nitrogen have a molecular heat of 5 calories over a range of several hundred degrees, whence it is concluded that, in addition to the translational degree of freedom, they possess two degrees of freedom with respect to rotation. They are capable, therefore, of rotating about two of the three possible axes of rotation. The third axis is evidently, from analogy with monatomic gases, that joining the centres of gravity of the two atoms constituting the molecule.

At higher temperatures the molecular heats of diatomic gases rise above 5 calories, and since this rise takes place at lower temperatures with gases like iodine, in which the atoms are loosely bound together, than with gases like oxygen, in which the binding of the atoms is very strong, it is inferred that intramolecular vibrations come into play.

The molecular heat of hydrogen falls at low temperatures from 5 to 3. This and other variations in specific heats with temperature can only be interpreted in terms of quantum dynamics, and the subjection of mechanical processes taking place among gas molecules to quantum principles must be taken into consideration in theories of chemical reaction mechanisms.

A detailed discussion of the quantum theory cannot be given here, but it will be well briefly to illustrate the general nature of its application in the kinetic theory of gases.

This may be done by considering the falling off in the specific heat of hydrogen at low temperatures.

When two molecules collide the rotational energy as well as the translational energy is, in general, changed by the impact. Molecules of the hydrogen type should be set in rotation by collision with other molecules. If we conceive a large number of hydrogen molecules to exist at $T°$, momentarily devoid of rotations, and to be in a position to draw heat from a reservoir also at $T°$, then, momentarily, the kinetic energy of the gas is $\frac{3}{2}RT$ per gram molecule. By collisions the kinetic energy is shared between the degrees of freedom, and the temperature would drop unless the molecules restored their translational energy to its original value by impacts upon the walls of the heat reservoir. The total energy of the gas should therefore reach $\frac{5}{2}RT$, and the specific heat should be $\frac{5}{2}R$. But, since the specific heat at low temperatures is much less than $\frac{5}{2}R$, the total energy evidently does not reach $\frac{5}{2}RT$. This is a result of the quantum principle, which states that when a collision takes place between two molecules the angular momenta of the molecules can only change by integral multiples of a definite quantum of angular momentum. The transfer of energy which, according to ordinary dynamical calculations, should occur does not, therefore, take place at all unless it corresponds to the transfer of at least one quantum of angular momentum. When this condition is fulfilled energy corresponding to this quantum is transferred, and any balance is retained. A molecule without rotational energy is not therefore set in gentle rotation by a gentle impact of a suitable kind. It is incapable of being set in rotation until it receives an impact of such violence, and so directed, that the transfer of angular momentum calculated according to the ordinary dynamical laws reaches a certain critical value. Thus the contribution it would normally make towards the $\frac{5}{2}RT$ is absent.

Analogous considerations apply to the vibrational energy of molecules. At high temperatures the specific heat of diatomic gases rises above 5 and approaches a value 7, indicating that the vibration of the two atoms within the molecule comes into play, and a new degree of freedom is operative. The kinetic energy of the vibrational degree of freedom is associated with an equal amount of potential energy, since, for small amplitudes, the vibration is nearly simple harmonic. The absence of vibrations at ordinary temperatures, and their gradual appearance at higher temperatures among larger and larger proportions of the molecules of the gas, shows once more the operation of the quantum principle.

The quantum law assumes different forms for different kinds of motion. Applied to rotational motions it has the form

$$\text{energy} = \frac{n(n+1)h^2}{8\pi^2 I},$$

where n is an integer, I is the moment of inertia, and h is a universal constant.

Applied to simple harmonic vibrations it becomes

$$\text{energy} = (n+\tfrac{1}{2})h\nu,$$

where n is an integer as before and ν is the frequency of the simple harmonic vibration: h is the same constant as before. $\frac{1}{2}h\nu$ represents the zero-point energy: that is, the energy which the oscillator retains at the absolute zero.

The vibrations of diatomic molecules being approximately simple harmonic, the quantum law takes the second form, namely, that the molecule must gain or lose vibrational energy in integral multiples of $h\nu$, where ν is the natural frequency of the vibration. Since the frequency of a simple harmonic vibration is given by

$$\nu = \frac{1}{2\pi}\sqrt{\frac{\text{restoring force per unit displacement}}{\text{mass}}},$$

it follows that the greater the restoring force, that is, the more tightly bound the atoms, the greater the frequency, the greater therefore the quantum, and thus the smaller the proportion of the molecules which, at a given temperature, can acquire it. Thus stable molecules like hydrogen are not set in vibration until high temperatures are reached, whilst unstable molecules like iodine have a small quantum and begin to possess vibrational energy at much lower temperatures. Thus iodine, the instability of which is shown by the very considerable thermal dissociation at 1,000°, has already at ordinary temperatures a specific heat well above 5.

The importance of all this in connexion with the theory of chemical change lies in the fact that molecules are not set in vibration by collision unless the impact is of a certain critical degree of violence: then a quantum of energy is taken up.

The study of the absorption and emission spectra of gases confirms and extends the information about molecular motions provided by the consideration of specific heats. We will confine ourselves to a statement of the results having a direct bearing on those aspects of molecular mechanics which may be important in the consideration of chemical change.

The kind of spectrum known as a band spectrum is that which is emitted by a molecule and not by an isolated atom or ion. The bands are not continuous, but consist of a large number of fine lines, which are more closely packed together towards the 'head' of the band.

Three kinds of phenomenon play their part in the production of these band spectra: electronic changes within the molecule, vibration of the atoms in the molecule, and rotation of the molecule as a whole. The electronic processes give rise to emission or absorption in the visible and ultra-violet regions, the intra-atomic vibrations to bands in the short infra-red region at wave-lengths of the order of several μ, and the molecular rotations to bands in the far infra-red at wave-lengths of the order $100\,\mu$.

According to the quantum theory of spectra the emission of each frequency depends upon a passage of the molecule from a condition of greater energy to one of smaller energy, or from what is called a higher energy level to a lower energy level. The energy so set free is converted by whatever mechanism it is which transmits radiation through space into waves, the frequency of which is determined by the relation $h\nu =$ energy set free by the passage of the emitting system (in this case the molecule) from the higher to the lower energy level.

Knowing the value of h ($6 \cdot 55 \times 10^{-27}$ erg-seconds), and the value of Avogadro's number, it is possible to calculate the energy changes per gram molecule associated with the various emission or absorption processes occurring within the molecule. Those producing the rotation bands in the far infra-red correspond to a few hundred calories per gram molecule, those producing the short infra-red vibration bands to something of the order of some thousands of calories, and the visible bands to some tens of thousands of calories, increasing to over a hundred thousand in the ultra-violet.

The rotation bands correspond to changes in the number of quanta of angular momentum possessed by the molecule; these represent the smallest energy change.

The vibration bands correspond to much larger energy changes. Since changes in the number of quanta of vibrational energy may be accompanied by simultaneous changes in rotational quanta, a single change in the vibrational state of the molecule may give rise to a number of bands corresponding to various rotational changes. As the energy changes involved in the rotational jumps are small compared with those involved in the vibrational jumps, there are produced a number of nearly equidistant lines, the spacing of which is small compared with the frequency of the central one. The frequency difference between the different rotational components of a vibration band gives the energy corresponding to a quantum of angular momentum. From this the moment of inertia of the molecule may be found. In the same way the superposition of vibrational and rotational changes on the electronic orbital changes produces a fine structure of the bands in the visible region, from which both the moment of inertia of the molecule and the frequency of the intramolecular vibrations can, in principle, be calculated.

In this way the study of spectra gives even more detailed information than the consideration of specific heats. It is found that infra-red rotation and vibration spectra are only given by those molecules, such as HCl, which are composed of a negative and a positive portion. Strictly homo-polar molecules do not absorb in the infra-red, although the theory of specific heats and the analysis of the visible spectrum leave no doubt about the existence of molecular rotations and, in such cases as iodine, of vibrations. We may note, therefore, the important conclusion that a molecule of homo-polar type, even though it possesses an appropriate natural frequency, is apparently not stimulated by radiation to execute either rotations or vibrations. Electronic processes within it are, however, influenced by radiation of the appropriate wave-length.

4. *Distribution of Energy among Molecules.*

The distribution of speeds given by Maxwell's law is a special case of the general law of distribution of energy. This law is derived on page 20. But it will be convenient to quote it here. If there are a series of quantized energy states $\epsilon_1, \epsilon_2,...$, then the number of molecules N_j in the jth state is given by

$$N_j = \frac{Ne^{-\epsilon_j/kT}}{\sum e^{-\epsilon_j/kT}},$$

where ϵ_j/kT may be replaced by E_j/RT.

For translational speeds in three or in two dimensions the law assumes the forms already quoted.

To a first approximation the different kinds of energy in a molecule can be regarded as independent of one another, and all expressed as a constant times the square of some quantity such as a speed, angular momentum, displacement, and so on. Thus the three components of translational velocity are associated with energies $\frac{1}{2}mu^2$, $\frac{1}{2}mv^2$, $\frac{1}{2}mw^2$, the rotational components with terms of the type $\frac{1}{2}I\omega^2$; the potential energy of a simple harmonic motion is proportional to the square of a displacement from the equilibrium position, $\frac{1}{2}\mu x^2$. Each of these is called a square term. In reality the different kinds of motion of which a molecule is capable interfere mutually: the moment of inertia, which determines the rotational energy, is a function of the state of vibration and so forth. But for many purposes the representation of the energy as a sum of square terms is legitimate.

The chance that a molecule possesses a total energy greater than some amount, E, in n square terms, without reference to how it is shared among them, will later be shown to be given approximately by the expression

$$\frac{e^{-E/RT}(E/RT)^{\frac{1}{2}n-1}}{(\frac{1}{2}n-1)!},$$

provided that E is great compared with RT. This no longer applies when n is as small as two. In this case a direct derivation gives the probability as

$$e^{-E/RT}.$$

The case of two square terms is an important one: it includes

(*a*) a single vibrational degree of freedom, in which the sum of the kinetic and potential energies is considered.

(*b*) A two-dimensional rotation.

(*c*) Two degrees of freedom of translation, one belonging to each of two approaching molecules, i.e. the kinetic energy associated with the relative velocity of two molecules along the line of centres. This will determine the violence of the impact and, therefore, in some circumstances, the amount of energy transferred.

The important term in all these expressions for the energy distribution is the exponential. The probability that a molecule possesses energy, E, considerably in excess of the average, is always small, and it is proportional to $e^{-E/RT}$. This exponential expression comes in throughout physical chemistry, and determines the form of vapour-pressure equations, the law for the dependence of equilibrium constants and velocity constants upon temperature, the variation of viscosity with temperature, and many other relations. It is interesting to inquire into its physical significance. The following is not in any sense intended to be a derivation of the formula, which is derived rigidly on page 20, but an illustration of the inner meaning of the exponential. A molecule may, in a given collision, gain or lose energy. Let us call one in which it gains energy, favourable, and one in which it loses energy, unfavourable. To accumulate energy much in excess of the average the molecule may be supposed to need a lucky run of favourable collisions. In a given collision let the chance of spoiling a favourable run be $1/X$. Then the chance of continuing it will be $(1-1/X)$.

The chance that the run continues for x collisions is therefore

$$\left(1-\frac{1}{X}\right)^x = \left(1-\frac{1}{X}\right)^{-(x/X)(-X)}.$$

Put
$$-X = n.$$

The chance is
$$\left\{\left(1+\frac{1}{n}\right)^n\right\}^{-x/X}.$$

The expression in brackets is the function which by definition becomes e when n is increased without limit.

Now x, the length of the necessary favourable series of collisions, will increase with E, the required accumulation of energy, while X, the number of collisions which occur before there is an unfavourable one, will increase with the temperature. Thus x/X will be proportional to some function like E/RT, and the chance, in the limit where only small changes occur at each collision so that large numbers are involved, will be given by the exponential of this ratio.

The above argument is intended simply to illustrate the fact that the exponential term in physico-chemical formulae arises directly from the form of the expression for the probability of runs of events, and from the definition of the quantity e itself.

5. *The Mean Free Path and the Collision Number.*

Knowledge of the number of collisions taking place in unit time between the molecules of a gas is obviously of great importance in the consideration of chemical reactions. It is found as follows.

Let the diameter of a molecule be σ. If we regard σ as a value of the effective diameter rather than a quantity with a strict geometrical significance, we may regard two molecules as entering into collision whenever their centres approach to within a distance σ of each other.

For the calculation of the number of collisions suffered by a given molecule all the other molecules can be regarded as stationary, and the given molecule imagined to be moving about among them with a definite velocity r. This is equal to the mean relative velocity, a quantity which is easily shown to be $\frac{4}{3}\bar{u}$. If the given molecule is further assumed to have a radius, instead of a diameter σ, all the others may be regarded as points. In one second the given molecule sweeps out a cylindrical space of length $\frac{4}{3}\bar{u}$ and cross-section $\pi\sigma^2$, the volume of which is $\frac{4}{3}\pi\sigma^2\bar{u}$. In this space $\frac{4}{3}\pi\sigma^2\bar{u}n$ point molecules will have been encountered, n being the number of molecules in a cubic centimetre. The cylinder will not have been straight but zigzag. $\frac{4}{3}\pi\sigma^2\bar{u}n$, therefore, gives the number of collisions suffered per second by any molecule. But each molecule undergoes the same process, so that the total number entering into collision in a second in one cubic centimetre is $\frac{4}{3}\pi\sigma^2\bar{u}n^2$. The number of collisions is exactly half the number of molecules entering into collision, since two molecules participate in each impact. The factor $\frac{4}{3}$ requires, moreover, slight correction when allowance is made for the distribution of velocities in accordance with Maxwell's law. The corrected value for the number entering into collision is $\sqrt{2}\,\pi\sigma^2\bar{u}n^2$.

The value of σ is obtained from viscosity data and has been determined for a great many gases and is always of the order 10^{-8} cm.

The viscosity is directly connected with the mean free path l. The number of collisions in unit time is $\bar{u}/l$ for each molecule, neglecting the difference between the mean velocity and the root mean square velocity. Thus $\dfrac{\bar{u}}{l} = \sqrt{2}\,\pi\sigma^2\bar{u}n$. The mean free path is connected with the viscosity by the relation

$$\eta = \tfrac{1}{3}\rho\bar{u}l, \quad \rho \text{ being the density.}$$

Rankine[*] and others have made numerous accurate measurements of η and calculated the molecular diameters from them. For calculating

[*] e.g. *Proc. Roy. Soc.*, 1910, A, **83**, 516; 1910, **84**, 181; 1912, **86**, 162; 1915, **91**, 201. *Phil. Mag.*, 1915, **29**, 552.

the number of molecules entering into collision in a gas it is therefore convenient to use tables of σ and the expression $\sqrt{2}\,\pi\sigma^2\bar{u}n^2$.

It might be objected that this formula is based upon assumptions about the nature of a collision which may not correspond to reality, and that therefore it cannot be an accurate one. This is not a real difficulty. The values of σ are obtained by use of the formula in question, the number of collisions being found from the mean free path which, in its turn, is derived directly from the viscosity. Thus the ordinary method of calculating the collision number from tables of σ for different molecules is in effect a direct calculation from the viscosity, the introduction of σ being merely a convenience but essentially irrelevant. In the theory of viscosity nothing whatever is assumed about the mechanical nature of a collision, whether, for example, it can be treated as an elastic impact of smooth spheres, or whether it should rather be regarded as analogous to the passage of a comet round the sun.

Some of Rankine's values are given below.

Gas	Molecular radius	Gas	Molecular radius
Chlorine	$1{\cdot}60 \times 10^{-8}$ cm.	Argon	$1{\cdot}28 \times 10^{-8}$ cm.
Bromine	$1{\cdot}71 \times 10^{-8}$	Krypton	$1{\cdot}38 \times 10^{-8}$
Iodine	$1{\cdot}88 \times 10^{-8}$	Xenon	$1{\cdot}53 \times 10^{-8}$

The question of molecular diameters is also dealt with by Sutherland, who gives a table of values.*

For collisions between unlike molecules in a mixture of gases the following formula is found (for derivation see page 35):

number of collisions per c.c. per sec.

$$= N_A\,N_B\,\sigma_{AB}^2\left\{8\pi RT\left(\frac{1}{M_A}+\frac{1}{M_B}\right)\right\}^{\frac{1}{2}}.$$

N_A and N_B are the numbers of molecules of the two kinds per cubic centimetre, σ_{AB} is the mean of the molecular diameters, M_A and M_B are the respective molecular weights.

It is sometimes necessary to calculate the number of collisions suffered by a molecule during the time that it has undergone a linear displacement x from its original position, x being measured in a straight line, and taking no account of the zigzag path actually traversed.

Einstein, in a paper dealing with the Brownian movement,† shows that the mean displacement is proportional not to the time, but to the square root of the time, being given by

$$\bar{x}^2 = 2Dt,$$

where t is the time and D the coefficient of diffusion.

* *Phil. Mag.*, 1910, **19**, 25.   † *Ann. Phys.*, 1905, **17** [IV], 549.

The coefficient of diffusion of gas molecules can be calculated from the kinetic theory: the simplest formula, which, however, is not quite exact, is due to Meyer.

$$D = \eta/\rho = \tfrac{1}{3}\bar{u}l,$$

whence $\qquad\qquad \bar{x}^2 = \tfrac{2}{3}\bar{u}lt.$

Meyer's formula is only approximate, but the error introduced by its use would not affect the order of magnitude of the result.

Smoluchowsky* finds the expression

$$\bar{x}^2 = \frac{4}{3\pi}\,\bar{u}lt,$$

which only differs from the above by a small numerical factor.

Now let Z be the number of collisions suffered during the displacement $\bar{x}$, then Zl is the total length of the zigzag path. Thus $Zl = \bar{u}t$.

Therefore

$$Z = \frac{\bar{u}t}{l},$$

$$= \frac{\bar{u}\bar{x}^2}{2lD} \quad \text{(from Einstein's formula)},$$

$$= \frac{3\bar{x}^2}{2l^2} \quad \text{(from Meyer's formula for } D\text{)},$$

or $\qquad\qquad Z = \dfrac{3\pi\bar{x}^2}{4l^2}$ (Smoluchowsky's formula).

These formulae are useful in calculating the number of collisions suffered by a molecule in the gas phase before it reaches the wall of the vessel at a distance x from the original position of the molecule. The difference in the numerical factor is unimportant in most applications.

When the diffusing molecule is surrounded by a mixture of gases a more complicated expression for D is required.

Liquids and Solids.

Molecules exert forces upon one another. In the gaseous state the thermal motion prevents the aggregation of all the molecules into a coherent mass. In the liquid state this aggregation has occurred. The characteristic of the solid state is that there is not merely aggregation but a very high degree of orientation, so that a space lattice with well-defined properties of symmetry is formed.

The phase changes from gas to liquid and from liquid to solid may take place at sharply defined temperatures. We will first consider the

* *Bull. Intern. Acad. Cracovie*, 1906, 202.

nature of these changes. In a gas the molecules, although moving too fast to aggregate in a wholesale manner, are not without influence on one another.

The potential energy of a given molecule is lower when it is in the neighbourhood of a second molecule than when it is remote from any other. By the Boltzmann principle (page 40), therefore, there is a slightly greater chance of finding certain molecules in incipient aggregates than of finding them all quite randomly spaced. These aggregates, however, will be temporary and rare. They will increase in size and in number as the temperature falls, since their probability is determined by a function of the form $e^{-U/RT}$, and we might therefore expect something like a continuous passage to a liquid, if a new factor did not enter. The larger an aggregate becomes the greater is its attraction for fresh molecules, because it contains several attracting centres reinforcing one another. But just because it is larger it is also more likely to lose molecules and disperse. Two factors thus oppose one another: and at a given temperature either the one or the other must be the greater. As long as the reversal tendency is called forth more strongly than the aggregating tendency by a small increase in size an equilibrium is reached. But as the temperature falls, there comes a point at which a small increase favours the further aggregation more than it favours the reversal, and here we have a discontinuity where small aggregates in equilibrium with single molecules begin to grow indefinitely. This is the condensation point. The relation of the liquid state to the solid state is similar, except that here it is a question of the growth of more completely orientated aggregates. The forces between molecules tend to arrange them in symmetrical arrays which thermal agitation breaks up. But by Boltzmann's principle, small elements of temporary orientation not only can but must exist in a liquid. When one molecule is striving to set itself in a symmetrical way in relation to a second, its efforts are rendered easier if neighbouring molecules already conform to the regular design. Thus here again there exists a limiting size for the orientated elements beyond which they will grow steadily rather than remain in equilibrium. This view of the matter explains the action of nuclei in facilitating phase changes.

The two problems which concern us from the point of view of chemical kinetics are those connected with energy distributions and with encounter rates respectively.

With regard to the first it may be said that the laws applicable to gases apply also to the condensed phases, although there may be difficulty in deciding such problems as whether or not the molecules of a condensed phase are in rotation.

The problem of encounter rates is much more difficult. In the solid state there is no translational motion. A certain limited degree of diffusion may occur but probably by complex mechanisms such as surface migration. A bimolecular reaction of two substances embedded in a continuous solid phase is practically impossible.

Liquids occupy a position intermediate between solids and gases, and in some respects must be regarded as resembling the one more closely and in other respects the other.

Debye especially has stressed the analogies between the liquid and the solid states,* and shown in particular that there is more regularity and order in liquids than would be expected if they were to be regarded simply as very highly compressed gases. This makes the calculation of the collision rate between molecules of a liquid difficult to define and almost impossible to calculate. A slightly more tractable problem is presented by the calculation of the encounters between two molecules of a solute in an independent substance as solvent. Even this is difficult enough. It receives a qualitative discussion in the following section.

Collision Rates in Liquid Systems. Solute-solute Collisions.

Two extreme cases present themselves. We may regard a solution as analogous to a gas on the one hand or to a solid on the other. The results will be different. Then we must try and see where, in between, the correct answer is to be found.

We may argue that the collision rate for solute molecules will be given as regards order of magnitude by the gas formula, since, in the derivation of this formula given on page 13, the presence of foreign molecules merely increases the number of bends in the cylinder swept out by the typical solute molecule, without seriously altering its volume. This is not true when the bends become too numerous, but we can say that up to a fairly high concentration of foreign molecules the rate of encounter of solutes A and B will not be affected. The question is at what concentration this argument breaks down. Starting from the other extreme, we can say that if A and B molecules were embedded in a solid their collision rate would be zero. The fall to zero may, however, occur very sharply when the last vestiges of mobility disappear. Just before this we have the state of affairs where mobility is very small and the chance of A's diffusing a long distance to meet B is

* Z. Elektrochem., 1939, **45**, 174.

C

very small, but is compensated for by the fact that an A molecule which has just collided with B will be hemmed in and sent back to collide with it again and again. Now, since in chemical reactions which we can measure, only one collision in millions leads to transformation, repeated collisions of the same pair of molecules are just as effective as collisions between changing partners. The compensation effect will only begin to fail when the diffusion has become so small or the reaction velocity is so great that the later members of a series of repeated collisions are useless, because the molecules will have reacted before the end of the series. In ordinary measurable chemical reactions, then, we should expect the gas formula to give us the correct order of magnitude, but to be subject to minor inexactnesses of a rather complicated kind. One of these will arise from the non-homogeneity of liquids. If half the liquid froze to solid, the concentration of solute would be doubled and the collision number quadrupled. If some of the liquid molecules aggregate into swarms, or develop other structural characters, as we should expect from Debye's discussion, the result will be in the same direction, namely, an increase in collision frequency of solute molecules. This, however, is not likely to amount to more than one order of magnitude.

The general ideas outlined above seem to be borne out by the detailed, though not absolutely assumption-free, calculations of Smoluchowsky and of Leontovitsch, and by the analysis of Fowler* and Slater. They are also confirmed in some measure by direct experiments on reaction velocity. The essentially bimolecular decomposition of chlorine monoxide, the interaction of ozone and chlorine, the ortho-para hydrogen conversion, and the addition reactions of quinone with dienes have all been studied both in the gas phase and in solution, and it can certainly be said that a rather varied selection of reactions proceed, at least in some solvents, with a velocity which is of the same order of magnitude as that which they would possess at the corresponding concentration in the gas phase.

Interesting results may be obtained by the use of a mechanical model such as that first introduced by Rabinovitsch and Wood.† In such a model solute and solvent molecules are represented by small balls, for example, by steel bearings which are agitated in a tray, and the encounters made between solutes can be recorded electrically or observed directly. It is found that as the density of the solvent is increased from small to large values by the addition of fresh balls to the tray,

* *Trans. Faraday Soc.*, 1938, **34**, 81.   † *Ibid.*, 1937, **33**, 1225.

pairs of solute 'molecules' become hemmed in and are caused to make repeated collisions with each other. But the solvent impedes diffusion and cuts down the number of collisions which a given solute makes with fresh partners. The two effects, however, nearly balance, so that if we count repeated collisions with the same partner on the same basis as collisions with new partners, the total number remains nearly constant.

It also appears* that if the solute balls are of a size which does not allow of convenient close packing with the solvent, then, at high densities of the latter, they may be squeezed out, as it were, from the structure of the solvent and make abnormally large numbers of collisions among themselves. This factor may be of some significance in connexion with reactions which take place in solvents possessing a high degree of structure in the Debye sense.

* Fairclough and Hinshelwood, *J. Chem. Soc.*, 1939, 593.

II

ELEMENTARY STATISTICAL MECHANICS AND THE THEORY OF CHEMICAL EQUILIBRIA

Introduction.

ELEMENTARY theory tells us that the equilibrium constant of a chemical change is the ratio of the velocity constants of the two opposing reactions.whose balance determines the final state of the system. There is thus the possibility that the value of an equilibrium constant may give us some indirect information about one or both of the velocity constants. Theoretical treatment of equilibrium constants has progressed much farther than that of velocities. Indeed, it may be said that equilibrium constants are, in principle, calculable *a priori* from thermodynamical and statistical laws.

It is the object of this chapter to consider the calculation of equilibria from statistical mechanical principles, and to inquire into the fundamental factors which determine the final state of chemical systems. The calculations will later assume some importance in connexion with the problem of reaction velocity itself.

It is so important to be clear about the basis of the calculations that the essential results of statistical mechanics will be developed *ab initio*.

Distribution of Molecules among Energy States.

The quantum theory has introduced an enormous simplification into this problem. We no longer have to deal with continuous ranges of coordinates, but can specify precisely defined states in each of which there will be a quite definite number of molecules. In accordance with the principles of wave mechanics this will apply even to the translational and position coordinates.

Let there be N molecules and let the possible energy states be such that there are N_1 in a state of energy ϵ_1, N_2 of ϵ_2, N_3 of ϵ_3, and so on.

We do not need at the moment to worry about the nature of the energy; every possible combination of all possible kinds of energy is included and constitutes a separate state.

The number of ways in which the N molecules can be assigned to the various states in the manner specified is given by

$$W = \frac{N!}{N_1! \, N_2! \, ...}.$$

The fundamental principle of the whole theory is that the condition of affairs which is realized most nearly and for most of the time in nature is that which makes W a maximum. This is because all possibilities are impartially explored in the course of the random molecular motion and the average is determined by mere frequency.

It is convenient instead of W to consider its logarithm.

By Stirling's approximation $\log N! = N \log N - N$, if N is a large number.

(Objection to the use of Stirling's approximation has been made on the ground that in some of the states the actual numbers of molecules are not large. This can be met by taking many instantaneous examples of the whole system and applying the calculations to the sum of the whole lot.)

We now have

$$\log W = N \log N - N - \sum N_1 \log N_1 + \sum N_1 = N \log N - \sum N_1 \log N_1.$$

Two other conditions must be fulfilled:

$$N_1 + N_2 + N_3 \ldots = N,$$
$$N_1 \epsilon_1 + N_2 \epsilon_2 + \ldots = E,$$

where E is the total energy of the system.

For W to be a maximum subject to the other two conditions we have

$$\sum (1 + \log N_1) \delta N_1 = 0,$$
$$\sum \delta N_1 = 0,$$
$$\sum \epsilon_1 \delta N_1 = 0.$$

There is a general method of dealing with such problems of conditioned maxima.

The second equation is multiplied by α and the third by β and they are then added to the first:

$$\sum \{(1 + \log N_1) + \alpha + \beta \epsilon_1\} \delta N_1 = 0.$$

Since α and β may be assigned any values we please, they may be chosen so that the coefficients of δN_1 and δN_2 are zero. Now the values of δN_3, $\delta N_4, \ldots$ are arbitrary. They represent the numbers transferred from one state to another in the small variation of conditions under which, by the conditions of the problem, W is to remain at its maximum. All possible values of δN_3, $\delta N_4, \ldots$ must be equally admissible. Therefore we take values of δN_4, $\delta N_5, \ldots$ equal to zero. This leaves us with every coefficient in the summation already made equal to zero except that of δN_3, which, since the sum is zero, must itself vanish.

Therefore the coefficient of every term must separately be equal to zero, since the argument applied to that of δN_3 applies equally well to all the others. We thus obtain a series of independent equations of the form

$$\log N_1 + 1 + \alpha + \beta \epsilon_1 = 0,$$

whence

$$N_1 = A e^{-\beta \epsilon_1},$$

where A is a constant, and similarly for N_2, N_3,.... .

The value of A is found from the condition

$$\sum N_1 = N = \sum A e^{-\beta \epsilon_1}.$$

Therefore

$$A = \frac{N}{\sum e^{-\beta \epsilon_1}}, \quad \text{and} \quad N_1 = \frac{N e^{-\beta \epsilon_1}}{\sum e^{-\beta \epsilon_1}} = \frac{N e^{-\beta \epsilon_1}}{f}.$$

f is a most important quantity known as the *partition function*. It is related to the important thermodynamic functions of the system. Chemical equilibria can be expressed in terms of it in a simple way.

The constant β is important. It will prove to be equal to $1/kT$, where T is the absolute temperature on the gas thermometer scale, and k is the gas constant per molecule (R/N).

The first step is to show that β is the same for different kinds of molecule and for different kinds of energy. Suppose the preceding calculation is repeated, not for a single kind of molecule, but for a mixture of the first kind with another kind having M_1 molecules in the first state of energy η_1, M_2 in the second state of energy η_2, and so on.

The two distributions among the respective states have to occur simultaneously so that the probability is the product of the separate probabilities. We therefore have

$$W = \frac{N!}{N_1! \, N_2! \dots} \times \frac{M!}{M_1! \, M_2! \dots}.$$

The numbers of each separate kind of molecule are constant:

$$\delta \sum N_1 = 0 \quad \text{and} \quad \delta \sum M_1 = 0,$$

but, although there can be no interchange of molecules, there can be an interchange of energy between the two kinds so that there is only *one* energy sum

$$\delta \sum (N_1 \epsilon_1 + M_1 \eta_1) = 0.$$

When the maximum problem is worked out as before, it is seen that the two conditions for constancy in total number of molecules have each to be multiplied by separate constants α_1 and α_2, whereas the single energy condition is only multiplied by a *single* constant β. When we proceed to show that in the summation of the terms the separate coefficients of δN_1, δN_2,..., δM_1, δM_2,...: are all equal to zero, a series of equations result which connect N_1, N_2,... with ϵ_1, ϵ_2,..., and M_1, M_2,... with η_1, η_2,..., but the multiplier β will be the *same* for both sets.

Further, it follows from the equation $N_j = Ne^{-\beta\epsilon_j}/f$ that the smaller the β, the greater is the probability that molecules will be in the jth energy state. In other words, β is a constant which defines the distribution of energy among molecules; it has the same value for different kinds of molecule and for different kinds of energy, and, the smaller it is, the greater is the chance that molecules can have energy of a given amount. It has thus the properties of an inverse temperature. It is therefore expedient to define a thermodynamic temperature which shall be related to β by the relation $\beta = 1/kT$, where k is the gas constant per molecule. In due course we can identify T with the ordinary absolute temperature of the gas scale. In the meantime we can write the distribution law in the form

$$N_1 = \frac{e^{-\epsilon_1/kT}}{f},$$

thinking of T as measured on a special scale.

Special Forms of the Partition Function

(a) Factorization of the Partition Function.

The partition function has been defined by the relation

$$f = \sum e^{-\beta\epsilon_1}.$$

Now the energy of a molecule consists in general of translational, vibrational, and rotational parts. The rotational and vibrational energies are not really independent, since, for example, the moment of inertia of the molecule, which determines the rotational energy, varies with the vibrational state of the structure. Thus the total energy will contain what are called cross terms. These, however, for many purposes can be neglected and we may write

$$\epsilon = \epsilon_T + \epsilon_V + \epsilon_R.$$

There will be separate series of translational, vibrational, and rotational states, and partial partition functions may be defined for each of these. For example, if the series of rotational and vibrational states are

$$\epsilon_{R_1}, \epsilon_{R_2},... \quad \text{and} \quad \epsilon_{V_1}, \epsilon_{V_2},....$$

then the rotational and vibrational partition functions are

$$f_R = \sum e^{-\beta\epsilon_{R_1}} \quad \text{and} \quad f_V = \sum e^{-\beta\epsilon_{V_1}}.$$

It is easily shown that the total partition function, when there are no cross terms in the energy, is simply the product of the separate functions referring to all the different kinds of energy which the molecule possesses—translational, rotational, and vibrational—each separate degree of freedom counting independently.

$$f = f_T f_R f_V,$$

and f_V itself will be composite, if there are several vibrational degrees of freedom:

$$f_V = f_{V_{\nu_1}} \cdot f_{V_{\nu_2}} \cdots .$$

This result is immediately obvious if the product of, say, f_R and f_V is inspected.

$$f_R = e^{-\beta \epsilon_{R_1}} + e^{-\beta \epsilon_{R_2}} + \ldots$$

$$f_V = e^{-\beta \epsilon_{V_1}} + e^{-\beta \epsilon_{V_2}} + \ldots$$

$$f_R f_V = e^{-\beta \epsilon_{R_1}} e^{-\beta \epsilon_{V_1}} + e^{-\beta \epsilon_{R_1}} e^{-\beta \epsilon_{V_2}} + e^{-\beta \epsilon_{R_2}} e^{-\beta \epsilon_{V_1}} + e^{-\beta \epsilon_{R_2}} e^{-\beta \epsilon_{V_2}} + \ldots$$

$$= e^{-\beta(\epsilon_{R_1} + \epsilon_{V_1})} + e^{-\beta(\epsilon_{R_1} + \epsilon_{V_2})} + e^{-\beta(\epsilon_{R_2} + \epsilon_{V_1})} + e^{-\beta(\epsilon_{R_2} + \epsilon_{V_2})} + \ldots .$$

In the final summation the quantities in brackets represent every combination of every rotational or vibrational state, that is to say, every possible energy state of the molecule. When these are arranged in the correct numerical order they constitute the series which was originally defined simply as $\epsilon_1, \epsilon_2, \ldots$.

(b) Vibrational States.

For a single series of vibrational states we may put the energy equal to $(n + \frac{1}{2})h\nu$, where ν is the frequency of vibration. If we measure from the zero-point energy, the successive energies are $nh\nu$, where n is an integer.

Therefore

$$f_V = \sum_{n=0}^{n=\infty} e^{-nh\nu/kT}.$$

This is a geometrical progression and the sum is given by

$$f_V = \frac{1}{1 - e^{-h\nu/kT}} = \frac{e^{h\nu/kT}}{e^{h\nu/kT} - 1}.$$

When ν is small, this reduces approximately to $kT/h\nu$.

The number of molecules in the nth and higher states is

$$\frac{N\{e^{-nh\nu/kT} + e^{-(n+1)h\nu/kT} + \ldots\}}{f_V}$$

$$= \frac{Ne^{-nh\nu/kT}}{f_V} \{1 + e^{-h\nu/kT} + \ldots\}$$

$$= \frac{Ne^{-nh\nu/kT}}{f_V} f_V = Ne^{-nh\nu/kT}.$$

If $\qquad nh\nu = \epsilon_n,$

then the number of molecules with energy greater than ϵ_n in one vibrational degree of freedom is $\qquad Ne^{-\epsilon_n/kT},$

a result of very frequent application in chemical kinetics.

(c) Translational States.

According to wave mechanics the translational energies are quantized, but the quantization depends upon the size of the enclosure containing the molecules. Thus the translational coordinates cannot be dealt with without simultaneous consideration of the positional coordinates. Let u be the component of velocity of the molecule along the x-axis. Suppose the molecules are enclosed in a rectangular vessel, the length of whose side parallel to the x-axis is l_1. Then, by the wave-mechanical condition, the wave-length of the particle is $\lambda = h/mu$, where m is the mass, and since, for a stationary state, an integral number of half wave-lengths must fit into the length l_1, we have $\frac{1}{2}(n\lambda) = l_1$.

Therefore $\qquad \dfrac{nh}{2mu} = l_1,$

whence $\qquad \frac{1}{2}mu^2 = \dfrac{n^2h^2}{8ml_1^2}.$

Thus the translational partition function for one degree of freedom is

$$\sum e^{-\frac{1}{2}mu^2/kT} = \sum e^{-n^2h^2/8ml_1^2\,kT}.$$

Since the energy steps are very small, this summation can be represented quite closely by the definite integral to which it would reduce were the steps made vanishingly small.

If $\qquad B = \dfrac{h}{2\sqrt{(2mkT)}\,l_1}$

the sum becomes

$$\sum e^{-B^2n^2} = \dfrac{\sum e^{-B^2n^2}\,\delta n}{\delta n}, \quad \text{where } \delta n = 1.$$

This is approximately

$$\int_0^\infty e^{-B^2n^2}\,dn = \dfrac{\sqrt{\pi}}{2B}.$$

Thus $\qquad f = \dfrac{\sqrt{(2\pi mkT)}\,l_1}{h}$

for one degree of freedom.

For the three translational degrees of freedom we have the product

$$f_T = \frac{(2\pi mkT)^{\frac{3}{2}}}{h^3} l_1 l_2 l_3 = \frac{(2\pi mkT)^{\frac{3}{2}} V}{h^3}.$$

For a non-rectangular vessel the geometry of the situation becomes rather complicated, but the final result, involving V, is the same.

The above result is reached without explicit reference to wave mechanics in the following way. We know that some kind of quantization of the translational motion is essential. Otherwise the number of possible states would be infinitely great, and, from the principle that the system spends most of its time in a condition near to that which can be realized in the greatest number of ways, we should have the result that all the energy would assume the translational form. Given that some law of quantization is to be found, it is natural to seek that which introduces the universal quantum constant, h, in the simplest possible way. If the momentum coordinates of a molecule along the three axes x, y, and z are p_1, p_2, and p_3, we may define a range of variation about these values by the product $dp_1 dp_2 dp_3 dxdydz$. This product has the same dimensions as h^3, $dp_1 dx$ having the dimensions of h. The simplest law possible, therefore, is that which declares all states corresponding to changes of coordinates within the range $dp_1 dp_2 dp_3 dxdydz = h^3$ to be indistinguishable from a single state. Enumeration of the states on this basis and their summation leads to the same result as that obtained above. It is the dimensional relation of h to $dpdx$ rather than to dp alone which demands the simultaneous treatment of position and momentum coordinates.

(d) Derivation of Maxwell's Law.

In its best-known form this law expresses the number of molecules which possess speeds between certain limits independently of the directions of these speeds. We can, with the aid of the above results, find an expression for the number of molecules with resultant velocities between c and $c+dc$. The first problem is to calculate the number of states, as defined in the last paragraph, which correspond to speeds between these limits. The velocity c corresponds to a momentum p. Let a diagram be constructed in which the three coordinates of momentum of the molecules in a given volume element $dxdydz$ are represented on three rectangular axes. The points corresponding to a resultant momentum p lie on a sphere of radius p. Those corresponding to a momentum between p and $p+dp$ occupy, therefore, a volume on the diagram of $4\pi p^2 dp$. The product of this volume, in the so-called momentum space, and of the actual volume element of the gas considered is $4\pi p^2 \, dp \, dx \, dy \, dz$. For the whole number of molecules this product is

$$4\pi p^2 \, dp \times V.$$

The size of a single state, also possessing the dimensions of a volume in momentum space times a volume in ordinary space, is h^3. Therefore the number of states is

$$\frac{4\pi p^2 \, dp \, V}{h^3}.$$

Since $p = mc$, the number becomes

$$\frac{4\pi m^3 c^2 \, dc \, V}{h^3}.$$

Now all the molecules in the range considered have energies nearly equal to $\frac{1}{2}mc^2$. The number in one state is therefore

$$\frac{Ne^{-\frac{1}{2}mc^2/kT}}{f_T} = \frac{Ne^{-\frac{1}{2}mc^2/kT}}{(2\pi mkT)^{\frac{3}{2}}V/h^3}$$

by the general result previously obtained.

The number (ΔN) in the whole system with velocities between c and $c+dc$ is therefore

$$\frac{4\pi m^3 c^2 \, dc \, V}{h^3} \frac{Ne^{-\frac{1}{2}mc^2/kT}}{(2\pi mkT)^{\frac{3}{2}}V/h^3}.$$

Hence

$$\frac{\Delta N}{N} = \frac{4}{\sqrt{\pi}(2kT/m)^{\frac{3}{2}}} c^2 e^{-\frac{1}{2}mc^2/kT} \, dc,$$

which is Maxwell's law.

At this stage the identification of T with the gas thermometer temperature could be made. The total change in momentum per second when gas molecules impinge on a surface can be calculated and integrated over all the velocity ranges: the result gives the gas pressure, which is related to the gas temperature by the equation $pV = RT$ Another method is, however, given later in full.

(e) Rotational States.

The partition function is formed by taking the sum of $e^{-\epsilon_{\text{rot}}/kT}$ over all the possible rotational states.

It can be represented approximately by an integral, as in the treatment of translational states.

For a rigid rotator which is a solid of revolution the result is

$$\frac{8\pi^2 IkT}{h^2},$$

where I is the moment of inertia. In other cases more elaborate formulae are found.*

Relation of Partition Functions to Thermodynamic Quantities.

From page 21 we have

$$\log W = N \log N - \sum N_1 \log N_1,$$

where

$$N_1 = \frac{N e^{-\epsilon_1/kT}}{f},$$

and

$$f = \sum e^{-\epsilon_1/kT}.$$

$k \log W$ proves to be the entropy.

We first express it in terms of f, assuming for the time being the identification.

If the values of N_1 and f are substituted in the expression for $k \log W$, we find

$$S = kN \log f + kNT \, d \log f/dT.$$

In making the substitution the following relation needs to be noted:

$$f = \sum e^{-\epsilon_1/kT}$$

$$\frac{df}{dT} = \sum \frac{\epsilon_1 e^{-\epsilon_1/kT}}{kT^2},$$

therefore

$$\sum \epsilon_1 e^{-\epsilon_1/kT} = kT^2 \frac{df}{dT}.$$

This also gives us the value for the total energy in terms of f, since the total energy is given by

$$E = \sum \epsilon_1 N_1 = \sum \frac{\epsilon_1 N e^{-\epsilon_1/kT}}{f}$$

$$= \frac{N}{f} kT^2 \frac{df}{dT}.$$

Therefore

$$E = NkT^2 \, d \log f/dT.$$

From the energy and the entropy the free energy is found by the thermodynamic relation

$$F = E - TS$$

$$= NkT^2 \, d \log f/dT - kNT \log f - kNT^2 \, d \log f/dT$$

$$F = -kNT \log f.$$

* See Fowler, *Statistical Mechanics.*

Thus, writing $kN = R$, we have

$$E = RT^2 d\log f/dT$$
$$S = R\log f + RT d\log f/dT$$
$$F = -RT\log f.$$

A more subtle problem is to express external work in terms of the statistical quantities. The key to it lies in the following consideration. If an external agency acts on a system so that all the molecules are affected and change their energies other than by going from one of the various states to another, i.e. so that the actual values of ϵ_1, ϵ_2,... are changed (as they will be, for example, if an electric potential is applied to the whole system uniformly, or if the whole system is set in motion so that every molecule receives a component of velocity distinguishable from its thermal motion), then we may say that external work is done on the system. If, on the other hand, there is no result which we can regard as common to all the molecules and express by a change in the various energy states themselves, but only a shift of molecules from lower into higher states, then we say that heat has been added to the system. To say that this distinction is not an absolute one, and that one process may quickly lead to the other, is only to express the inter-convertibility of heat and work.

Suppose some external variable x changes by dx so that ϵ_1 changes by $\frac{\partial\epsilon_1}{\partial x}dx$, then all the N_1 molecules in the first state change their energies, and similarly for other states. The external work done by the system will conversely be represented by a corresponding negative expression so that we have: work done by the system

$$dA = -\sum N_1\frac{\partial\epsilon_1}{\partial x}dx,$$

where dx is the change in the external variable.

Since

$$f = \sum e^{-\epsilon_1/kT},$$

$$\frac{\partial f}{\partial x} = -\sum e^{-\epsilon_1/kT}\frac{1}{kT}\frac{\partial\epsilon_1}{\partial x}.$$

Transposing, multiplying by N, and dividing by f,

$$RT\frac{\partial\log f}{\partial x} = -\sum\frac{Ne^{-\epsilon_1/kT}}{f}\frac{\partial\epsilon_1}{\partial x} = -\sum N_1\frac{\partial\epsilon_1}{\partial x}.$$

That is

$$RT\frac{\partial\log f}{\partial x}dx = dA.$$

Since $dA/dx = -\partial F/\partial x$, this completes the identification of $-RT\log f$ with the free energy.

From the equations at the top of page 29

$$S - \frac{E}{T} = R\log f.$$

Therefore

$$dS - \frac{dE}{T} = R\frac{\partial\log f}{\partial x}dx = \frac{dA}{T},$$

$$dS = \frac{dE+dA}{T} \quad \text{if } T \text{ is constant.}$$

$dE+dA$ represents the *total* heat supplied, so that

$$dS = \frac{dQ}{T}.$$

This identifies dS with the change in the ordinary thermodynamic entropy.

The Equipartition Law. Relation of the Statistical Temperature to the Gas Scale.

In its familiar form the equipartition law only applies in so far as the continuous distributions of the classical theory are regarded as adequate approximations to the quantum laws.

The number of molecules in a given state of energy ϵ is $Ae^{-\beta\epsilon}$, where A is a constant. With continuous ranges of variables a state has to be replaced by a range of coordinates $dq_1\,dq_2...dp_1\,dp_2...dp_n$, and the number of molecules in a given range is given by

$$dN/N = Ce^{-\beta\epsilon}\,dq_1\,dq_2...dp_1\,dp_2...dp_n,$$

where C is constant.

Since the total number in all ranges is N, we have

$$\iiint ... Ce^{-\beta\epsilon}\,dq_1\,dq_2...dp_1\,dp_2...dp_n = 1.$$

We carry out an integration of this expression by parts, regarding it as a product of dq_1 and of the remainder. By the ordinary rule the integration gives

$$\left[\iint ...q_1\,Ce^{-\beta\epsilon}\,dq_2...dp_1\,dp_2...dp_n\right]_{\text{lower limit}}^{\text{upper limit}}$$

$$+ \iiint ...q_1\,Ce^{-\beta\epsilon}\left(\beta\frac{\partial\epsilon}{\partial q_1}\right)dq_1\,dq_2...dp_1\,dp_2...dp_n.$$

The limits of q_1 are $+\infty$ and $-\infty$. Since the value of the energy is infinite for an infinite value of any variable on which it depends, and since $e^{-\infty}$ is of a higher order of smallness than $1/\infty$, the expression in the square brackets is zero.

Thus
$$\int\int\int \ldots \left(q_1 \frac{\partial\epsilon}{\partial q_1}\right) Ce^{-\beta\epsilon}\, dq_1\, dq_2\ldots dp_1\, dp_2\ldots dp_n = \frac{1}{\beta}.$$

The expression on the left is a value of $q_1(\partial\epsilon/\partial q_1)$ multiplied by the number of molecules for which the function has this value, integrated over all possible values of the variables and divided by the total number of molecules. It is, in fact, the average value of $q_1(\partial\epsilon/\partial q_1)$. The same result will be found for any other variable of which the energy is a function.

Therefore
$$\left[q_1\frac{\partial\epsilon}{\partial q_1}\right]_{\text{mean}} = \left[q_2\frac{\partial\epsilon}{\partial q_2}\right]_{\text{mean}} = \ldots = \frac{1}{\beta}.$$

Usually the energy can be expressed as a constant times the square of one of the variables, e.g. $\frac{1}{2}mv^2$, which is $p^2/2m$, $\frac{1}{2}I\omega^2$, or, for the potential energy of a simple harmonic oscillator, $\frac{1}{2}ax^2$.

If
$$\epsilon = aq^2,$$

$$\frac{\partial\epsilon}{\partial q} = 2aq,$$

$$q\frac{\partial\epsilon}{\partial q} = 2aq^2 = 2\epsilon.$$

Thus
$$\bar{\epsilon} = \frac{1}{2\beta}.$$

This will apply also to a single degree of freedom of translational motion. For the total translational energy we have, therefore,

$$\bar{E} = 3 \times \frac{1}{2\beta}.$$

From the theory of the pressure exerted by a gas we have
$$pV = RT = \tfrac{1}{3}Nm\bar{u}^2,$$

therefore   kinetic energy $= \tfrac{3}{2}RT$.

That is
$$\bar{E} = \tfrac{3}{2}kT,$$

but
$$\bar{E} = \frac{3}{2\beta},$$

whence
$$\beta = 1/kT.$$

Chemical Equilibrium.

The great principle underlying all statistical calculations is that systems composed of large numbers of individuals spend most of their time in conditions which differ very little from that corresponding to the maximum probability. The probability is measured by the number of ways in which the individuals can be assigned to the various possible states. Fundamental physical laws are involved in deciding what exactly constitutes a state.

So far we have only considered the assignment of molecules to energy states, the molecules themselves having been regarded as unchangeable individuals. But a diatomic molecule AB is capable of splitting up into atoms A and B, and, for a complete treatment, the individuals with which the statistical calculation must deal are the atoms themselves. If we consider the equilibrium

$$AB \rightleftharpoons A + B,$$

then we can define two conditions of an atom, namely free and combined. If all the atoms are free, or, on the other hand, if they are all combined, we have only one possible way of realizing each of these contingencies.

But if some are free and some combined, then large numbers of permutations of individuals between the free and combined conditions become possible. For arithmetical reasons, therefore, there will be a tendency for equilibria not to lie wholly on one side. The maximum probability corresponds to some intermediate position, and differs according to the form of the chemical equation, that for

$$AB \rightleftharpoons A + B$$

differing from that for $A_3 B \rightleftharpoons 3A + B.$

But the assignment of atoms to free or combined states is not the only assignment to be made. The free atoms have in their turn to be assigned to their various energy levels, and so have the molecules. Furthermore, the number and nature of the energy levels available depend upon the character of the molecules themselves, and therefore the final state of equilibrium is by no means simply that which makes the number of permutations between the free and combined conditions greatest, but that which makes the grand total of all possible permutations between free and combined and between the various energy levels of these two conditions the greatest.

It is a mere extension of the calculation already given for the energy distribution law to calculate the distribution of the atoms between all possible states and so to estimate the proportion which are free and the proportion which are combined. The calculation is rather cumbrous to perform *ab initio*. It involves, however, the repetition of operations which have already been performed and summarized in the formulae of the preceding sections. We therefore proceed as follows, making use of results already obtained.

The entropy of a gram molecule was shown to be

$$S = R\log f + E/T,$$

where f is the partition function of the molecular species in question.

E is the thermal energy. For a reason which will appear in a moment, we write $E = U - U_0$, where U is the total energy and U_0 the zero-point energy, i.e. the energy which molecules possess at the absolute zero, which does not change unless the molecule itself is changed chemically and which does not come into consideration when purely thermal changes occur.

U_0 has been introduced here because, when molecules suffer chemical change, the products formed may be presented with, or mulcted of, a supply of internal electronic energy, i.e. the heat of reaction, which does not enter into any calculation of their own properties as molecules so long as they retain their identity.

Thus $$S = R\log f + (U - U_0)/T$$

and the free energy of a gram molecule is

$$F = U - TS$$
$$= U_0 - RT\log f.$$

In the expression for the free energy U rather than E has now been written because we are going to envisage the possibility of chemical change, and when this occurs external work may be done at the expense not merely of the thermal energy of the molecules but also at that of the internal stores which become available when these molecules change their chemical identity.

If we now consider a chemical reaction such as

$$2H_2 + O_2 = 2H_2O,$$

then, counting reaction products as positive, we have the increase of free energy accompanying the change from left to right represented by $\sum nF$ when two gram molecules of steam are formed:

$$\Delta F = \sum nF = \sum nU_0 - RT\sum n\log f.$$
$$\sum nU_0 = \Delta U_0,$$

D

the heat of reaction (energy absorbed).

$$\Delta F = \Delta U_0 - RT \sum n \log f.$$

As has been shown, the partition functions are products of factors referring separately to the translational, vibrational, and rotational energies, and the translational partition function contains the volume. It is convenient to write $f = f_0 V$. Then, remembering that the concentration c is $1/V$, we have

$$\Delta F = \Delta U_0 - RT \sum n \log f_0 + RT \sum n \log c.$$

If all the concentrations happen to correspond to the equilibrium values, the change in free energy is zero:

$$\Delta F = \Delta U_0 - RT \sum n \log f_0 + RT \log K,$$

since by definition $\quad \log K = \sum n \log c_{equil}.$

Therefore
$$\log K = \sum n \log f_0 - \Delta U_0 / RT,$$
$$K = \prod (f_0) e^{-\Delta U_0 / RT},$$

where $\prod (f_0)$ is a product of partition functions built on the exact plan of the equilibrium constant, each f_0 replacing the corresponding c. For example, in the equilibrium of the system represented above

$$K = c^2_{H_2O} / c^2_{H_2} c_{O_2} = (f^2_{0\,H_2O} / f^2_{0\,H_2} f_{0\,O_2}) e^{-\Delta U_0 / RT},$$

a result of remarkable elegance and simplicity.

This expression for K shows clearly what factors determine the equilibrium between various chemical species at a given temperature. First, the form of the chemical equation determines whether there are more factors in the numerator or in the denominator of the equilibrium constant. Other things being equal, there is therefore less likely to be a favourable yield of product when many molecules associate to form few than when few dissociate to give many. Secondly, the values of the individual partition functions have an important influence, in the sense that the more energy states a molecule possesses the more likely it is to be formed. Thirdly, the heat of reaction exerts an influence which, at lower temperatures, is often nearly a decisive one (Berthelot principle). The greater the energy liberated in the reaction the larger the equilibrium constant.

It is of interest to observe directly the statistical reason for the appearance of the term $e^{-\Delta U_0 / RT}$ in the equilibrium constant. Suppose a single molecule A is transformed into another B with evolution of heat Q per gram molecule or q per molecule. In the dynamic equilibrium between the species A and B, whenever B molecules are formed from A they are formed as it were with a bonus of energy q. This is equivalent to a raising of the energy-zero of the B molecules by q. Thus the probability of any given state of energy η of the B molecules is no longer proportional to $e^{-\eta/kT}$ but to $e^{-(\eta-q)/kT}$. Every single state on the right of the chemical equation becomes increased in probability relative to the corresponding state on the left by the amount $e^{q/kT}$, that is, by $e^{-\Delta U_0/RT}$.

Consideration of Collision Numbers and of Rate Phenomena.

Consider first the equilibrium between two atoms A and B and the diatomic molecule AB:

$$K = \frac{[AB]}{[A][B]}.$$

This equilibrium constant is equal to $(f_{AB}/f_A f_B)\,e^{-\Delta U_0/RT}$. The partition functions for A and B contain factors for translational energy only, while that for AB contains in addition factors for rotational energy and for one degree of freedom of vibrational energy.

The value of K, therefore, is given by

$$\frac{\dfrac{\{2\pi(m_A+m_B)kT\}^{\frac{3}{2}}}{h^{3}}\dfrac{8\pi^2 IkT}{h^2}\dfrac{1}{1-e^{-h\nu/kT}}}{\dfrac{(2\pi m_A kT)^{\frac{3}{2}}}{h^3}\dfrac{(2\pi m_B kT)^{\frac{3}{2}}}{h^3}}e^{-\Delta U_0/RT},$$

where m_A and m_B are the masses. I, the moment of inertia, is given by $I = \{m_A m_B/(m_A+m_B)\}\sigma_{AB}^2$, σ_{AB} being the diameter of AB, and ν is the vibration frequency.

A particularly interesting case arises when the binding force between the two atoms is very weak, so that ν is small. The value of the vibrational partition function now reduces to $\dfrac{1}{1-(1-h\nu/kT)} = \dfrac{kT}{h\nu}$. Substituting this value and rearranging the terms, we obtain for the equilibrium constant

$$\frac{N_{AB}}{N_A N_B} = \frac{1}{\nu}\left(\frac{1}{m_A}+\frac{1}{m_B}\right)^{\frac{1}{2}}(8\pi kT)^{\frac{1}{2}}\sigma_{AB}^2\, e^{-\Delta U_0/RT}.$$

When the binding force is small enough $\Delta U_0 \to 0$, and the exponential term approaches unity. Therefore

$$\nu N_{AB} = N_A N_B\left(\frac{1}{m_A}+\frac{1}{m_B}\right)^{\frac{1}{2}}(8\pi kT)^{\frac{1}{2}}\sigma_{AB}^2.$$

In the limiting case now reached the binding force is so small that the molecule AB must dissociate at the end of a single vibration period, and indeed will only exist for one such period. In other words, the molecule AB is nothing but a pair of atoms in collision. The dissociation frequency νN_{AB} is thus simply the rate at which the atoms A and B emerge from collisions. The expression found for it is, in fact, identical with that already quoted for the collision rate of two unlike molecules (page 14). The calculation just given, although made for a pair of atoms, would apply equally well to a pair of molecules, because in the limiting case of such weak chemical interaction that the binding force vanishes, all the partition functions relating to complex internal vibrations are common both to the separate molecules A and B and to the pair AB and so cancel out, leaving only the terms which were used above for the diatomic system.

This example shows how we can pass from a consideration of equilibrium to a consideration of velocity. The statistical calculation gave us the number of pairs: the assumption that each pair broke up again at the end of a single period enabled us to calculate the rate of formation of the pairs. The process was in essence not very different from the direct calculation of a collision rate by the kinetic theory. It must, however, be emphasized very strongly indeed that the calculation of any rate from any equilibrium condition can only be done with the aid of an auxiliary assumption. This was clearly stated in the calculation just carried out, but in more difficult examples the corresponding assumption may not be so obvious. It is, however, always present either explicit or implicit. We see that this must be so when we remember that any equilibrium constant is a ratio of two velocity constants, and realize that a given *ratio* of a/b may be satisfied by an infinite set of values of a and b.

Distribution of Energy in Complex Molecules.

For some purposes we need to know the number of molecules which possess a total energy greater than an assigned amount in many degrees of freedom, without reference to the way in which it is shared between them. The calculation depends upon the following considerations.

Let p be a momentum coordinate of some particular kind, referring to any one of the possible types of motion. The corresponding energy is related to the momentum by an equation of the type

$$p = mx, \qquad \epsilon = \tfrac{1}{2}mx^2,$$

whence
$$\epsilon = p^2/2m.$$

The number of molecules N_1 in a given energy state is given by the general formula
$$N_1/N = e^{-\epsilon/kT} \Big/ \sum e^{-\epsilon/kT}.$$

Let q be the positional coordinate associated with p. Then the magnitude of a quantum state is given by $dpdq = h$.

It is convenient to pass from the quantum theory to the classical theory as an approximation, and to consider the number of molecules whose momenta lie between p and $p+dp$. Since the size of a state is as defined above, the number of states in the range, dp, will be equal to $dpdq/h$. Thus the number of molecules dN in this range is given by

$$dN/N = \frac{e^{-\epsilon/kT}\, dpdq/h}{\sum e^{-\epsilon/kT}}.$$

The summation can be represented approximately by a definite integral as follows:

$$\sum e^{-\epsilon/kT} = \frac{\sum e^{-\epsilon/kT} dpdq}{dpdq} = \frac{\int_0^\infty e^{-p^2/2mkT}\, dpdq}{h}$$

$$= \tfrac{1}{2}\sqrt{\pi}\,\sqrt{(2mkT)}\, dq/h.$$

Therefore
$$\frac{dN}{N} = \frac{e^{-\epsilon/kT}\, dpdq/h}{\tfrac{1}{2}\sqrt{\pi}\,\sqrt{(2mkT)}\, dq/h} = \frac{2e^{-\epsilon/kT}\, dp}{\sqrt{(2\pi mkT)}}.$$

Since $\epsilon = p^2/2m$, $\qquad p\,dp = m\,d\epsilon,$

$$dp = m\,d\epsilon/\sqrt{(2me)} = me^{-\frac{1}{2}}\,d\epsilon/\sqrt{(2m)},$$

$$\frac{dN}{N} = \frac{2e^{-\epsilon/kT}\, me^{-\frac{1}{2}}\, d\epsilon}{\sqrt{(2m)}\sqrt{(2m)}\sqrt{(\pi kT)}} = \frac{\epsilon^{-\frac{1}{2}} e^{-\epsilon/kT}\, d\epsilon}{\sqrt{(\pi kT)}}.$$

If E is $N\epsilon$ and $R = Nk$, then

$$\frac{dN}{N} = \frac{E^{-\frac{1}{2}} e^{-E/RT}\, dE}{\sqrt{(\pi RT)}}.$$

Thus the fractional number of molecules with energies corresponding to one single momentum coordinate is given. There is nothing in the argument which cannot be applied to any kind of energy.

Thus the expression just recorded for dN/N need not be restricted to kinetic energy of translation but may be applied to any form, since rotational energy and vibrational kinetic energy may be expressed in a quadratic form, as may also the potential energy associated with simple harmonic motion.

Now let us consider a molecule of complex structure; the total energy may be made up in many different ways. Let each kind of energy, potential and kinetic, in each degree of freedom be representable by a 'square term' and let there be n such terms. The chance of an energy between Q and $Q+dQ$ in one particular term, e.g. one particular component of translational motion, or a particular vibration, is given by

$$\frac{Q^{-\frac{1}{2}}}{(\pi RT)^{\frac{1}{2}}} e^{-Q/RT} dQ.$$

The chance that simultaneously the energy in one term is between Q_1 and Q_1+dQ_1 and in another term between Q_2 and Q_2+dQ_2 is the product of the expressions for Q_1 and Q_2, namely

$$\frac{1}{\pi RT} Q_1^{-\frac{1}{2}} e^{-Q_1/RT} dQ_1 \times Q_2^{-\frac{1}{2}} e^{-Q_2/RT} dQ_2.$$

Suppose $$Q_1+Q_2 = E.$$

We may now inquire what is the chance of a total energy between E and $E+dE$ in the two terms together without reference to how it is shared between them. This is given by putting $Q_2 = E-Q_1$ and then integrating with respect to Q_1 from 0 to E. Thus

$$\frac{dN}{N} = \frac{1}{\pi RT} \int_0^E Q_1^{-\frac{1}{2}} e^{-Q_1/RT} dQ_1 (E-Q_1)^{-\frac{1}{2}} e^{-(E-Q_1)/RT} dE.$$

$$= \frac{e^{-E/RT} dE}{\pi RT} \int_0^E Q_1^{-\frac{1}{2}} (E-Q_1)^{-\frac{1}{2}} dQ_1.$$

The value of the expression under the integral sign is π, as may be found by substituting $E \sin^2\theta = Q_1$.

Thus $$\frac{dN}{N} = \frac{e^{-E/RT} dE}{RT}.$$

If we now wish for the number of molecules with energy greater than E in the two terms jointly we integrate with respect to E from E to ∞ and obtain

$$\frac{1}{RT} \int_E^{\infty} e^{-E/RT} dE = e^{-E/RT}.$$

This expression is most important: it is the result already obtained for the probability of an energy greater than E for an oscillator, where the degree of freedom involves two square terms corresponding to the kinetic and the potential energy. But its importance lies in the fact that it also represents the chance of an energy greater than E in any other two terms jointly.

In a similar way we may represent the fractional number of molecules for which the total energy in n terms is between E and $E+dE$ by the expression

$$\frac{1}{(\pi RT)^{\frac{1}{2}n}} \int_0^E \int_0^E \cdots Q_1^{-\frac{1}{2}} e^{-Q_1/RT} \, dQ_1 \times Q_2^{-\frac{1}{2}} e^{-Q_2/RT} \, dQ_2 \cdots$$

$$\cdots \{E - (Q_1 + Q_2 \cdots)\}^{-\frac{1}{2}} e^{-\{E - (Q_1 + Q_2 \cdots)\}/RT} \, dE,$$

where $$Q_1 + Q_2 + \cdots = E.$$

This is because the total energy can be made up with anything from 0 to E in each term, subject to the condition that the total does not exceed E; and in general the chance of Q_1 in one term, Q_2 in the next, and so on, is the product of the separate probabilities.

The integral is equal to

$$\frac{e^{-E/RT} E^{(\frac{1}{2}n-1)} \, dE}{\Gamma(\frac{1}{2}n)(RT)^{\frac{1}{2}n}}.$$

The chance that a molecule possesses energy greater than E is

$$\frac{1}{\Gamma(\frac{1}{2}n)(RT)^{\frac{1}{2}n}} \int_E^\infty e^{-E/RT} E^{(\frac{1}{2}n-1)} \, dE.$$

This integral is equal to

$$e^{-E/RT} \left[\frac{1}{(\frac{1}{2}n-1)!} \left(\frac{E}{RT} \right)^{\frac{1}{2}n-1} + \frac{1}{(\frac{1}{2}n-2)!} \left(\frac{E}{RT} \right)^{\frac{1}{2}n-2} + \cdots + 1 \right].$$

When E/RT is large, as in most chemical applications, we may take the first term only of the expansion

$$\frac{e^{-E/RT}(E/RT)^{\frac{1}{2}n-1}}{(\frac{1}{2}n-1)!}.$$

This gives the chance of a total energy in the whole n terms which exceeds E without any restriction as to how the energy is shared among the separate terms.

This expression will be found of importance in dealing with chemical changes of complex molecules with many internal degrees of freedom. Each internal vibration contributes two quadratic terms, one for the kinetic energy and one for the potential energy. It should be realized that when we are dealing with the statistics of a large number of molecules the kinetic energy and the potential energy of a vibration are quite independent quantities. Some molecules at a given instant may have a large kinetic energy and a small potential energy and vice versa.

Distribution of Molecules in Fields of Force. The Boltzmann Principle.

Suppose that there are two regions of space in which the values of the potential energy of a molecule are respectively u_1 and u_2. If a molecule with other energy ϵ is transferred from one region to the other its total energy changes from $\epsilon + u_1$ to $\epsilon + u_2$. It may now be regarded as in a new state.

By the general law the relative numbers of molecules in the two states will be

$$N_2/N_1 = \frac{e^{-(\epsilon + u_2)/kT}}{e^{-(\epsilon + u_1)/kT}} = e^{-(u_2 - u_1)/kT} = e^{-\Delta u/kT}.$$

If the first region is one where the molecules are free from the action of any external forces, then it may be taken as the state of reference from which potential energy is measured, and we have the result that the density of molecules at a point where the potential energy is Δu is to the density in free space in the ratio $e^{-\Delta u/kT}$. It should be remembered that in the neighbourhood of an attracting centre the potential energy is negative if that remote from the centre is taken to approach zero: i.e. the molecules cluster more densely round the attracting centre, a result intuitively obvious.

III

THE ENERGY OF ACTIVATION

THE configuration of a stable molecule represents a minimum of potential energy. If stable molecules rearrange themselves by a chemical transformation to give fresh ones, the new configurations also represent minima of potential energy. There must be intermediate states where the potential energy is greater than in the initial or final states. Somewhere in the intermediate region there must be a maximum, which may be likened to a pass over which the molecules must travel in the course of the reaction. The top of this pass is what is sometimes called the transition state. In the transition state of the reaction $2HI = H_2 + I_2$ the two molecules of hydrogen iodide, or, if we consider the reverse reaction, the molecules of hydrogen and of iodine, have been so dislocated that reactants and products are indistinguishable. The energy which must be supplied to the reacting substances to make them capable of chemical transformation into the products is called the activation energy. The slowness of many chemical reactions is due to the fact that activated molecules are but rarely produced according to the chances of the molecular thermal motions. This is shown clearly by the study of the influence of temperature on the rate of reaction.

The Arrhenius Equation for the Variation of Reaction Velocity with Temperature.

In a balanced reaction, where the velocity constant of the direct reaction is k_1 and that of the reverse reaction is k_2, the variation with temperature of the equilibrium constant K, which equals k_1/k_2, is given by the van't Hoff equation

$$\frac{d \log K}{dT} = \frac{Q}{RT^2},$$

where Q is the heat of reaction.

Since
$$\log K = \log k_1 - \log k_2,$$

$$\frac{d \log k_1}{dT} - \frac{d \log k_2}{dT} = \frac{Q}{RT^2},$$

and therefore
$$\frac{d \log k_1}{dT} = \frac{A_1}{RT^2} + B$$

and
$$\frac{d \log k_2}{dT} = \frac{A_2}{RT^2} + B,$$

where
$$A_1 - A_2 = Q.$$

It does not follow from this that B is independent of temperature, but Arrhenius found empirically that the variation of the velocity constant k with temperature can be expressed satisfactorily by the simplified equation

$$\frac{d \log k}{dT} = \frac{A}{RT^2} \quad \text{or} \quad \log k = C - A/RT.$$

The method of testing this equation is to plot the logarithm of the velocity constant against the reciprocal of the absolute temperature. A straight line is obtained if the equation is satisfied. The slope of the line gives the value of A. The quantity A has the dimensions of energy, and if R is taken as $1 \cdot 98$ calories, then A is measured in calories per gram molecule.

Arrhenius[*] interpreted the equation by suggesting that there exists an equilibrium between normal molecules and what he called 'active' molecules, and that only the active molecules undergo chemical change. The active molecules were supposed to be formed endothermically from the normal molecules. The rapid increase in the rate of chemical change with rising temperature is therefore caused by the shift in the equilibrium between the two kinds of molecule, and, since k is proportional to the number of active molecules, the equation $d \log k/dT = A/RT^2$ represents this shift in the ordinary thermodynamic way. A is the heat absorbed in the formation of an active molecule from a normal one and is therefore called the heat of activation.

This view, though indefinite, is accepted as essentially correct. It is, however, no longer believed that anything of the nature of a tautomeric change is involved in the conversion of an ordinary molecule into an active one; it is, indeed, difficult to imagine what change simple molecules like hydrogen and iodine could suffer as a preliminary to chemical transformation. The active molecules are regarded simply as those endowed with exceptionally large amounts of energy. In this sense they are formed endothermically from the normal ones. The more precise physical significance of A will be discussed presently.

The Arrhenius equation applies equally well to homogeneous and heterogeneous reactions, as shown by various examples in Figs. 1 a, 1 b, 1 c, 1 d.

---

[*] *Z. physikal. Chem.*, 1889, **4**, 226.

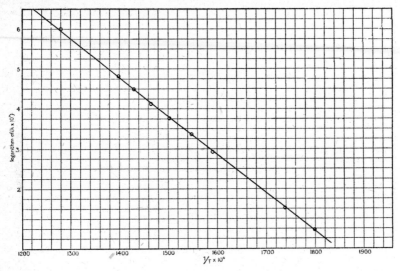

FIG. 1 *a*.—Influence of temperature on the rate of decomposition of hydrogen iodide.

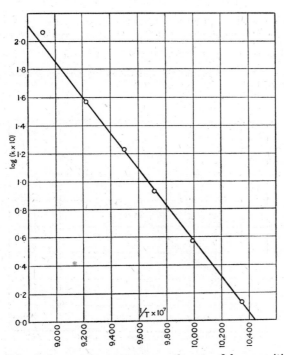

FIG. 1 *b*.—Influence of temperature on the rate of decomposition of nitrous oxide.

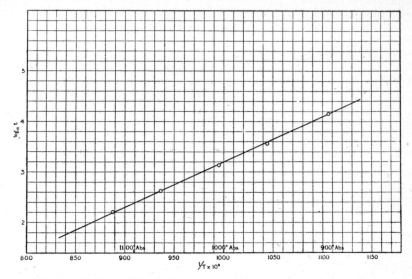

Fɪɢ. 1 c.—Influence of temperature on the rate of thermal decomposition of ammonia on a tungsten filament.

Instead of log k the values plotted in these two diagrams (figs. 1 c, 1 d) are those of log t, where t is the *time* required for a definite fraction of the reaction to accomplish itself at a given pressure. Since $t \propto \dfrac{1}{k}$, log k is equal to constant $-$ log t. This means that the slope of the curve is unchanged, but the curve runs up instead of down with increasing values of $1/T$.

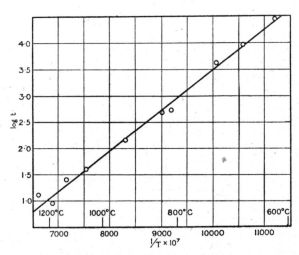

Fɪɢ. 1 d.—Influence of temperature on the heterogeneous decomposition of nitrous oxide on a platinum wire.

Heterogeneous and catalytic reactions also give straight lines over as wide ranges of temperature as can be investigated. For example, in the catalytic decomposition of ammonia on the surface of a tungsten wire the value of A remains constant over the range 904° to 1,129° abs. in a manner which confirms the equation completely.

The idea of activation applies to these catalytic reactions also, but

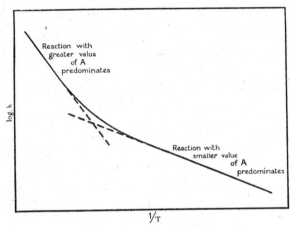

FIG. 2.—Influence of temperature on the speed of
a composite reaction.

A is naturally a function of the catalyst as well as of the reacting substances.

If when $\log k$ is plotted against $1/T$ there is any marked deviation from a straight line, this is an almost certain indication that the observed reaction is a composite one made up of two or more con-current reactions differently influenced by temperature. At low temperatures one of the reactions may preponderate so that the slope of the curve corresponds to the value of A proper to this reaction. If the second reaction has a larger temperature coefficient, its velocity will increase relatively to that of the first as the temperature rises, and ultimately it will constitute the major portion of the total change. The slope of the $(\log k, 1/T)$ curve now corresponds to the greater value of A characteristic of the second reaction. The influence of temperature on the composite reaction is represented by a curve similar to that shown in the figure.

Quite small deviations from the Arrhenius equation, only detectable by very careful experiment, occur for other reasons which will be referred to in a later section.

Statistical Meaning of the Arrhenius Equation.

Since general statistical considerations, as outlined in earlier chapters, show that the number of molecules with energy exceeding an amount E is proportional to a function which always contains the factor $e^{-E/RT}$, and in several important cases is represented exactly by this factor: and since molecules may reasonably be supposed to require dislocation before rearrangement, the natural interpretation of the Arrhenius equation is simply given. We suppose that the number of molecules reacting in unit time is proportional to the number whose energy exceeds E, an activation energy. Then we have

$$\text{rate of reaction} = Ce^{-E/RT},$$

where C is a quantity either independent of temperature, or whose temperature variation is small compared with the rapid variation of the exponential term.

If k is a velocity constant which defines the rate at a given temperature, we have

$$k = \chi e^{-E/RT},$$

whence

$$d \log k / dT = E/RT^2.$$

A Simple Example.

Nothing has so far been said about the constant χ of the equation given at the end of the last section. In certain simple examples it proves to be determined merely by the collision rate of the molecules. This may be illustrated by the decomposition of hydrogen iodide.

Experimental data relating to this reaction are discussed later. At the moment it suffices to say that the rate is proportional to the square of the hydrogen iodide concentration, showing that reaction is determined by collisions between pairs of molecules, as indeed the equation $2HI = H_2 + I_2$ suggests.

As shown in the first chapter, the number of molecules entering into collision per c.c. per second is given by

$$Z = \sqrt{2}\,\pi\sigma^2 \bar{u} n^2.$$

If we assume that the molecules at the moment of collision must between them have energy greater than E in two square terms, as would be required if, for example, the kinetic energy corresponding to the relative velocity of approach had to exceed E, then the rate would be given by

$$\sqrt{2}\,\pi\sigma^2 \bar{u} n^2 e^{-E/RT}.$$

That is, we assume

$$\frac{\text{number of effective collisions}}{\text{total number of collisions}} = e^{-E/RT}.$$

This very simple expression proves to be remarkably near the truth for the hydrogen iodide decomposition.

From the temperature coefficient of the rate of decomposition E is found to be 44,000 calories.

At 556° abs. $\bar{u}$ is found by the method of the first chapter to be $3\cdot3\times10^4$ cm. per second.

σ may be taken approximately as $3\cdot5\times10^{-8}$ cm.

If the concentration of the hydrogen iodide is one gram molecule per litre and Avogadro's number is $6\cdot1\times10^{23}$, then $n = 6\cdot1\times10^{20}$.

The value of $\sqrt{2}\,\pi\sigma^2\bar{u}n^2\,e^{-E/RT}$ is thus found to be $3\cdot25\times10^{14}$. This is the number of collisions per second between the activated molecules in one c.c.

Thus the number of molecules which should react in each second is $3\cdot25\times10^{14}$ per c.c. or $3\cdot25\times10^{17}$ per litre.

Expressing this as a fraction of a gram molecule by division with Avogadro's number the value

$$\frac{3\cdot25\times10^{17}}{6\cdot1\times10^{23}} = 5\cdot3\times10^{-7}$$

is obtained.

This gives the fraction of one gram molecule reacting in one second when the concentration is one gram molecule per litre. It is therefore the velocity constant k expressed in gram molecules per litre per second.

It agrees well with the experimentally obtained velocity constant $3\cdot5\times10^{-7}$.

This is a very striking calculation of the absolute velocity of a reaction, but we must examine carefully the exact significance of the degree of numerical agreement between the two values of k.

The value taken for σ is inevitably not very accurate, and, since k is proportional to the square of σ, a somewhat different value for the molecular diameter would completely destroy any close numerical agreement. Even more serious would be a change in the value of E, since small changes in E make a great difference in the exponential term $e^{-E/RT}$. The numerical concordance of the two values of k must therefore be considered as good as could possibly be expected.

The point of real significance is that an absolute value of k can be calculated which is of the right order of magnitude. The theory allows a calculation of the velocity constant from an experimentally determined value of E. E is subject to certain experimental errors which, from the nature of the relation between E and k, appear as proportional errors not in k itself but in the logarithm of k. The accuracy, therefore, with which the logarithm of k can be calculated is a just test of the theory; the accuracy with which k itself can be calculated is an excessively severe test, having regard to the inevitable errors involved in the determination of E.

The calculation in no way depends upon interpolation, but is absolute, there being nothing in the form of the equations which constrains $\log k$ to lie between fixed values. It might have almost any value, and an essentially wrong theory could lead to results tens of millions of times too large or too small. Hence an even less exact agreement than that obtained here would have been satisfactory from the point of view of ascertaining the general correctness of the assumptions made.

The best method of calculation is one which gives the experimental errors a proportional effect on the results. In this instance such a method is to compare the value of E calculated from the Arrhenius equation with that found from the relation

$$\frac{\text{number of effective collisions}}{\text{total number of collisions}} = e^{-E/RT}$$

When the comparison of the two values of E is made for the hydrogen iodide decomposition, practically identical values, namely 44,400 and 44,000 calories, are obtained.

General Significance of the Activation Energy.

The calculation outlined in the preceding section cannot be expected to apply very generally as far as the precise details are concerned.

For one thing, it is only in the very simplest molecules that we should expect activation to be a sufficient as well as a necessary condition for reaction. Factors such as the orientation of the molecules at the moment of impact, and the state of their internal vibrations, would be expected to play an important part. Secondly, the use of the simplest form of the distribution law can hardly be expected to be accurate for all purposes.

Nevertheless the above calculation gives us a very useful starting-point, in showing that a quite simple theory gives the correct order of magnitude for the absolute rate of a rather simple reaction. This helps to convince us of the reality of the activation energy.

Still more striking evidence, however, of the significance of the activation energy is provided by a comparison of the values of this energy for different reactions.

The function $e^{-E/RT}$ varies so rapidly with E and with T that for a very wide range of reactions it is far more important than any other factor in determining the rate of the reaction, and, in particular, changes in E are very often more important than other factors in determining the relative rates of different reactions.

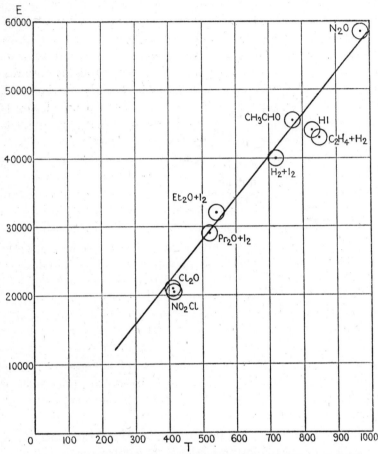

FIG. 3. Relation between heat of activation and temperature at which collision reactions attain an assigned rate.

(The reactions are the decompositions, or interactions of the substances indicated by the various formulae.)

If the constant χ in the equation $k = \chi e^{-E/RT}$ were the same for all reactions, then the temperature at which a reaction attained a given speed would be higher the higher the activation energy, and there would be a direct proportionality between the two. For quite an impressive number of reactions this conclusion is strikingly verified, as shown by Fig. 3.

E

E is the heat of activation calculated from the influence of temperature by applying the Arrhenius equation. T is the absolute temperature at which the several reactions would attain equal speeds. The actual speed chosen for purposes of illustration is one such that the total change would be half completed in ten minutes when the concentration of any reacting substance was 0·01 gram molecule per litre.

The parallelism between E and the absolute temperature at which the reaction attains an assigned speed is evident. It is also to be noted that the line drawn through the points is directed roughly towards the absolute zero. The various points would lie exactly on the line only if (1) all molecular diameters and velocities were identical, and (2) if the equation given above were quite rigidly applicable and all the reactions were built strictly upon the same kinetic plan. The non-fulfilment of the first condition is not very serious. The variation in the collision number from case to case will not exceed a factor of about five, which corresponds to twenty or thirty degrees of temperature on the average. There is obviously much more room for variations arising from non-fulfilment of the second condition. The reactions in question are all built roughly upon the same plan to the extent that they depend upon collisions and involve relatively simple activation processes. But nearly all reactions have kinetic peculiarities of their own which make them difficult to compare in detail, as will be seen when some of the examples are considered more fully. The curve in the figure, however, shows without any reasonable doubt that the factor $e^{-E/RT}$ is by far the most important one determining the rate of these collisional reactions. This is perhaps the most striking piece of evidence for the reality of the energy of activation. The deviations which are evident show that other factors besides activation are not without influence. Sometimes these factors become much more serious.

In the above examples the ratio of E/T is about the same as for the hydrogen iodide decomposition, where, as we have seen, the absolute rate is given as regards order of magnitude by the equation

$$\text{number of molecules reacting} = Z\,e^{-E/RT}.$$

Many examples are much more complex, and are not even approximately expressed by this simple formula. But, even then, the general parallelism of activation energy and reaction temperature remains discernible, as shown by the following table, which includes some reactions where chain processes make a certain contribution to the velocity.

Reaction, decomposition or transformation of	Temperature of equal reaction velocity (absolute)	Energy of activation (calories per gram molecule)
N_2O_5	328°	24,700
$C_3H_7.N{=}N.C_3H_7$	545°	40,900
$C_{10}H_{16}$	556°	43,700
$CH_3.N{=}N.CH_3$	599°	51,200
C_2H_5CHO	792°	51,000
$CH_3.O.CH_3$	800°	62,000
$C_2H_5.O.C_2H_5$	812°	67,000
$CH_3.CO.CH_3$	835°	68,500
C_2H_6	947°	74,500

It is convenient to widen the scope of the equation given on page 50 by writing

$$\text{number of molecules reacting} = PZe^{-E/RT},$$

where P is a factor representing the other unknown conditions which must be fulfilled.

Even when P is far removed from unity, we may still find, for a group of related reactions, that changes in E itself are all important in determining the changes in velocity which occur on passing from one to another. The best examples of this are found in solution. If we study, for example, the reactions of a series of benzene derivatives, the velocity may be varied over a very wide range by the introduction of different substituents, the general structure of the reactants, and the kinetic form of the reaction remaining strictly comparable throughout. If the velocity constant, which is proportional to the number of molecules reacting, is written according to the above equation,

$$\ln k = \ln C + \ln P + \ln Z - E/RT,$$

where C is a factor for the conversion of units, we see that on plotting $\log_{10}(k/Z)$ against the value of E from the Arrhenius equation, we shall obtain a straight line, provided that P is constant. Furthermore, the slope of this line will be $-2 \cdot 303 RT$.

This is illustrated in Fig. 4, which represents the results of experiments on the reaction between benzoyl chlorides and substituted anilines.* By varying the substituents the reaction rate can be changed over a range of more than 10^4. In this reaction the encounters occur between unlike molecules, and from the formula on page 14 it will be seen that Z_{AB} will be proportional to $1/M^{\frac{1}{2}}$, where $1/M = (1/M_A + 1/M_B)$, the diameters being assumed not to vary from case to case. Therefore, in the figure, $\log k\sqrt{M}$ is plotted. The line drawn through the point

* Williams and Hinshelwood, *J. Chem. Soc.*, 1934, 1079.

representing the reaction between the two unsubstituted compounds
has been given the slope $-2 \cdot 303 RT$. It is evident that the wide variations in velocity are in the main accounted for by the changes in the
activation energy.

These and many other examples leave us in no doubt about the
reality and the fundamental significance of the activation energy as

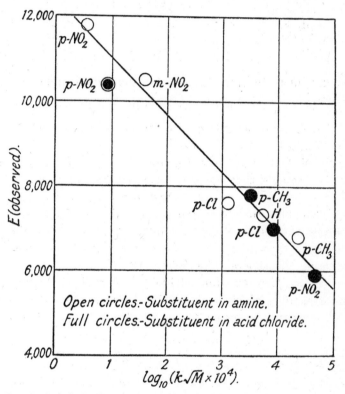

FIG. 4. Correlation between variations in velocity and changes in the
activation energy.

one of the major factors determining the absolute rate of chemical
reactions.

There is a not inconsiderable number of reactions, both in the gas
phase and in solution, where the absolute rate approximates in order
of magnitude to the collision number $\times e^{-E/RT}$. But this relation is
probably never exactly fulfilled: in very many cases it is not even
roughly true. But the regularities of a general statistical nature so far
disclosed will prove of great help in guiding us through the increasing
tangle of experimental fact.

Some Corrections Applicable to the Arrhenius Equation

(a) *Activation of Molecules with many Degrees of Freedom: Energy of Activation and 'Critical Increment'.*

The simple exponential factor $e^{-E/RT}$, as we have seen, is only applicable strictly to represent the probability of a total energy E of the colliding molecules in two quadratic terms. As an approximation it may be used for any quite small number of terms. In fact its applicability with such success in many examples might be taken to show that the activation process in such reactions was a relatively simple one, whatever its exact nature might be.

If we regard two colliding molecules as one system, the fraction of such systems which possess energy greater than E in n quadratic terms is approximately

$$\frac{e^{-E/RT}\left(\dfrac{E}{RT}\right)^{\frac{1}{2}n-1}}{(\tfrac{1}{2}n-1)!},$$

which is much larger than $e^{-E/RT}$ when n becomes considerable. (For very large values of n the expression passes through a maximum.)

The form of the Arrhenius equation for the variation of the velocity constant with temperature requires some consideration when n is large.

If k is proportional to $\dfrac{e^{-E/RT}\left(\dfrac{E}{RT}\right)^{\frac{1}{2}n-1}}{(\tfrac{1}{2}n-1)!}$, we have

$$\log k = \text{constant} - \frac{E}{RT} - (\tfrac{1}{2}n-1)\log T,$$

whence

$$\frac{d\log k}{dT} = \frac{E}{RT^2} - \frac{(\tfrac{1}{2}n-1)}{T}$$

$$= \frac{E-(\tfrac{1}{2}n-1)RT}{RT^2}.$$

Since the average energy of the molecules is $\tfrac{1}{2}RT$ for each of the n terms, $\tfrac{1}{2}nRT$ is the average energy of all the molecules. Thus we have $\dfrac{d\log k}{dT} = \dfrac{E+RT-\overline{U}}{RT^2}$, where $\overline{U}$ is the average energy. The formula $\dfrac{e^{-E/RT}\left(\dfrac{E}{RT}\right)^{\frac{1}{2}n-1}}{(\tfrac{1}{2}n-1)!}$ is only an approximation formula itself, the more correct expression being $\dfrac{1}{(\tfrac{1}{2}n-1)!\,(RT)^{\frac{1}{2}n}}\displaystyle\int_{E}^{\infty} e^{-E/RT}E^{\frac{1}{2}n-1}\,dE$. By employing this we may show that the really correct form of the Arrhenius equation is

$$\frac{d\log k}{dT} = \frac{\text{average energy of the activated molecules} - \text{average energy of all the molecules}}{RT^2} = \frac{\bar{E} - \bar{U}}{RT^2}.$$

For
$$k = \frac{A}{(\tfrac{1}{2}n-1)!}(RT)^{-\tfrac{1}{2}n}\int_E^\infty e^{-E/RT}E^{\tfrac{1}{2}n-1}\,dE,$$

where A is constant.

Differentiating under the integral sign with respect to T we find

$$\frac{dk}{dT} = \frac{A}{(\tfrac{1}{2}n-1)!}(RT)^{-\tfrac{1}{2}n}\int_E^\infty \frac{E}{RT^2}e^{-E/RT}E^{\tfrac{1}{2}n-1}\,dE -$$

$$-\frac{\tfrac{1}{2}nA}{(\tfrac{1}{2}n-1)!}R^{-\tfrac{1}{2}n}T^{-\tfrac{1}{2}n-1}\int_E^\infty e^{-E/RT}E^{\tfrac{1}{2}n-1}\,dE$$

$$\frac{1}{k}\frac{dk}{dT} = \frac{\displaystyle\int_E^\infty Ee^{-E/RT}E^{\tfrac{1}{2}n-1}\,dE}{RT^2\displaystyle\int_E^\infty e^{-E/RT}E^{\tfrac{1}{2}n-1}\,dE} - \frac{\tfrac{1}{2}n}{T}$$

$$\frac{d\log k}{dT} = \frac{\dfrac{\displaystyle\int_E^\infty Ee^{-E/RT}E^{\tfrac{1}{2}n-1}\,dE}{\displaystyle\int_E^\infty e^{-E/RT}E^{\tfrac{1}{2}n-1}\,dE} - \tfrac{1}{2}nRT}{RT^2}$$

$$= \frac{\text{average energy of all molecules with energy greater than } E - \text{average energy of all molecules}}{RT^2}$$

$$= \frac{\bar{E} - \bar{U}}{RT^2}.$$

For this reason the constant of the Arrhenius equation is sometimes called the critical increment of energy. When n is small E and $\bar{E} - U$ are very nearly equal.*

(b) Modification of the Arrhenius Equation for Reactions depending on Molecular Collisions at High Temperatures.

We have for a collisional reaction the equation

$$k = \text{const. } \bar{u}e^{-E/RT}.$$

* For a fuller discussion cf. Tolman, *J. Amer. Chem. Soc.*, 1925, **47**, 2652.

The term $e^{-E/RT}$ is the only one which varies considerably with temperature.

Strictly, however, the variation of $\bar{u}$ should be taken into account. Since $\bar{u}$ varies at $T^{\frac{1}{2}}$,

$$k = \text{const.} \sqrt{T} e^{-E/RT},$$

$$\log k = \log \text{const.} + \tfrac{1}{2} \log T - E/RT,$$

$$\frac{d \log k}{dT} = \frac{1}{2T} + \frac{E}{RT^2}$$

$$= \frac{E + \tfrac{1}{2}RT}{RT^2}.$$

For the decomposition of nitrous oxide, the slope of the $(\log k, 1/T)$ curve gave an uncorrected value E equal to 59,500 calories. The temperature varied by about 150 on either side of 1,000° abs. The corresponding values of $\tfrac{1}{2}RT$ varied, therefore, between 850 and 1,150 approximately. $\tfrac{1}{2}RT$ thus equals $1,000 \pm 150$. The uncorrected value of E, obtained directly from the Arrhenius equation, must therefore be diminished by this amount. Since 150 in 59,500 is considerably smaller than the experimental error, it is easily seen that no deviation of the curve from a straight line could have been detected. Nevertheless the mean correction amounting to 1,000 calories is appreciable, and reduces the value of E to that given, namely 58,500 calories. The correction might be automatically applied by plotting $\log k/\sqrt{T}$ instead of $\log k$ against the reciprocal of the temperature.

(c) *Variation of Activation Energy with Temperature.*

Although $\log k$ plotted against $1/T$ usually gives a straight line to a high degree of approximation, very careful experiment can sometimes detect a curvature, which means that E is varying slightly with temperature. Heat of reaction varies with temperature according to the well-known thermodynamic law which makes $d/dT(\Delta U) = \sum c$, the c terms being the specific heats of the substances involved in the chemical equation. Since heat of reaction is the difference of the activation energies of the direct and reverse reactions, it follows that, in principle, E is temperature-variable also. In practice the variation amounts to a few per cent. only over the range usually accessible to experiment.

The explanation depends upon facts of the following kind: suppose all molecules with energy greater than an amount E_0 can react: some molecules will always be present with energy much greater than E_0, and these may react more easily than those with a bare margin over the minimum: thus the reacting molecules have a complete spectrum of

E values, most, however, being confined to a narrow band near E_0. The contributions from the more energetic ones become relatively greater the higher the temperature of the system as a whole. Hence the slight shift in the value of the quantity which determines the slope of the Arrhenius line.

Rate of Reaction and Rate of Activation.

When molecules are activated in the actual collision by which they are transformed chemically, there is no distinction between rate of activation and rate of reaction. This corresponds to the simplest interpretation, namely, that reaction follows collisions in which the molecules possess or receive the requisite energy.

If the activation process is an independent one for the two molecules, such, for example, as the absorption of radiation, 'active molecules' exist in definite concentration, and have a definite average life, which may be terminated either by chemical transformation or by simple loss of energy, a process conveniently called deactivation.

In general we may distinguish two extreme cases: where all the molecules which are activated are transformed at once or at least before they lose their energy again, and, at the other extreme, where only a small proportion of the molecules which possess enough energy to react are actually transformed, most of them being deactivated again. When the second state of affairs prevails there is a definite concentration of active molecules in the system expressed by the appropriate energy distribution law.

The relations actually existing between rate of activation and rate of reaction may be roughly analysed as follows.

(a) In some reactions no activation of the molecules is required: this applies particularly to certain reactions involving free atoms, which are discussed further in a later section.

(b) The chemical transformation takes place in the activating collision. The efficiency of the process need not be unity, since some of the collisions, even though violent enough, may merely lead to 'reflection'. But in quite a number of examples the efficiency appears to approach unity.

(c) The production of the activated molecules may be quite independent of the collision in which they are chemically transformed, or indeed the final transformation may not depend upon a collision. The rate of activation and deactivation may both be great compared with the rate of reaction: this will appear to be characteristic of many unimolecular reactions.

(d) In exothermic reactions the energy liberated may be handed on to molecules of the reacting substance and activate them more rapidly than the normal process of collision. This gives rise to what is called a 'chain reaction'.

(e) If the initial activation process is vigorous enough, free atoms or free radicals may be formed, and these in their turn may cause a long series of reactions in which fresh atoms or radicals are continually regenerated with little or no fresh activation. This, indeed, is a very much commoner type of chain reaction than (d).

Reactions involving Free Atoms.

It is noteworthy that many chemical reactions, especially those in which halogens play a part, involve the intervention of free atoms. Atomic chlorine is involved at some stage of the reaction between hydrogen and chlorine and in the reaction between carbon monoxide and chlorine. Atomic bromine is involved in the reaction between hydrogen and bromine. In a number of photochemical reactions in solution between halogens and other substances the rate of reaction is proportional to the square root of the light intensity which indicates, as shown on page 104, that the primary process is the resolution of the halogen molecule into atoms. In addition to these examples we have the reactions, studied by Polanyi and others, between alkali metal atoms and halogen compounds. Some typical examples of these atomic reactions are tabulated below.

$$
\begin{array}{llll}
\text{(1 a)} & Cl_2 = Cl + Cl & \text{(1 b)} & Cl + Cl = Cl_2, \\
\text{(2 a)} & Br_2 = Br + Br & \text{(2 b)} & Br + Br = Br_2, \\
& \text{(3)} & Cl + Cl_2 = Cl_3, & \\
& \text{(4)} & H + HBr = H_2 + Br, & \\
& \text{(5)} & Na + Cl_2 = NaCl + Cl. &
\end{array}
$$

It is quite understandable that resolution into atoms should sometimes occur, since this is nothing but the limiting case of ordinary activation. Ordinarily activation of two molecules, AB and CD, consists in a loosening of the attachment of A to B and of C to D by a collision of sufficient violence to impart a considerable number of vibrational quanta to each molecule—normal heats of activation correspond to about 10 such quanta. AB and CD usually rearrange themselves to AC and BD without first being completely resolved into atoms. Resolution into atoms, however, as the study of band spectra shows, is the natural limit of the activation process, and indeed the amount of energy required to resolve the halogens into their atoms is of the same order of magnitude as the usual heats of activation. Thus the appearance of free atoms, especially as part of a complex series of changes, is far from being anomalous, or from constituting a sharp contrast with the class of reaction where complete resolution does not occur.

For a reaction between two atoms such as (1 b) or (2 b) no activation can be required. This is not necessarily true of reactions between an atom and a molecule, such as (4) or (5), although it is certainly fair to expect that the extent of the activation demanded, if any is demanded, will be much smaller. This anticipation is fully confirmed for exothermic reactions of this type.

Polanyi finds that in reaction (5) every collision is effective.

Formally, we might exemplify the extreme types of behaviour thus:

$$(a) \quad A_2 + B_2 + \text{energy} \rightarrow 2AB,$$
$$(b) \quad \begin{cases} A_2 + \text{energy} & \rightarrow A + A \\ A + B_2 & \rightarrow AB + B. \end{cases}$$

There is no theoretical reason why the second stage of (b) should not require some energy, though we expect it to be small. Actually a number of experimental results indicate that the amount required approaches zero in many exothermic reactions.*

Processes in which two atoms combine to give a single molecule demand further consideration. No activation is required, but another condition has to be fulfilled, as Herzfeld† and Polanyi‡ have pointed out. When two atoms collide, the nascent molecule which is formed contains all the energy of formation, and this, moreover, must be exactly quantized. Unless therefore its energy can be adjusted by a collision with a third molecule or with the wall of the vessel it will be incapable of continued existence and will fall apart again. Reactions of the type $A + BC = AC + B$ are not affected by these considerations, since the kinetic energy with which the two products of the reaction fly apart adjusts itself in accordance with the quantum demands of the molecule AB.

In the reaction between hydrogen and bromine Bodenstein found that a fraction of the order 1/1000 of the collisions between bromine atoms leads to combination at about 200° C., but how exact this esti-

---

* If the change were endothermic, a heat of activation equal to, but no greater than, the heat of reaction would correspond to the zero activation of the exothermic case.

† Z. Physik, 1922, 8, 132.

‡ Ibid., 1920, 1, 337. Compare also Born and Franck, Ann. Phys., IV, 1925, 76, 225.

mate is cannot easily be judged. At quite low gas-pressures, however, a still smaller value was found, which indicates that the ternary collisions were here beginning to be insufficient to stabilize all the potential bromine molecules.

The recombination of hydrogen atoms is often a wall reaction, where the requirements of the theory are automatically fulfilled. There is also a good deal of evidence that a process $2N + N_2 = 2N_2$ plays a part in the decay of active nitrogen.

The Potential-Energy Curves of Diatomic Molecules.

For the interpretation of the physical and chemical behaviour of diatomic molecules consideration of the potential-energy curve is often

of great help. This curve represents the potential energy of the molecule as a function of the distance between the atoms, and has the form shown in Fig. 5. At the point where $r = r_0$ the energy is a minimum and the molecule is in its normal equilibrium state. When it is vibrating the atoms may be at distances greater or smaller than r_0. For the smaller separations the energy increases very rapidly towards indefinitely great values, since the compressibility of a molecule is very limited. As the separation of the atoms exceeds the equilibrium value

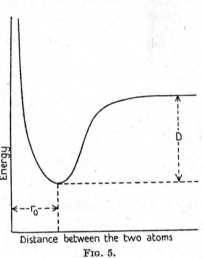

FIG. 5.

the energy increases at first rapidly and in approximate accordance with the law of a simple harmonic oscillator, and then more slowly as the binding forces between the atoms get weaker and weaker. Finally the energy reaches a constant limiting value corresponding to complete dissociation of the molecule. The length D in the figure represents the energy of dissociation. An exact theoretical equation for the form of this curve is hardly possible to obtain, since it will depend upon the variation of binding force with distance, but various semi-empirical equations are used, the constants in which can be evaluated by the aid of data obtained from band spectroscopy. One of the most convenient of these equations is that of Morse.*

* *Phys. Rev.*, 1929, **34**, 57.

The energy of the molecule is represented by the expression

$$E(r) = De^{-2a(r-r_0)} - 2De^{-a(r-r_0)}.$$

$E(r)$ is the energy for a displacement r of the two atoms, D is the dissociation energy, and a is a constant.

This expression possesses the following properties: as r approaches ∞, E comes asymptotically to the value zero, i.e. the energy of the completely separated atoms is taken as the standard level; E has a single minimum of $-D$ at $r = r_0$; when $r = 0$ the value of E, although not infinite as it should be, is very great, which is a good enough approximation. Thus the general shape of the curve is provided for. The equation has a further important property: if we write down Schrödinger's wave equation for an oscillator and substitute the above value for the potential energy and then determine the allowed values for the various energy levels of the vibrating system, we obtain a series of the same form as one of the best of the empirical spectroscopic equations. The constants of the two expressions can be equated, and thus a can be expressed in terms of spectroscopic data. For the nth level Morse's equation gives

$$W(n) = h\omega_0(n+\tfrac{1}{2}) - (h^2\omega_0^2/4D)(n+\tfrac{1}{2})^2.$$

The spectroscopic vibrational levels can be well expressed by the formula $W(n) = h\omega_0[(n+\tfrac{1}{2}) - x(n+\tfrac{1}{2})^2]$: ω_0 is the frequency of oscillations small enough to be simple harmonic; from the original equation it is easily found to be equal to $\dfrac{a}{2\pi}\left(\dfrac{2D}{\mu}\right)^{\frac{1}{2}}$, where μ is the 'reduced mass'.

After equation of constants and simplification, the value finally found for a is $0.2454(M\omega_0 x)^{\frac{1}{2}}$, where $M = M_1 M_2/(M_1+M_2)$, M_1 and M_2 being the atomic weights of the two nuclei on the oxygen scale and ω_0 being expressed in wave numbers. Morse also gives an empirical rule for finding r_0, viz. $r_0^3 \omega_0 = 3000$ Å.^{3}/cm.: the latter, however, is not regarded as of universal validity.

The qualitative application of the potential-energy curve in discussions about the behaviour of molecules on electronic excitation has already been mentioned. It finds a further application in calculations of interatomic forces, and, what is of special interest for the present purpose, in predictions of the magnitude of the activation energy of simple reactions.

Theoretical Calculation of Activation Energies.

From the point of view of chemical kinetics, the heat of activation is in one sense the fundamental quantity, and the principal problem is this: given the energy of activation for a chemical change of a definite type, what is the rate of reaction? In this way heat of activation bears to velocity the same sort of relation as that borne by the total heat of reaction to the equilibrium constant in applications of the third law of thermodynamics.

But the establishment of these connexions takes us only one definite stage: the further problem then arises of calculating heats of reaction and heats of activation in terms of molecular structures and forces.

The calculations can only be made in very simple cases, and then only rather roughly, but although they are unlikely to be applicable to most experimentally accessible reactions, they are of the greatest interest in principle.* They depend upon the Heitler-London theory of valency, aided by the more direct information that band spectra yield about the actual potential-energy curves of simple molecules.

The force between two atoms is made up of two parts: an electrostatic part called the Coulomb force, and the force depending upon the quantum-mechanical resonance phenomenon, this force being known usually as the 'exchange' force. In molecule formation the exchange force is the more important. In simple examples the magnitude of these different forces can be calculated.

Now in attempting to estimate the magnitude of an energy of activation we have to consider the forces existing between a number of atoms present together, and at various distances from one another, e.g. the forces between three atoms for a simple reaction of the type $Y+XZ = YX+Z$, or four atoms for one of the type

$$WX+YZ = YX+WZ.$$

This is made possible by the use of some approximate formulae of London's, which give the total energy of a system of three or four atoms in terms of the energies which these atoms would possess if they existed as isolated pairs (diatomic molecules) at their actual distances apart. Thus for three atoms the total energy is given by

$$E = Q+[\tfrac{1}{2}\{(\alpha-\beta)^2+(\alpha-\gamma)^2+(\beta-\gamma)^2\}]^{\frac{1}{2}},$$

where $Q = A+B+C$, the sum of the three Coulomb energies for the three atoms taken in pairs, and α, β, and γ are the exchange energies of the three possible isolated diatomic molecules (the atoms being taken in pairs at their actual distances in the triatomic system). For four atoms,

$$E = Q+[\tfrac{1}{2}\{(\alpha_1+\alpha_2-\beta_1-\beta_2)^2+(\alpha_1+\alpha_2-\gamma_1-\gamma_2)^2+(\beta_1+\beta_2-\gamma_1-\gamma_2)^2\}]^{\frac{1}{2}},$$

* Eyring and Polanyi, *Z. physikal. Chem.*, B, 1931, **12**, 279; Eyring, *J. Amer. Chem. Soc.*, 1931, **53**, 2537; *Trans. Faraday Soc.*, 1938, **34**, 3.

where Q is the sum of the six Coulomb energies, and α_1, α_2,..., etc., are the exchange energies of the six diatomic combinations.

The next step is to find the values of the exchange and Coulomb energies for the diatomic systems. This requires some rather drastic approximations. The total energies of the diatomic combinations can be found from the band spectra of the corresponding molecules as described in the previous section. A rough estimate, based upon the analogy of very simple examples such as the hydrogen molecule, where actual calculation is possible, is then made of the proportion of the total energy which is Coulomb energy and the proportion which is exchange energy: thus the separate terms in the above formulae are found. To assume that the proportion is constant for different distances of the atoms is obviously a rough and ready procedure, but is more or less justified by the fact that the Coulomb energy is in general only a small fraction of the total. We can now calculate, in principle, the total energy of any configuration of three or four atoms and can thus study its variation as one molecule approaches another from a great distance and comes into chemical reaction with it.

Starting with XZ as a molecule with its atoms at the normal equilibrium distance apart, and with the atom Y at a great distance, we can calculate the energy changes which occur as Y is brought up adiabatically to the molecule, and as Z subsequently recedes to an infinite distance, leaving YX as a molecule. It transpires that intermediate configurations possess a greater energy than the initial or final ones. In fact for the reaction to occur an 'energy pass' must be climbed. The minimum height of this pass is the energy of activation. One way for it to be climbed would be for the approaching atom to possess the necessary store of kinetic energy. Analogous considerations apply to the type of reaction involving two diatomic molecules. Corrections for change in the so-called zero-point energy of the molecules must be applied. The actual mass of calculation to be performed in estimating the energy of activation is reduced by the use of one or two simplifying principles, e.g. London showed that reactions of the type $Y+XZ$ require least activation when the three atoms are in a straight line.

Eyring and Polanyi in the above manner estimated the energy of activation of the reaction $H_{2\,para}+H = H_{2\,ortho}+H$ to be 13 kg.-cals., the experimental value being uncertain but between 4 and 11 kg.-cals. Their picture of what occurs during the reaction is as follows: in the molecule the atoms are separated by 0·76 Å.; the atom approaches and the potential energy of the system increases adiabatically until all three atoms are 0·96 Å. apart: the reaction may now go to completion or the system may return to its initial state.

They also estimate the heat of activation of

$$H+HBr = H_2+Br$$

to be about 10 kg.-cal. and of

$$H+Br_2 = HBr+Br$$

to be zero, which agrees in a general way with the experimental result that atomic reactions possess small inertia.

For bimolecular reactions of the types

$$H_2+X = HX+H; \quad H+X_2 = HX+X;$$

and

$$X_2+X' = XX'+X,$$

where X is a halogen, Eyring has made similar calculations. Only in the reaction $H_2+I_2 = 2HI$ is comparison with experiment possible. If the Coulomb energy is taken *ad hoc* as 3·5% of the total, an activation energy of 40,000 cals. in agreement with experiment is found: if it is taken as 10%, the value becomes 28,000 cals. Thus numerically the method is as yet undeveloped. The most interesting result of Eyring's calculations, however, is that the thermal reaction between hydrogen and iodine should involve molecular iodine, while with the other halogens reaction by way of atoms should be easier. This is in agreement with observation.

It should be mentioned that before Eyring and Polanyi, Villars* applied the information derived from potential-energy curves to get a fairly good value for the energy of activation of the reaction $2HI = H_2+I_2$, basing his calculation on an analogy to Franck and Condon's spectroscopic principle, namely, that the reaction should occur most readily when no change in nuclear distances had to accompany the process. Franck and Rabinowitsch† elaborated this idea, and deduced from it that reactions between halogen molecules should require little activation, while reactions between molecules such as hydrogen, oxygen, and nitrogen should possess great heats of activation.

Factors determining the Magnitude of Activation Energy.

In order to form a picture of the factors influencing the activation energy, we may consider how the activation energy is made up in a simple system such as $A+BC = AB+C$. According to the Heitler-London theory of the interaction of atoms and molecules, BC will repel A. This repulsion prevents the close approach of A, and preserves BC

* *J. Amer. Chem. Soc.*, 1930, **52**, 1733.   † *Z. Elektrochem.*, 1930, **36**, 794.

from reaction. For the mechanism of activation two extreme cases are imaginable: (1) A is forced up against the repulsion of BC until it is so close that it competes for B on equal terms with C, which is finally expelled; (2) BC is given so much energy that the bond between B and C is disrupted, after which A and B can combine without further opposition. As the calculations of Eyring and Polanyi showed,[*] it is usually more economical for the reaction to proceed by a compromise between these two mechanisms, A being forced up against the repulsion and the bond between B and C being stretched at the same time until A and C can compete on equal terms for B. Thus we can regard the activation energy as being made up of two parts: that required to overcome the repulsion of the approaching reagent, and that required to weaken the existing bond. In extreme cases one or the other of these might conceivably be the only factor. In practice we know, of course, that sometimes, though not usually, dissociation of one reactant is the controlling step in a reaction. The general case is represented below.

$$A \qquad\qquad\qquad B\text{———}^{r_0}\text{———}C \quad \text{(normal)}$$

$$A\text{-----}^{r}\text{-----}B\text{-----}^{r_1}\text{-----}C \quad \text{(activated)}$$

From the point of view of an Eyring-Polanyi diagram, four energies come into consideration: (1) the bond strength of the link BC, (2) the repulsion between A and BC, (3) the repulsion between AB and C, and (4) the bond strength of the link AB which is formed. Fig. 6 shows an energy diagram, which consists of two curves.[†] Curve I is a normal attraction curve with a minimum for any given distance between A and BC. As the distance between A and BC becomes smaller, this curve shifts upward on the diagram. Curve II is the repulsion curve for AB and C. The intersection of the two curves, slightly rounded off owing to resonance between two states, corresponds to the energy of the activated state, and the energy of activation is given by the vertical distance between the minimum of the BC attraction curve when A is at infinity and the intersection.

Of the energies enumerated above, positive increments in (1), (2) and (3) increase E, that in (1) by deepening the depression in curve I at all separations between A and BC, that in (2) by raising curve I without affecting the curve for infinite separation of A and BC, and that in (3) by the vertical displacement of curve II. On the other hand, a positive increment in (4) lowers the activation energy by lowering

---

[*] *Z. physikal. Chem.*, 1931, B, **12**, 279.

[†] Cf. Evans and Polanyi, *Trans. Faraday Soc.*, 1938, **34**, 11.

curve II, since a higher bond strength results in a lower potential energy· of the system $AB + C$. In the terminology of Evans and Polanyi, (1), (2), and (3) are sources of inertia, (4) of driving force.

For some purposes it is convenient, instead of considering all four terms separately, to consider the repulsion energy which must be overcome in bringing A up to the distance r of the transition state, and

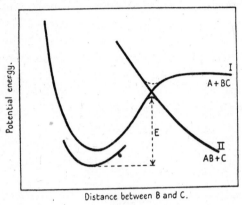

Distance between B and C.

FIG. 6.

energy which must be utilized in stretching BC from the length r_0 to r_1; r and r_1 are functions of the four terms referred to above, but the regrouping into two terms is convenient for approximate treatments. We may therefore speak of the activation energy as consisting of two parts: reagent repulsion energy, or simply *repulsion energy*, and *bond-stretching energy*.

This point of view is helpful in discussing the direction of the influence of substituents on the reactivity of organic compounds. Electron attracting or repelling groups may have opposite effects according as the mechanism of the reaction makes changes in bond energy or repulsion energy more important.*

ACTIVATION BY LIGHT

The mechanism of photochemical reactions and of thermal reactions is by no means always the same. For example, the decomposition of hydrogen iodide by light occurs by a direct resolution of a single molecule into an atom of hydrogen and an atom of iodine. The thermal reaction takes place by the interaction of two molecules with the splitting off of molecules of iodine and hydrogen: its heat of activation is

---

* Hinshelwood, Laidler, and Timm, *J. Chem. Soc.*, 1938, 848.

only 44,000 calories, whereas the process $HI = H+I$ would require the absorption of 69,000 calories. A quantum of the active light is large enough to supply this energy. (On the other hand, the thermal reaction of hydrogen bromide almost certainly proceeds by the atomic mechanism.) It is not at all difficult to see in a general way why there should be some sort of difference between the mechanism of thermal and of photochemical reactions. In the latter, the first stage is electronic excitation by a quantum of energy usually comparable with, or larger than, the heat of dissociation of the molecule into atoms or radicals: on the other hand, in thermal reactions, energy in varying amounts is continually entering and leaving the vibrational degrees of freedom of the molecules, and if the 'economical' bimolecular reaction is possible it will often take place without waiting for the more 'wasteful' reaction by the atomic mechanism.

The majority of photochemical reactions appear to depend on the primary production of free atoms or radicals. These can often be detected by direct chemical means, as, for example, when Pearson showed that a stream of aldehyde vapour, irradiated by ultra-violet light, contained particles capable of reacting with metals, and possessing the characteristics of methyl radicals. Resolution into atoms represents the extreme limit to which the activation of the vibrational degrees of freedom of a molecule can proceed: in this sense there is no discontinuity between the thermal and the photochemical process. But there is, of course, a profound difference in the way in which the energy reaches the vibrational degrees of freedom. The theory of the direct photochemical dissociation of a simple molecule has been given by Franck, and is illustrated in the figure on page 67.

The two curves represent the potential energy of the molecule, which for simplicity is assumed diatomic, as a function of the distance between the atoms. The lower one refers to a normal molecule, the upper one to a molecule electronically excited by the absorption of light. The point of minimum energy corresponds to the equilibrium position of the two atoms. If the molecule possesses a few quanta of vibrational energy it will vibrate, so that the extreme distances between the atoms correspond to $a_1 a_1$. With more quanta the vibration will be between the limits $b_1 b_1$, while if the vibrational energy is great enough an oscillation starting at c_1 will carry the atoms completely outside the range of the interatomic forces and result in dissociation. Suppose a molecule almost devoid of vibrational energy is electronically excited by absorption of light. According to Franck, this process is instantaneous compared with the vibration period: the interatomic distance has not time to change during absorption. The molecule arrives therefore at the point y vertically above the starting-point x. The electronically excited state possesses its own potential-energy curve, and commonly the minimum energy point of the excited state corresponds to a greater separation of the atoms than that of the unexcited state, i.e. electronic

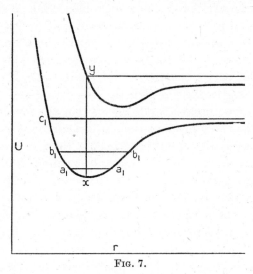

FIG. 7.

excitation weakens the binding of the atoms. The point y corresponds, therefore, to a high vibrational level of the new state, and as soon as the next half-period of oscillation is over the molecule will have fallen apart.

In one sense, therefore, this form of photochemical excitation is an indirect way of activating vibrational degrees of freedom.

This is not the only way in which dissociation takes place. Dissociation by rotation is known.* Occasionally bands break off suddenly at high values of the rotational quantum number, showing that the molecule in the higher rotational states is unstable; an example is found in the mercury hydride bands.

The higher electronic level is not necessarily unstable,† and direct dissociation of the molecule at the end of its vibration period is by no means bound to occur. But sometimes another extremely interesting phenomenon takes place. There may exist two (possibly several) excited

* Oldenburg, *Z. Physik*, 1929, **56**, 563.

† e.g. the minimum point of the upper curve in Fig. 7 may lie to the left of the minimum of the lower curve.

electronic levels of about the same energy. Transitions are possible from the one excited level to the other. The level to which the molecule is first raised may be stable: that to which it can subsequently make a transition unstable. Then we have the following sequence: excitation, time interval, spontaneous electronic rearrangement, dissociation within a period less than the time of rotation. This kind of transition from the original excited to a new unstable electronic state is revealed spectroscopically in a phenomenon discovered by Henri, who found that with decreasing wave-length, but before the region of continuous absorption is reached, the rotational fine structure of bands sometimes disappears, the bands themselves remaining quite distinct. At still shorter wave-lengths the fine structure may reappear. The occurrence of the diffuse structureless bands means that the rotations cease to be quantized while the vibrations remain quantized. This depends upon the fact that after absorption of the light there is a redistribution of energy within the molecule, the process occurring within a period which is small compared with the time of a rotation (about 10^{-11} second), but long compared with the time of a vibration (about 10^{-13} or 10^{-14} second). The rearrangement involves the actual dissociation of the molecule,* hence the continuous nature of the bands in spectral regions where this takes place.

The molecular process is called predissociation. Two types are distinguished, spontaneous and induced. In the latter the excited molecules only decompose when they suffer a collision which induces the redistribution of the energy. This form is recognized by a dependence upon pressure of the appearance of diffuseness in the spectrum. It should be mentioned that in actual practice with molecules other than the simplest it may be difficult to distinguish diffuseness arising from predissociation from diffuseness due to unresolvably complex structure.

The phenomenon of predissociation is important because it shows that spontaneous redistributions of energy involving the dissociation of a molecule are possible. The existence of an upper frequency limit to predissociation, and the analogous upper frequency limit of certain continuous spectra is important because it shows that not so much the total energy of the molecule, as its actual distribution in the right places, is the important factor in chemical change.

The first conclusion drawn from the combination of photochemical and spectroscopic evidence was that, in general, the primary act in most photochemical reactions was the resolution of the molecule into

* Bonhoeffer and Farkas, *Z. physikal. Chem.*, 1927, **134**, 337.

atoms: this would mean that, if the light quantum were great enough to cause dissociation, the chemical reaction would take place, but not otherwise. The existence of photochemical thresholds, or frequencies below which the quantum efficiency diminished steeply to zero, seemed to confirm this idea. But further investigation has shown that the relations between spectrum and photochemical behaviour are very complicated and difficult to analyse.

The really important contribution of photochemistry was that it first gave us the idea of chain reactions, because one light quantum was observed to bring about the change of many molecules. Chain reactions are most simply explained in terms of free atoms and free radicals, and thus we became familiar with their intervention in chemical mechanisms.

IV

COLLISION REACTIONS IN GASES

Homogeneous and Heterogeneous Reactions.

MANY reactions which at first sight might be thought to be reactions in the gaseous phase are found on closer investigation to take place entirely on the walls of the containing vessel. A true gas reaction is called a homogeneous reaction; a reaction taking place at the surface of a solid, and in particular on the walls of the containing vessel, is called a heterogeneous reaction. A reaction may be partly homogeneous and partly heterogeneous. In very many instances, however, the velocity of the heterogeneous reaction is relatively so great that the homogeneous reaction remains an insignificant fraction of the total change throughout the whole range of temperature where measurement of reaction velocity is practically possible. This circumstance renders the detection and measurement of the homogeneous part difficult or impossible. Examples of the very large number of predominantly heterogeneous changes are the thermal decomposition of the hydrides of arsenic and antimony, and the thermal decomposition of ammonia and of phosphine. In all these reactions, the progress of which has been observed in vessels of either glass, quartz, fused silica, or porcelain, the wall reaction predominates overwhelmingly at all temperatures where the speed is not too great to be measured.

The first necessity, therefore, in an experimental investigation is to determine whether the reaction dealt with is homogeneous or heterogeneous. The criterion of a homogeneous reaction is that the velocity is independent of the area of the surface of the vessel in which the reacting gases are contained; that of a heterogeneous reaction that the velocity is, for vessels of the same material and volume, directly proportional to the internal area.

If the volume, as well as the surface area, is varied, the velocity of reaction should be proportional to the ratio surface/volume. The usual way of varying this ratio is to have vessels of different shapes and volumes, or to add a packing of tubes of the same material. It may be desirable to obtain information as to whether a heterogeneous reaction accounts for any fraction of a change which is known to be at least predominantly homogeneous, and the method is to introduce into the reaction vessel, in the form of powder, a considerable quantity of the material of which the vessel is made. In this way a very large increase of surface is produced, and a heterogeneous reaction taking place to the extent of a few per cent. only of the total change can be detected.

If the homogeneous and heterogeneous reactions proceed at rates of the same order it is found that the curve obtained by plotting velocity of reaction against the ratio surface/volume does not pass through the origin. The velocity corresponding to zero value of this ratio is that of the homogeneous part of the reaction.

The Order of Gaseous Reactions.

The classical division of chemical reactions is into those of the first, second, and third order. These were also called unimolecular, bimolecular, and termolecular.

Those of the first order follow the equation

$$\frac{dx}{dt} = k(a-x),$$

whence
$$kt = \ln a/(a-x),$$

where a is the initial concentration, or pressure, and $(a-x)$ the concentration, or partial pressure of the reacting substance after time t.

For reactions of the second order the equation is

$$\frac{dx}{dt} = k(a-x)^2,$$

whence
$$kt = x/a(a-x),$$

and correspondingly for the third order.

Taking the time of half-change, that is, the time required for the concentration to fall to half its initial value, as τ, then for the first-order reaction $\tau = \frac{1}{k}\log 2$, and for the second-order reaction $\tau = 1/ka$.

Thus the 'half-life' in the first-order reaction is independent of the initial concentration, while in the second-order reaction it is inversely proportional to it. In general it is easily shown that in a reaction of the nth order, following the equation $-dc/dt = kc^n$, the time of half-change, or half-life, is inversely proportional to the $(n-1)$th power of the initial concentration. In dealing with gases concentration is proportional to the partial pressure if the volume of the system remains constant.

The sharpness of this criterion is illustrated by the two examples given below. The thermal decomposition of nitrous oxide at ordinary pressures is kinetically more nearly of the second order than of any other: that of phosphine, although really a heterogeneous reaction, follows the first-order law.

Thermal decomposition of nitrous oxide

Initial pressure (millimetres)	Half-life in seconds
296	255
139	470
52·5	860

Thermal decomposition of phosphine

Initial pressure	Half-life
707	84
79	84
37·5	83

The marked difference in the influence of initial pressure in the two examples is obvious.

Attempts to judge from the constancy or otherwise of k would give much less unequivocal results, since k sometimes shows a drift in value, caused by the catalytic action of the products, the imperfection of the experimental arrangements, side reactions, and other factors.

At first it was natural to assume that reactions of the first order involved the transformation of isolated molecules, that those of the second order required the presence of two molecules, and so on. Thus it was supposed that if the decomposition of nitrous oxide took place in accordance with the equation $N_2O = N_2+O$ it would be of the first order, while if it depended upon the process

$$2N_2O = 2N_2+O_2,$$

it would be of the second order.

As the above figures show, the reaction is more nearly of the second order than the first. If we say that this proves collisions to play a fundamental part in determining reaction, then we are on safe ground: but if we go on to infer that two molecules must actually be present at the moment when the chemical transformation is completed, then we are ignoring certain subtler aspects of the collision mechanism which will be explained below. A reaction which is, in fact, accomplished by a single molecule may be of the second order. This has led to a convention that the terms unimolecular, bimolecular, and termolecular should be reserved for the specification of the actual number of molecules involved in the crucial act of chemical change, while first order, second order, and so on should be used to describe the form of the differential equation governing the variation of reaction rate with pressure or concentration.

The way in which the distinction became clear was as follows. At first the classical division into well-defined orders was tacitly accepted as logical and natural, although there was very little experimental material with which it could be tested.

Comparatively rough tests for the pressure dependence of the reaction rate were obviously enough to distinguish between reactions where the half-time varied with pressure and those in which it was independent of the pressure. Reactions such as the decomposition of nitrous oxide or of ozone were classified as bimolecular, while the decomposition of nitrogen pentoxide proved by the same criterion to be unimolecular.

An interesting theoretical discussion of unimolecular reactions led to the realization that the matter must be more complex than the classical division suggested. Perrin* in 1919 argued that since the time for the completion of a given fraction of the change in a gaseous unimolecular reaction is independent of the pressure, it should be possible to expand the gas to infinite volume without influencing the number of molecules which undergo transformation in unit time. In some way, therefore, isolated molecules, cut off from all communication of energy by collision, become activated for chemical change. Perrin suggested that the cause of reaction was therefore to be sought in the action of radiation upon the molecules. This striking thesis seemed to lend support to the general radiation theory of chemical change put forward originally in an obscure form by Trautz,† and considerably developed by W. C. McC. Lewis,‡ but since abandoned.

Lindemann§ answered Perrin's argument by pointing out that molecules might actually receive their energy of activation by impact from other molecules, and nevertheless be transformed chemically at a rate which was independent of the pressure over a very large range, though not to the limit of infinite dilution, as Perrin had postulated.

It is only necessary to assume that a certain period of time elapses between the moment when a molecule receives the energy by collision and the moment of chemical transformation. This assumption is quite reasonable, for, in virtue of the internal motions, molecules must pass through maxima and minima of stability.

One may suppose the molecule to be activated by collision, and to decompose only when it passes through its next minimum of stability.

* *Ann. Phys.*, IX, 1919, **11**, 1.
† *Z. wiss. Photochem.*, 1906, **4**, 160. Compare also the reference given by Perrin, *Trans. Faraday Soc.*, 1922, **17**, 546.
‡ See, for example, *J. Chem. Soc.*, 1916, **109**, 796; 1917, **111**, 457; 1918, **113**, 471.
§ *Trans. Faraday Soc.*, 1922, **17**, 598.

If the average time elapsing between activation and chemical transformation is large compared with that between two impacts, most of
the molecules activated by one collision will lose their energy again by
a second collision before they have a chance to react. According to this
view, rate of activation is a very different thing from rate of reaction.
The state of affairs may be represented as follows:

$$\text{normal molecules} \leftrightharpoons \text{activated molecules}$$
$$\downarrow$$
$$\text{products of reaction.}$$

The processes indicated by the horizontal arrows take place very
rapidly compared with that indicated by the vertical arrow. A stationary state is thus set up, in which a constant fraction of the molecules, nearly proportional to $e^{-E/RT}$, possess the energy of activation,
and are liable to suffer transformation if they pass through the phase
of minimum stability before their next collision. A small fraction only
are so transformed, the majority being deactivated. The chemical
reaction, therefore, disturbs the concentration of active molecules very
little. The fraction $e^{-E/RT}$ is independent of pressure, and the number
of molecules reacting in unit time is a small constant fraction of this.
Thus the number reacting in unit time is also independent of the pressure, and all the conditions of a unimolecular reaction are realized.

At sufficiently low pressures, however, the time between two collisions
must become comparable with the period elapsing between activation
and reaction, so that the removal of molecules by chemical change
seriously diminishes the stationary concentration of activated molecules. When the pressure is very much reduced there must therefore
ultimately come a point where the unimolecular velocity constant
falls off.

The acceleration of many chemical reactions by light shows that there
is nothing improbable in principle about the supposition that molecules
are activated by the absorption of ordinary temperature radiation.
Only the fact that the amount of radiational energy contained in a
gaseous system at ordinary temperatures is small in comparison with
the molecular kinetic energy, except at very low pressures, as was long
ago shown, seems at first sight to render the hypothesis of activation
by infra-red radiation rather superfluous.

It was not long before experimental examples appeared of reactions
which followed the first-order law over a considerable range of pressure
but tended to adapt themselves more nearly to the second-order law
at lower pressures. These are found chiefly among the decompositions

of organic vapours such as propionic aldehyde,* various ethers,† azo-methane derivatives,‡ and many others. It proved, even, that the decomposition of nitrous oxide tended more and more towards the first order at high pressures.§ Other complexities also have appeared in the picture, but through the whole tangle it is clear that variable order rather than constant order is the characteristic of most gas reactions. The simplest treatment of variable order is given in the following section.

Transitions from First to Second Order. Activation by Collision.

The original idea about a unimolecular or a first-order reaction was that the molecules were activated independently of collisions. There is, however, no reasonable alternative mechanism to the collisional one. Although the collision process itself is of the second order, nevertheless the reaction as a whole may be of the first order over a wide range. This state of affairs is due to the fact that we have in principle two opposing processes of activation and deactivation. Rate of activation is proportional to number of collisions, and thus to the square of the concentration of the normal molecules: let us call this rate $k_1 c^2$, Rate of deactivation of active molecules, by loss of their energy, to normal molecules is proportional to the concentration of the active molecules and to c: let it be $k_2 ca$. But besides this physical deactivation, the active molecules suffer chemical transformation, in favourable cases, at a rate which may be called $k_3 a$. For a stationary concentration of active molecules,

$$k_1 c^2 = k_2 ca + k_3 a;$$

whence $k_3 a$, the rate of the chemical reaction, is

$$k_1 c^2 \Big/ \left(1 + \frac{k_2}{k_3} c\right).$$

This gives us a reaction the rate of which is proportional to a power of the concentration between the first and the second, i.e. in principle neither unimolecular nor bimolecular. *For a given reaction*, when c is small enough, the behaviour approaches as closely as desired to that of a bimolecular change in the classical sense; and when c is large enough, to that of a unimolecular reaction. *For a given concentration*, different reactions are nearly of the second order when k_2/k_3 is small,

* Hinshelwood and Thompson, *Proc. Roy. Soc.*, 1926, A, **113**, 221.

† Hinshelwood, ibid., 1927, A, **114**, 84; Hinshelwood and Askey, ibid., 1927, A, **115**, 215.

‡ Ramsperger, *J. Amer. Chem. Soc.*, 1927, **49**, 912, 1495.

§ Volmer and Nagasako, *Z. physikal. Chem.*, B, 1930, **10**, 414.

and nearly of the first when it is large. The former alternative involves a relatively small rate of deactivation, i.e. the molecule reacts before it has time to lose its energy. This condition is most easily fulfilled with a simple molecule where complex internal redistributions of the activation energy are not necessary for actual chemical transformation. Conversely, the latter alternative applies to complex molecules where such redistributions are likely to be necessary.

In spite of this blurring of the contrast between reactions of the first and second orders, there remains a sense in which a sharp distinction can be drawn between a unimolecular and a bimolecular reaction. Consider, for example, the decomposition of nitrous oxide. When this was first investigated from the kinetic point of view, the prominent question was simply whether the decomposition rate depended on the number of collisions or not. In this sense the reaction turned out to be bimolecular. The natural interpretation of this fact was that the process of decomposition occurred according to the equation $2N_2O = 2N_2 + O_2$. It is also possible, however, that after activation by collision the molecules part and that one (or each) independently suffers the process $N_2O = N_2 + O$. This can be called a unimolecular change, although the reaction is of the second order. In other words, we can call the reaction unimolecular when the *completion* of the chemical change after activation only requires the presence of one of the molecules which participated in the activation process: similarly, we can restrict the term bimolecular to reactions where the two molecules must be transformed simultaneously if they are to be transformed at all. If the molecular oxygen which is the product of the nitrous oxide decomposition has to be formed at the moment of reaction, and not by the subsequent combination of two separately produced atoms, then, in the present sense, the reaction is bimolecular. Conversely, the decomposition of acetaldehyde would be called unimolecular, even though of the second order, since the actual transformation does not demand the simultaneous presence of the two molecules—although activation does.

The difficulty now arises that the criterion just discussed is not an experimental one, like order of reaction, and doubts may arise whether a given reaction is unimolecular or bimolecular, even after kinetic measurements have been made. If the half-life varies with pressure at low pressures, more or less according to a second-order law, and becomes independent of the pressure at higher pressures, as in the examples which have been mentioned above, then it is evident that the activated molecules have survived the collision which produced them, and the reaction is unimolecular in the present sense. When, however, the reaction is observed to be of the second order up to the highest pressures to which the measurements have been carried, the interpretation is uncertain. It must always remain as a possibility that at a pressure still higher than any of those employed in the experiments the reaction would become of the first order, and thus reveal itself as unimolecular. This uncertainty affects reactions of the type $2XY = X_2 + Y_2$: reactions of the type $X_2 + Y_2 = 2XY$ must naturally have two molecules (or at any rate an atom and a molecule) present at the actual moment of chemical transformation. In a reaction of the former type it is sometimes found that the energy absorbed in the process $XY = X + Y$ is greater than the heat of activation of the observed reaction, as, for example, with the decomposition of hydrogen iodide, where the heat of activation is 44,000 calories while the heat of dissociation of HI into atoms is 71,000 calories. The heat of dissociation of oxygen was formerly thought to be very great: thus a process such as $N_2O = N_2 + O$ would have been considered impossible unless the observed heat of activation had been very much greater. But it is now known that the heat of dissociation of the oxygen molecule is not very much greater than 100,000 calories, i.e. the production of a single atom involves the absorption of not much more than 50,000 calories. The nitrous oxide molecule is formed endothermically from molecular nitrogen and oxygen, and the heat of activation of the decomposition is considerably greater than 50,000 calories, so that here, in contrast with the hydrogen iodide example, the unimolecular mechanism is possible as far as considerations of energy are concerned.

There must, then, as far as purely kinetic measurements go, remain an element of uncertainty about any second-order decomposition reaction of a single molecular species. No matter how extended the pressure range over which experiments have been made, there exists doubt about what will happen at still higher pressures. If experiments made at very high pressures reveal a transition to a reaction of the first order, another kind of doubt may arise, which although perhaps less important, should be mentioned. At high pressures the number of ternary collisions is not negligible.

Suppose, for example, that two nitrous oxide molecules at the time of impact require to remain in contact for a small but finite interval before the splitting off of an oxygen molecule is completed. (There is no difficulty in supposing that the activated molecules remain together as a sort of complex for a short interval before rearrangement.) If during this period a third molecule arrives, deactivation may occur. Let the activated complex be denoted by X. Its rate of formation will be $k[N_2O]^2$; it will be destroyed by chemical transformation at a rate $k'[X]$, and deactivated at a rate $k''[N_2O][X]$. The stationary concentration which is established is given by

$$k[N_2O]^2 = k'[X] + k''[N_2O][X];$$

thus the rate of reaction, which is proportional to $[X]$, is proportional to $k[N_2O]^2/(k' + k''[N_2O])$. When the nitrous oxide concentration becomes large enough this reduces to a first-order expression. The essential condition for a reaction to become kinetically of the first order is that something should emerge from the activating collision and be exposed to the possibility of deactivation before chemical transformation is completed. This something is usually assumed to be one molecule; but it might be a complex of two molecules, about to split off molecular oxygen, just as much as the single molecule about to lose an atom of oxygen. Thus, even first-order behaviour at very high pressures may not be quite certain proof of a unimolecular reaction, unless the influence of ternary collisions can be shown to be negligible.

Rate of Activation Processes.

The decomposition of various substances of fairly simple structure occurs at a rate whose order of magnitude is not far from that indicated by the equation

number of molecules reacting = collision number $\times e^{-E/RT}$.

This is roughly true for the decomposition of nitrous oxide, of hydrogen iodide, of acetaldehyde, and other reactions. But reactions were soon found where the number of molecules reacting in unit time was calculated to be several powers of ten greater than that predicted by the simple equation.

Nitrogen pentoxide decomposes at room temperatures about 10^5 times as rapidly as expected, at $400°$ propionic aldehyde 10^2 to 10^3 as rapidly, and at $800°$ acetone about 10^5 times as rapidly.

Two explanations of this interesting fact were soon forthcoming. On the one hand, that the numerous internal degrees of freedom were involved in the activation processes of complex molecules;[*] and, on the other hand, that the reactions were chain reactions.[†]

---

[*] Lewis and Smith, *J. Amer. Chem. Soc.*, 1925, **47**, 1508; Hinshelwood, *Proc. Roy. Soc.*, A, 1926, **113**, 230; Fowler and Rideal, ibid., A, 1927, **113**, 570.

[†] Christiansen and Kramers, *Z. physikal. Chem.*, 1923, **104**, 451.

Contribution to Activation Energy from Internal Degrees of Freedom.

The apparent difficulty of accounting for the activation rate in reactions of the kind referred to in the preceding section can be overcome by taking into account the internal degrees of freedom of the reacting molecules. If we assume that every kind of energy in all degrees of freedom can constitute or be converted into activation energy, then the possible activation rate may be up to a million times greater than that predicted by the simple formula. The chance that a molecule contains in n square terms an amount of energy greater than E is approximately

$$\frac{e^{-E/RT}(E/RT)^{\frac{1}{2}n-1}}{(\frac{1}{2}n-1)!}.$$

In this expression the factor multiplying the exponential factor becomes very large when n is considerable. The physical meaning of this is simply that if the total E can be made up by contributions in any proportion from any degree of freedom, then the total number of ways in which the energy can be stored in the molecule is very great. The essential idea is that in the activating collision the molecule acquires the energy in any form, and indeed goes on accumulating it in its various degrees of freedom until it possesses enough. Even then there is no reaction unless, as a result of the surging of the energy from one part of the molecule to another, there is a concentration in a particular bond or bonds. Chemical transformation then becomes possible. Since the energy may be in the molecule without finding its way to the right place, the time lag postulated in the Lindemann mechanism and the likelihood of deactivation rather than transformation follow naturally.

One great advantage of this theory is that the values of n, the number of degrees of freedom, which need to be invoked to account for the observed activation rates are very plausible, at least in the great majority of examples.

The simplest way of making an estimate of n is to observe the pressure at which the transition of the reaction from the first order to the second order begins to set in. If the rate is expressed by a first-order velocity constant k, there is usually found a pressure below which k begins to fall away from its steady value.

The following simple method of calculation is probably as accurate as is needed in the present state of our knowledge.*

* For more elaborate methods of treatment, which, however, yield *essentially* the same result, see Rice and Ramsperger, and Kassel (references on page 85).

Let it first be assumed that no chemical reaction is taking place in the gas. Of N molecules present let N_1 possess energy greater than E, the energy being distributed in n 'square terms'. These are the active molecules

$$N_1 = Nf(E)$$
$$= \frac{Ne^{-E/RT}(E/RT)^{\frac{1}{2}n-1}}{(\frac{1}{2}n-1)!}.$$

Let Z_1 be the number of molecules which enter the active state in unit time as a result of collisions, and Z_2 the number which leave it, also as a result of collisions.

For statistical equilibrium $Z_1 = Z_2$.

Active molecules are very exceptional ones, so that nearly every collision undergone by an active molecule results in its deactivation, rather than its activation to a higher degree. Thus Z_2 is very nearly equal to the number of collisions suffered in unit time by active molecules. Therefore

$$Z_2 = \text{total number } (Z) \text{ of collisions} \times \frac{\text{number of active molecules}}{\text{total number of molecules}}$$
$$= \frac{ZN}{N} \frac{e^{-E/RT}(E/RT)^{\frac{1}{2}n-1}}{(\frac{1}{2}n-1)!},$$

leaving out of account the very small number of collisions in which both the molecules have very high energy. This expression must also equal Z_1, since $Z_1 = Z_2$. If, now, the statistical equilibrium is disturbed by the removal of active molecules in chemical change, Z_1 is the maximum rate at which they can be re-formed. This determines the maximum rate that the chemical change can attain without the aid of chain mechanisms. This maximum rate of activation, in the region where k is constant, should be at least several times greater than the observed rate of reaction.

At the point where k begins to fall away from its normal value, it may be assumed that the rate of activation is just great enough to keep up the rate of reaction. By equating, therefore, the number of molecules reacting at the pressure where k begins to fall, to the expression for the rate of activation, the value of n may be found.

For the purposes of this calculation the value of E cannot be derived simply from the formula $d\log k/dT = E/RT^2$. Since the value of k is proportional to

$$\frac{e^{-E/RT}(E/RT)^{\frac{1}{2}n-1}}{(\frac{1}{2}n-1)!},$$

we find by taking logarithms and differentiating

$$\frac{d\log k}{dT} = \frac{E - (\tfrac{1}{2}n - 1)RT}{RT^2}$$

Thus the value obtained from the Arrhenius equation must be increased by $(\tfrac{1}{2}n - 1)RT$. This correction is relatively small, though not negligible.

Suppose, for example, that k begins to fall at about 400 mm. at 800° abs., the number of collisions per c.c. per second under these conditions being $1\cdot73 \times 10^{28}$ and the number of molecules reacting per c.c. per second being $6\cdot8 \times 10^{15}$. Suppose the value of E is

$$58500 + (\tfrac{1}{2}n - 1)RT.$$

Thus
$$\frac{e^{-\left\{\frac{58500 + (\frac{1}{2}n - 1)RT}{RT}\right\}}\left(\dfrac{58500 + (\frac{1}{2}n - 1)RT}{RT}\right)^{\frac{1}{2}n - 1}}{(\tfrac{1}{2}n - 1)!} = \frac{6\cdot8 \times 10^{15}}{1\cdot73 \times 10^{28}},$$

whence
$$\frac{e^{-(\frac{1}{2}n - 1)}\{36\cdot93 + (\tfrac{1}{2}n - 1)\}^{\frac{1}{2}n - 1}}{(\tfrac{1}{2}n - 1)!} = 4300.$$

If $n = 10$, the left-hand side is 2140, while if $n = 12$ it is 7270. n may therefore be taken as 11.

To account for the behaviour of dimethyl ether about 10 terms are needed, for diethyl ether 18; azomethane would require about 25, and germanium tetraethyl* about 8 to 10.

Since each internal vibration contributes two square terms, kinetic energy and potential energy, 5 to 9 internal vibrations must be involved in the activation of the ethers, and about 12 would be needed in the activation of azomethane. In general, having regard to the formulae of these molecules, the result is plausible.

The conclusion is interesting, since it is precisely for molecules of this complex internal structure, with several simultaneous vibrations, that complicated phase relations might be expected, leading to the time-lag between activation and reaction which is the essential condition of the Lindemann mechanism. There are two independent pieces of evidence. On the ne hand, the decrease of the velocity constant at lower pressures and its approach to a limiting value at higher pressures is most simply explained in terms of increasing deactivation by collision at higher pressures, and this can only occur when the time-lag exists. On the other hand, the complexity of the activation process, as revealed by the number of degrees of freedom which have to be

* Geddes and Mack, *J. Amer. Chem. Soc.*, 1930, **52**, 4372.

assumed to account for the rate, make the existence of such a time-lag appear very probable. The value of n required to account for the fact that the velocity constant for the decomposition of azoisopropane does not fall off at 0·25 mm. is from 45 to 50. This is rather a large value, but by no means an impossible one. The specific heat of gaseous acetone, which contains 10 atoms, is about 20 calories per gram molecule at about 150° C.; azoisopropane contains 22 atoms to the molecule, and might therefore have a specific heat of 40 to 50 calories. Since each square term in the energy expression contributes $\frac{1}{2}R$ calories per gram molecule there is obviously nothing unreasonable about the value which must be assigned to n to account for the constancy of k. If the velocity constant were found not to diminish at still lower pressures serious difficulties would begin to arise.

Such a difficulty does actually arise in the decomposition of nitrogen pentoxide. At low pressures nitrogen pentoxide reacts at a rate which looks like being rather greater than the maximum possible rate of activation by collision, however great a value of n be assumed. There is a limit to the maximum rate theoretically possible, since, when n is increased beyond a certain point, the increase in the term

$$E = E_{\text{Arrhenius}} + (\tfrac{1}{2}n - 1)RT$$

produces a decrease in the calculated rate which more than compensates for the increase due to the term $(E/RT)^{\frac{1}{2}n-1}$ multiplying the exponential term.

The nitrogen pentoxide decomposition is the only reaction definitely known to be anomalous in this respect, but the azoisopropane decomposition may have to be added to the list. Various explanations of the anomaly have been offered. Fowler and Rideal suggested that all the energy of two molecules in collision might flow into one of the molecules, and activate it. By considering the statistical equilibrium between activated and unactivated molecules, it can easily be shown that if it is possible for all the energy of two molecules in collision to become concentrated in one, then the effective radius of a molecule for deactivating collisions must be very many times greater than for activating collisions. This result is not a very plausible ore, though not definitely impossible. To explain, for example, the variation with pressure of the polarization of the resonance radiation of mercury vapour, the effective radius of the mercury atom has to be assumed considerably greater than that indicated by the kinetic theory.

It has also been suggested that the molecular diameter of nitrogen pentoxide is effectively much greater for activating collisions, as well as for deactivating collisions, than that calculated in the ordinary way from the kinetic theory. The difficulty about this suggestion is that the calculation of so many reaction rates can be carried out satisfactorily with the ordinary diameters; it is therefore rather an *ad hoc* procedure to alter them to explain one or two anomalous reactions.

The quantum-mechanical resonance phenomenon, and the actual existence of abnormal collision diameters in other connexions, must be remembered, of course, but a definite conclusion about this is hard to reach.

When the question of chain reactions has been considered it will be realized that forced or improbable explanations of high activation rates are now quite unnecessary, and can only be entertained when there is positive evidence against the existence of chains.

The observed rate of the cis-trans isomerization of the dimethyl ester of maleic acid,* in contrast with the examples referred to above, is very much slower than the possible rate of activation would allow it to be. Even if two square terms only are taken for the activation energy, the number of potentially activating collisions is about 10^4 times greater than the number of molecules reacting. For some reason, therefore, the collisions are peculiarly unfruitful. Some 'phase' factor plays an important part in determining the actual rearrangement of the molecule. Kistiakowsky and Nelles suggest that this rather unusual circumstance is connected with the fact that the reaction depends upon a special kind of mechanical motion, namely a rotation of heavy groups around the double bond. It may be mentioned here that very many other examples of reactions are known in which the efficiency of the potentially activating collisions is small. This applies especially to bimolecular reactions in solution.

Behaviour of Certain First-order Reactions at Low Pressures

(a) Influence of Foreign Gases.

It is true of large numbers of reactions that the first-order velocity constant has a more or less steady value at higher pressures and falls away at lower pressures. According to the theory outlined in the preceding sections, the fall is due to the failure of the collisions to maintain the Maxwell distribution at the lower pressures. The presence of foreign gases might therefore be expected to prevent or delay it. Their action seems to be a highly specific one.

* *J. Amer. Chem. Soc.*, 1932, **54**, 2208.

It is, however, a remarkable fact that in the presence of a sufficient concentration of hydrogen the velocity constant in a number of examples (propionic aldehyde, diethyl and other ethers) does not diminish but retains its normal value exactly when the partial pressure of the reacting gas is decreased (see page 129). There is apparently no question of any reducing or other purely chemical action of the hydrogen, because it is without influence when the initial pressure of the reacting gas is above a certain limit, and, moreover, no pressure of hydrogen can increase the velocity constant to a value greater than the normal limiting value characteristic of higher pressures. The hydrogen thus appears to act merely by maintaining the Maxwell distribution of energy among the molecules of the reacting gas, when the supply of active molecules would otherwise begin to fall short of that required to keep the constant at its normal value.

All this is in complete accordance with expectation; but it is remarkable that the action of hydrogen is so specific, and that helium, nitrogen, and other gases do not have a similar effect. The molecular velocity of hydrogen is much greater than that of any other gas, being nearly four times as great, for example, as that of nitrogen. Thus the molecules of the reacting gas will suffer approximately four times as many collisions with hydrogen as they would with nitrogen at the same pressure. Helium, which is the only gas with a molecular velocity approaching that of hydrogen, has only three degrees of freedom as compared with the five of hydrogen and therefore could communicate less energy than hydrogen. Qualitatively therefore the exceptional position of hydrogen is understandable, but quantitatively the differences seem to be greater than can be accounted for in this way. The advantage that hydrogen possesses in virtue of its great velocity over all gases except helium, and over helium in virtue of its five degrees of freedom, appears to be reinforced by some specific factor.* This influence of hydrogen as a distributor of energy, although exceptional and specific, is not unique. The reaction products in the decomposition of azomethane appear to be able to keep the velocity constant at its normal value, since the constant does not drop in the course of the reaction in the way which would be expected from the falling partial pressure of the reacting gas.

Studies of the dispersion of sound waves in gases show that energy exchanges are in general highly specific. The principle of the method

---

* Before a purely 'chemical' explanation can be accepted we must show that it would account for the inability of hydrogen to increase the rate beyond the 'normal' rate (see above).

is as follows. The velocity of sound in a gas depends upon γ, the ratio of the specific heats. At very high frequencies the adiabatic changes accompanying the passage of sound through a gas are too rapid to allow the establishment of equilibrium between the translational and vibrational degrees of freedom of the molecules: thus the effective value of γ will change at frequencies where the failure of complete energy equilibrium sets in. From the curve of this variation it is possible to calculate the number of collisions which, on the average, are necessary for the transfer of one quantum of energy from the vibrational to the translational form. The influence of other gases on the excitation of the vibrations of nitrous oxide has, among other examples, been carefully studied. The results are by no means simple to interpret, but show that the efficiency of different gases varies between very wide limits indeed.

From the theoretical point of view it appears that the important factor in energy transfers is the degree of mutual disturbance of the potential-energy curves of the two molecules between which they occur. This naturally leaves room for the most diverse specific influences.*

(b) Form of the Curve Connecting k and Pressure.

This problem has been treated in detail by Rice and Ramsperger† and by Kassel,‡ who show that the exact form of the curve may be used to decide how the transformation probability of the molecule depends upon its energy content. Since in a complex molecule the energy must become concentrated before actual chemical transformation takes place, the chance of reaction ought to increase steadily with any excess of energy over the minimum requirement E. The larger this excess the sooner will a specified amount find its way into a given linkage.

The following is a simplified treatment of the problem.

Taking the equation, given on page 75, for the balance between activation, deactivation, and transformation, and rewriting it, we obtain
$$k_1 c^2 - k_2 c a - k_3 a = 0.$$
The rate of reaction is
$$k_3 a = k_1 c^2 \Big/ \left(1 + \frac{k_2}{k_3} c\right).$$

---

* See Eucken and Becker, *Z. physikal. Chem.*, 1933, B, **20**, 467; Franck and Eucken, ibid., 460; Eucken and Küchler, *Physikal. Z.*, 1938, **39**, 831; Eucken, *Oesterr. Chemiker-Zeitung*, 1935, no. 20, 1; and for discussion of relation to kinetics, Patat, *Z. Elektrochem.*, 1936, **42**, 85, 265.

† *J. Amer. Chem. Soc.*, 1927, **49**, 1617; ibid., 1928, **50**, 617.

‡ *J. Physical Chem.*, 1928, **32**, 225.

This may be written kc, where k is the variable first-order constant.

Therefore
$$\frac{1}{k} = \frac{1}{k_1 c} + \frac{k_2}{k_3 k_1}.$$

Thus the reciprocal of k plotted against the reciprocal of the initial pressure should give a straight line. This argument tacitly assumes k_3 to be constant. It is, however, reasonable to suppose that the molecules with greater energies are more readily transformed chemically, while those with smaller energies require longer and, therefore, are relatively more often deactivated. The lower the pressure, however, the longer is the time during which molecules are left undisturbed: therefore the greater is the *relative* contribution to the reaction from the molecules with the smaller transformation probabilities. Now the intercept of the curve of $1/k$ against $1/c$ on the axis is $k_2/k_3 k_1$. The lower the pressure the greater is the contribution from molecules with small values of k_3, so that the intercept is steadily changing: in other words, the line will not be straight but will show a characteristic curvature.

Taken as a whole the experimental results conform best to the idea that k_3 increases with the energy. Unfortunately, however, two sets of complications, which will be outlined in the following sections, make the detailed analysis of the curves in some cases meaningless and in others doubtful, so that at the moment the idea is supported more by its inherent reasonableness than by unquestionable experimental evidence.

Chain Mechanisms.

That first-order reactions might take place by a chain process was first suggested by Christiansen and Kramers* to account for difficulties which were felt about the activation rate before the magnitude of the contribution from internal degrees of freedom was realized. The kind of chain suggested was one in which the energy of activation, augmented by the heat liberated in the reaction itself, was handed on from the products to fresh molecules of reactant. It was shown that reactions depending on such a process could follow a first-order law. The objection to the theory in its original form was that inert gases, including the reaction products themselves, should have helped to dissipate the energy and so retard the change. Such retardation is not generally observed.

Several discoveries, however, contributed to place the whole chain theory in a new light.

* *Z. physikal. Chem.*, 1923, **104**, 451.

The combination of hydrogen and oxygen, and other combustion reactions proved to possess very unusual kinetic characteristics which gave unmistakable evidence that long chains were involved.

The revision of the values for the dissociation energies of simple molecules made it clear that the primary formation of free atoms and radicals was a less difficult process than had hitherto been imagined, and that, therefore, their participation in chemical reactions might be plausibly assumed. The undoubted chain reactions involved in combustion processes proved to be most easily interpretable in terms of mechanisms depending upon atoms and radicals rather than activated molecules.

Paneth discovered that in pyrolytic reactions at high temperatures organic radicals such as methyl could be produced, and that they could be detected by passage over mirrors of mercury or tellurium with which they combined giving metal alkyl derivatives. It was, therefore, reasonable to use free organic radicals in making hypotheses about reaction mechanisms.

F. O. Rice devised possible free radical mechanisms for many reactions, such as the decomposition of hydrocarbons, without, however, producing positive evidence that the reactions did in fact take place in this way. Photochemical investigations, nevertheless, showed that several organic decomposition reactions could occur by the radical mechanism, the photolysis of acetaldehyde at 300° C., for example, being found to have a quantum yield of several hundred.*

Rice and Herzfeld† investigated the reaction orders to which various hypothetical chain mechanisms would lead: and with plausible assumptions about various dissociation energies showed in a large number of examples that the propagation of radical chains should be possible. This still leaves open the question as to how far the radical mechanisms do in reality operate in thermal reactions, especially at temperatures where the rates can be measured.

The problem now assumes the following aspect. In the decomposition of a substance such as acetaldehyde, the initial production of a free radical by a process such as $CH_3CHO = CH_3 + CHO$ will require a much higher activation energy than the alternative process of direct molecular rearrangement to CH_4 and CO. It will indeed require an energy equal to the strength of the carbon-carbon link, which is not less than about 80,000 calories per gram molecule: while the observed

* Leermakers, *J. Amer. Chem. Soc.*, 1934, **56**, 1537.
† Rice and Herzfeld, ibid., 1934, **56**, 284.

activation energy of the reaction is about 47,000 calories. On the other hand, once the first free radicals are produced, they will enter into chains of reactions in which they are repeatedly regenerated: and these reactions will require very little activation energy in comparison with the primary process, or even compared with the direct molecular rearrangement. Therefore chains of great length may be propagated. We have then the possibility of two competing processes: on the one hand, the relatively easy rearrangement of the original molecule to give saturated products in a single act; and, on the other hand, the much less likely process of radical formation, the effect of which, however, is magnified many times over by its catastrophic consequences. Which mode will on balance predominate and contribute most to the observed reaction is impossible to predict. Experiment alone can decide.

The upshot of various investigations seems to be that the chances are rather evenly balanced: that in some reactions the chain processes play an important part, and in others a negligible one. Sometimes the photochemical reaction may take place by a mechanism involving long chains, while the corresponding thermal reaction is a direct molecular rearrangement. On the whole it may be said that chain processes play an important but not a predominant role. General statements of this kind are, of course, often enough subject to modification as the number of examples investigated grows larger.

It seems probable, to quote a few examples, that the thermal and photochemical decompositions of acetone are not chain reactions, that the thermal decomposition of acetaldehyde is chain-free while the photochemical reaction at 300° involves chains of several hundred units: that with the ethers there is a mixture of chain reaction and direct rearrangement, the proportion of chain reaction diminishing as the homologous series is ascended.

If free radicals are introduced artificially into a reaction system, they may initiate chain processes which would not be making an appreciable contribution in the normal way. Many interesting observations of this kind have been made:* they show the possibility of chain processes in various systems, and sometimes their non-occurrence in others, but cannot be taken to show that the normal reaction of a given substance is necessarily of the chain type.

Before discussing the criteria by which the presence of radical chains may be judged, it will be convenient to consider the relation between

---

* Sickman and Allen, *J. Amer. Chem. Soc.*, 1934, **56**, 1251; Rice, Rodowskas, and Lewis, ibid., 1934, **56**, 2497.

reaction rate and pressure in such changes. It will appear that this does not differ so much from that predicted by the Lindemann theory as to make a decision between the two mechanisms easy without the aid of independent information.

Relation between Rate and Pressure in Radical Chain Reactions.

Case 1. This may be illustrated by calculations based upon a hypothetical mechanism for the thermal decomposition of acetaldehyde.

$$CH_3CHO = CH_3 + CHO \tag{1}$$

$$CH_3CHO + CH_3 = CH_4 + CO + CH_3 \tag{2}$$

$$2CH_3 = C_2H_6. \tag{3}$$

The concentration of methyl radicals in the system will increase until the rate of formation is equal to the rate of removal. *Assuming* the primary reaction (1) to be of the first order, and (2) and (3) to be of the second order, we have:

$$\frac{d[CH_3]}{dt} = k_1[CH_3CHO] - k_3[CH_3]^2 = 0,$$

whence

$$[CH_3] = \sqrt{\left(\frac{k_1}{k_3}\right)}[CH_3CHO]^{\frac{1}{2}}.$$

The reaction rate is

$$-\frac{d[CH_3CHO]}{dt} = k_1[CH_3CHO] + k_2[CH_3CHO][CH_3],$$

and since the first term is negligible compared with the second when the chains are long, this becomes

$$-\frac{d[CH_3CHO]}{dt} = k_2\sqrt{\left(\frac{k_1}{k_3}\right)}[CH_3CHO]^{\frac{3}{2}}.$$

Although some violence must in fact be done to the experimental data for acetaldehyde itself to make them fit this equation (e.g. by ignoring the results for part of the pressure range studied), it is obvious that a reaction of the order three-halves may be difficult to distinguish over a limited range from one showing a gradual transition from the first order to the second. This is especially true when the form of this transition is itself a matter of some uncertainty, as the discussion of the last section but one showed, and that of the next but one will show still more clearly.

Case 2. The essential characteristics of this case can be illustrated by the following *hypothetical* chain which would account for most of the decomposition products of diethyl ether.

$$C_2H_5OC_2H_5 = CH_3 + CH_2OC_2H_5 \tag{1}$$

$$CH_3 + C_2H_5OC_2H_5 = C_2H_6 + CH_2OC_2H_5 \tag{2}$$

$$CH_2OC_2H_5 = CH_3 + CH_3CHO \tag{3}$$

$$CH_3 + CH_2OC_2H_5 = \text{end of chain.} \tag{4}$$

(As a matter of fact, ethyl radicals could also be produced in (1), and (2) might be $C_2H_5 + C_2H_5OC_2H_5 = C_2H_6 + CH_3.CH.OC_2H_5$. Free radicals probably attack hydrogen atoms more readily than they attack saturated carbon atoms, so that the latter scheme may be the more nearly correct one. It leads to the same result as that written out, though not quite so simply.)

Assuming (1) and (3) to be of the first order, and (2) and (4) to be of the second order, and writing the concentration of CH_3 as $[R]$, that of $CH_2OC_2H_5$ as $[S]$, and that of the ether as $[A]$, we have:

$$\frac{dR}{dt} = k_1[A] - k_2[R][A] + k_3[S] - k_4[R][S] = 0,$$

$$\frac{dS}{dt} = k_1[A] + k_2[R][A] - k_3[S] - k_4[R][S] = 0.$$

Solving, we find $\qquad [R] = \sqrt{\left(\frac{k_1 k_3}{k_2 k_4}\right)},$

and since nearly all the ether is supposed to be decomposed in (2) rather than (1), we have

$$-\frac{d[C_2H_5OC_2H_5]}{dt} = k_2 \sqrt{\left(\frac{k_1 k_3}{k_2 k_4}\right)}[C_2H_5OC_2H_5].$$

Thus the overall reaction appears as one of the first order.

Several things in these two calculations must be observed closely. In the first place, the primary process has been assumed to be strictly of the first order. The question of its own mechanism then arises. If it remained of the first order at all pressures, the well-known difficulty with which Perrin started the whole modern discussion of unimolecular reactions would arise afresh. In reality, therefore, the pressure dependence of both types of reaction must be more complex than that which we have just worked out. In case (2), the fact that the overall order works out to be the same as that of the primary process means that the chain-length is independent of pressure. If, therefore, a reaction did occur according to this scheme, and if it showed a characteristic pressure dependence, then that dependence would be characteristic of the primary process itself, and we should have the opportunity of applying, as it were at one remove, the Lindemann mechanism to explain it.

The second thing to observe is what difference in the assumed mechanisms makes case (1) yield the order 1·5, while case (2) yields the order unity. The crucial matter is the mode of chain-breaking. In case (2) the radical $CH_2OC_2H_5$ is postulated: which is not actually a chain propagator, but must be assumed to *suffer a thermal decomposition of its own* before it yields something capable of continuing the chain: and the chains are broken by the combination of the methyl radicals themselves with this non-participating radical. In case (1), on the other hand, the chains are broken by recombination of two of the actual participating radicals with each other. These distinctions are important (cf. page 131).

Criteria of Radical Chains in Thermal Reactions

(a) The Para-hydrogen Method.

In presence of hydrogen a methyl radical will readily undergo the following reaction:

$$CH_3 + H_2 = CH_4 + H,$$

and in the steady state the concentration of hydrogen atoms will bear a definite ratio to the concentration of the methyl radicals. If para-hydrogen is used it will be transformed into the equilibrium mixture of ortho- and para-hydrogen at a rate which is proportional to the concentration of atoms, the mechanism of the transformation being known to be

$$p\text{-}H_2 + H = H + o\text{-}H_2,$$

and the velocity constant having been established.

Patat and Sachsse* adapted this method to determine the concentration of methyl radicals prevailing during the thermal decomposition of such substances as dimethyl ether, acetaldehyde, ethane, and acetone. They concluded that, although free radicals were usually detectable in the system, the concentration was very much smaller than would be required by the reaction mechanisms of Rice and Herzfeld. The fraction of the total number of molecules decomposing which yielded radicals was estimated at between 0·1 and 1%. According to this result the chain processes play the part only of side reactions, the main contribution coming from the direct rearrangement to stable molecules.

* Z. physikal. Chem., 1935, B, **31**, 105; 1936, B, **32**, 294.

The quantitative results of Patat and Sachsse, however, depend upon a knowledge of the ratio of the velocity constants for the interaction of methyl radicals with hydrogen, and of hydrogen atoms with the organic substance. This introduces some uncertainty into the results.

(b) The Nitric Oxide Method.*

The most direct evidence for the participation of radical chains in the decomposition of certain organic compounds comes from the study of the influence of small quantities of nitric oxide, which exert, in some instances, a remarkable inhibiting effect.

One millimetre of nitric oxide may reduce to a fraction of its original value the rate of reaction of several hundred times its own amount of the organic substance. The nitric oxide is gradually used up, but usually only slowly. For example: 2 mm. nitric oxide will last out the decomposition of 400 mm. diethyl ether which in the meantime is reacting at about one-third the normal rate. Sometimes the nitric oxide may be used up before the decomposition is over. This occurs with dimethyl ether, but even here some 20 molecules of the ether decompose at a greatly reduced rate before the one of nitric oxide is consumed and the rate rises rather abruptly to normal again. The first detectable products are oxidation products of the organic compound, reduction products of nitric oxide, such as ammonia,† and sometimes traces of cyanide,‡ but these must be the result of a series of changes, probably starting with the direct union of an organic radical and the nitric oxide, which, electronically, is itself a free radical.

A plausible scheme which explains these facts is as follows:

$$CH_3 + NO = CH_3NO = H_2C : NOH = HCN + H_2O,$$

together with other secondary reactions.

Since one molecule of nitric oxide, by reacting with something in the system, can stop the reaction of several hundred molecules of an organic compound, the something which it removes in its own reaction must normally have been responsible for the decomposition of a large number of molecules. This process is, by definition, the breaking of a chain.

The next important fact is that in many examples the nitric oxide reduces the reaction rate, not to zero but to a quite definite limit. The

---

* Staveley and Hinshelwood, Nature, 1936, 137, 29; Proc. Roy. Soc., A, 1936, 154, 335; J.C.S., 1936, 812; Proc. Roy. Soc., A, 1937, 159, 192; J.C.S., 1937, 1568; Hinshelwood and Staveley, J.C.S., 1936, 818; Mitchell and Hinshelwood, Proc. Roy. Soc., A, 1937, 159, 32; Staveley, Proc. Roy. Soc., A, 1937, 162, 557; Hobbs and Hinshelwood, Proc. Roy. Soc., A, 1938, 167, 439, 447; Hobbs, ibid., 456.

† Thompson and Meissner, Nature, 1937, 139, 1018.

‡ Küchler, private communication.

rate does not in general simply fall to a minimum and then rise again, but remains steady at the limit over a relatively wide range. With ether, for example, it falls rapidly over the range 0–2 mm. and then remains nearly constant for about ten times this range. Later the rate rises again, large amounts of nitric oxide showing a positive catalytic effect as well as undergoing an appreciable reaction with the ether.

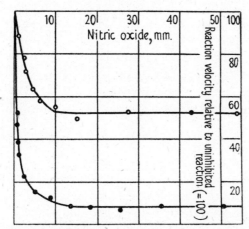

FIG. 8. Showing how the reaction velocity reaches a steady limiting value as the nitric oxide pressure increases. The upper curve (open circles) is for 100 mm. of hexane at 530° C., the lower (full circles) for 150 mm. of ethane at 620° C.

The activation energy of the reaction which remains after the nitric oxide has exerted its maximum inhibiting effect is often much smaller (by 20,000 calories or more) than could correspond to the breaking of a bond and the production of a free radical. It is therefore natural to suppose that it corresponds to the direct rearrangement process, rather than simply to the primary process of the chain-reaction itself. There is good reason to believe from independent evidence that a negligibly small proportion of molecules are concerned in the primary radical formation, as will appear presently.

The doubt naturally arises as to whether the limiting rate really has quantitative significance or whether it may not be simply a minimum, representing a state where nitric oxide starts as many chains as it stops. This view is difficult to reconcile with several facts. (1) The extreme definiteness of the limit in many examples. In Fig. 8 the limit does not in the least resemble a minimum of the kind suggested. (2) The reduction of the quantum yield in the photochemical decomposition of acetaldehyde from several hundred to nearly unity by the addition of nitric oxide. (3) The admission of minute amounts of nitric oxide into a stream of ether issuing from a furnace at 800° C. inhibits the removal of tellurium mirrors. (4) The positive catalytic effect which appears at higher pressures of nitric oxide is a phenomenon on a different scale from that of the inhibition and could hardly be supposed to compete on equal terms with it.

These and other facts led to the hypothesis that nitric oxide can suppress all the chains, and that absence of inhibition may in suitable cases be taken as evidence for the absence of chains. For example, the decomposition of dimethyl ether is subject to a marked inhibition: that of acetone, which should give quite similar radicals, shows no inhibition at corresponding temperatures, and is therefore probably not a chain reaction at all.

According to the hypothesis, the ratio of the original rate to the limiting rate gives information about the proportion of chain reaction present in a given example. The ratio may be called for convenience the mean chain-length: the convention underlying this is that a direct rearrangement to saturated products is called a chain of unit length. The values found for the mean chain-length are usually rather small: they fall from 17 for dimethyl ether to 1·4 for di-isopropyl ether at 540°; from 17·8 for ethane at 100 mm. pressure and 600° to 1·9 for hexane at 530° and 100 mm. pressure. The values for acetaldehyde and for acetone are unity, i.e. there is no evidence of chains.

The variations of mean chain-length with pressure conform to two types corresponding closely to types 1 and 2 of the preceding section.

The mean chain-lengths are small because very few of the primarily decomposing molecules give radicals at all. But the average absolute length of the chains set up by these few radicals must be great. It may be estimated in the following way. Photochemical measurements show that approximately one molecule of nitric oxide is used up for every chain broken. Assuming that the same is true of the thermal reactions, and estimating the consumption of nitric oxide during the inhibition period, we know how many chains are broken, and dividing this into the number of molecules which would have reacted we obtain the chain-length. It works out at about 400 for dimethyl ether, and is probably longer for diethyl ether, the numerical values being difficult to obtain, since the consumption of nitric oxide is small.

Summarizing, we may say that the application of the nitric oxide method shows quite certainly that chains are present in many organic decomposition reactions: that it shows them probably to be entirely absent in others under comparable conditions; and that it suggests, in general, a competition between frequent molecular reactions of low activation energy and infrequent radical formation followed by long chains. In other words, many such decomposition reactions appear to be kinetically composite. Before drawing conclusions, therefore, from kinetic measurements, it is necessary to determine what contributions come from chain processes, and then, if desired, to suppress these and re-examine the kinetics of the residual reaction.

Taking the most careful stock of all the facts known at present it seems to be just to say the following of one typical example: the thermal decomposition of diethyl ether. There is a considerable contribution from a chain reaction, which shows in detail the characteristics of type 2 (Rice and Herzfeld) of the last section: that there is also a non-chain reaction which shows the characteristics discussed in the earlier parts of this chapter, and involves the direct decomposition of the molecule activated in about nine degrees of freedom. The experimental evidence for this statement is more fully reviewed in the next chapter.

Some confusion may arise in the discussion of chain processes unless we distinguish between two senses in which we might refer to the contribution of chain reactions to the total change. Since the activation energy for the initial production of radicals is usually from 10,000 to 30,000 calories greater than that for the direct molecular reaction, it is obvious that the number of primary processes which initiate chains is extremely small compared with the number which give saturated products directly. In this sense we may refer to the chain-producing reaction as a relatively unimportant side reaction. On the other hand, the length of the chains may be such that if we compare, not the numbers of primary processes but the actual numbers of molecules decomposed, then we may have to say that the contribution of the chain reaction is considerable.

If the hypothesis that the nitric oxide in the limit suppresses all the chains, despite its probability, proves to be incorrect, it will be necessary to explain the distinction between the repressible and the irrepressible types, and this will doubtless lead to a further increase in our understanding of the processes concerned.

Another Form of Composite Reaction Mechanism which may be shown by Molecules of Intermediate Complexity.

The considerations which follow are to be taken to apply to reactions in which chain processes are absent, or have been allowed for.

As has appeared in previous sections, the relation between reaction rate and pressure in a large class of reactions is such that the reciprocal of τ, the half-life of the reacting substance, gives a curve of type 1 or 2 when plotted against the initial pressure. (The precise shape of the curve before it has become horizontal depends, as already mentioned,

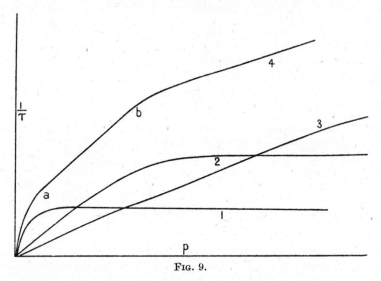

Fig. 9.

upon how the probability of transformation of the activated molecules varies with the total energy.)

In a molecule of moderate but not too great complexity it is not impossible that there may be several distinct modes of activation, corresponding to particular divisions of the energy among a limited number of vibrational (or rotational) degrees of freedom.* To a first approximation each of these modes may be associated with a separate probability of transformation, because internal redistribution may be difficult without collisions. Thus the total rate of reaction will be roughly the sum of several virtually independent rates, each varying according to a curve of the type 1, 2, or 3. Since each of these reaches its limit at a different pressure, the total rate may vary with pressure according to a composite curve of type 4, with fairly rapid changes of direction at a, b, and so on. The simplest types of molecule may give curves which do not bend at all, at least up to high pressures, moderately simple molecules curves with a limited number of segments of decreasing slope, while complex molecules with many degrees of freedom will give

* Hinshelwood and Fletcher, *Nature*, 1933, **131**, 24.

curves in which the segments merge into a single line without any noticeable changes of direction at particular stages.

The equation of the composite curve in a real example would be complicated, since the assumption of virtually independent reactions is to some extent an idealization. Further, the variation of all the transition probabilities with total energy may also complicate matters.

It is quite possible, however, that some kind of composite curve is the most general form for molecules of 'intermediate complexity'. The behaviour of nitrous oxide at lower pressures, in comparison with its behaviour at higher pressures, can be accounted for if we assume the complete curve to consist of several segments in this way.

The behaviour of acetaldehyde, and especially the *gradation in behaviour shown in the series* formaldehyde, acetaldehyde, propionic aldehyde, chloral,* may also be interpretable in this way—though, as will have become evident in the course of this chapter, decisions between possible theories are not always easy.

* See page 137.

NOTE ADDED JULY 1945

A useful inhibiting agent for the detection of radical chain reactions is provided by propylene.† Its action is generally similar to that of nitric oxide, but much larger quantities are needed to give comparable degrees of inhibition. Its action depends upon direct union with free radicals, a process which, in appropriate circumstances leads to polymerization of the propylene itself.‡

The limiting rate of reaction observed with nitric oxide and with propylene has been shown, for certain examples, to be identical. This lends support to the idea that this limiting rate observed in presence of the inhibitor is more probably that of an independent non-chain process than that characteristic of a stationary state where the inhibitor starts and stops chains with equal efficiency.

† Rice and Polly, *J. Chem. Phys.*, 1938, **6**, 273; Smith and Hinshelwood, *Proc. Roy. Soc.*, A, 1942, **180**, 237.
‡ Cf. Danby and Hinshelwood, *Proc. Roy. Soc.*, A, 1941, **179**, 169.

H

V

SOME TYPICAL UNIMOLECULAR AND BIMOLECULAR REACTIONS

In this chapter we shall consider more fully the experimental results relating to a series of typical reactions.

The classification of chemical reactions proves to be very much more difficult than used to be thought. The established variability of the order of reaction removes one valuable criterion; the uncertainty whether a second-order reaction is really bimolecular, or whether it may prove at higher pressures to become of the first order and so reveal itself as essentially unimolecular, removes a second criterion. The frequent occurrence of composite mechanisms, as when chain processes take place side by side with molecular rearrangements, increases the difficulty of classification. The real unities and regularities reside in the underlying statistical principles. Some of these have been discussed in the course of the foregoing pages: and it now remains to try and discern their existence in some special examples.

Some Typical Reactions of the Halogens and their Compounds

The examples chosen are the union of hydrogen with iodine, bromine, and chlorine respectively; the decomposition of hydrogen iodide; the combination of bromine atoms; and some typical decomposition reactions of oxides of chlorine.

The first set illustrate the interplay of atomic and molecular mechanisms. Hydrogen and iodine combine by way of activated molecules: with bromine and chlorine, however, there is a more economical reaction path by way of the initial dissociation of the halogen into atoms. This arises simply from a quantitative difference in the activation energies—a natural consequence of the gradation in properties of the halogens in the periodic system. Yet it makes the kinetics of the various reactions almost unrecognizably different. The formation and decomposition of hydrogen iodide illustrate the kinetics of two opposing reactions: and each is a good example of the simplest type, where the observed rate of change is nearly equal to the rate of activation by collision. The combination of bromine atoms provides an interesting example of indirect analysis; while the decomposition reactions of chlorine oxides show how chemical complexities may be superposed on an underlying kinetic simplicity.

The study of the reactions of the halogens and their compounds has played an important part in the understanding of mechanisms involving free atoms, and of the relation of atomic to molecular mechanisms.

(a) The Union of Hydrogen and Iodine.

The velocity of combination of hydrogen and iodine was measured by Bodenstein. Known amounts of hydrogen and iodine were sealed in bulbs and heated for given times, after which the fraction of iodine transformed into hydrogen iodide was determined.

It was impossible to work with equimolecular amounts, and the velocity equation therefore assumes the form

$$\frac{dx}{dt} = k'\left(a - \frac{x}{2}\right)\left(b - \frac{x}{2}\right) - kx^2,$$

where a is the initial concentration of hydrogen, and b that of iodine. x is the amount of hydrogen iodide formed at time t.

In Bodenstein's experiments a, b, and x are all expressed as fractions of 'normal concentration', that is, the concentration at which the substances would each exert a pressure of 760 mm. at $0°$ C.

Integration by means of partial fractions gives

$$k' = \frac{2}{mt}\left(\ln\frac{\dfrac{a+b-m}{1-4K} - x}{\dfrac{a+b+m}{1-4K} - x} + \ln\frac{a+b-m}{a+b+m}\right),$$

where
$$m = \sqrt{\{(a+b)^2 - 4ab(1-4K)\}}$$

and $K = k/k'$, k being known from previous experiments on the hydrogen iodide decomposition.

The following is a typical series of experiments carried out at $393°$ C.

t (minutes)	a	b	x	k'
120	0·4681	0·2797	0·3239	0·0394
120	0·4681	0·3703	0·4061	0·0392
60	0·4681	0·5492	0·3561	0·0358
30	0·4681	0·9865	0·3534	0·0378
30	0·4681	1·2230	0·4019	0·0336
122	0·9086	0·2101	0·3599	0·0416
45	0·9086	0·4608	0·4405	0·0370
30	0·9086	0·6039	0·4448	0·0390
15	0·9086	1·3890	0·5190	0·0358
15	0·9086	2·2410	0·8076	0·0393

The considerable range of variation of a and b is to be noted, the constancy of k' under these circumstances being good evidence that the bimolecular law is followed.

The measurements showing the influence of temperature are given in the following table. The units are the original ones of Bodenstein, namely time in minutes, and concentrations in gram molecules per 22·4 litres.

T (abs.)	k'
781	3·58
716	0·375
700	0·172
683	0·0659
666	0·0379
647	0·0140
629	0·00676
599	0·00146
575	0·000353
556	0·000119

From these, using the equation $d \log k'/dT = E/RT^2$, Lewis derived a value of E of 40,000 calories for the gram molecule of hydrogen plus the gram molecule of iodine, and investigated whether it is possible to calculate the absolute rate of reaction by assuming that all collisions between activated molecules lead to combination.

At 700° abs., taking σ as 2×10^{-8} cm., the calculated value of k' was 14×10^{-2}.

The experimental value with the time measured in minutes and the concentration in gram molecules per 22·4 litres is 0·172. When the units are changed to seconds and gram molecules per litre the value becomes $6·4 \times 10^{-2}$, which must be regarded as good agreement with the calculated value when it is borne in mind that the calculation is absolute.

(b) The Thermal Decomposition of Hydrogen Iodide.

Bodenstein* also made a comprehensive study of the equilibrium between hydrogen, iodine, and hydrogen iodide, and a complete series of measurements of the velocity of decomposition of hydrogen iodide at various temperatures. We are concerned now with the kinetic measurements only. He used the method of sealing up the reacting gases in bulbs and analysing the products after keeping for a known time in a thermostat, usually a vapour bath. The bulbs used in the decomposition experiments were filled with hydrogen iodide at 0° and 760 mm., and contained initially, therefore, one gram molecule in 22·4 litres. If x is the fraction of the hydrogen iodide decomposed after time t, then since the reaction is a reversible one,

$$\frac{dx}{dt} = k(1-x)^2 - k'(x/2)^2.$$

* Z. physikal. Chem., 1899, **29**, 295.

If ξ is the fraction decomposed at equilibrium,

$$k(1-\xi)^2 = k'(\xi/2)^2,$$

whence
$$k = \frac{\log_{10}\left[\dfrac{\dfrac{\xi}{2\xi-1}-x}{\xi-x}(2\xi-1)\right]}{0\cdot8686\dfrac{1-\xi}{\xi}t}.$$

Thus k can be calculated from the amount decomposed in time t and the amount decomposed at equilibrium. The values of k calculated in terms of x and ξ in this way are not independent of the initial concentration, which, in the experiments, was actually one gram molecule in 22·4 litres. In the second column of the table below, Bodenstein's values of k are given, the time unit being the minute, and in the third column are given the values of k recalculated, with the time expressed in seconds, and the concentrations in gram molecules per litre instead of per 22·4 litres.

Decomposition of hydrogen iodide

T (abs.)	k Time in minutes. Conc. in gram molecules per 22·4 litres	k Time in seconds. Conc. in gram molecules per litre
781	0·1059	0·0395
716	0·00670	0·00250
700	0·00310	0·00116
683	0·00137	0·000512
666	0·000588	0·000220
647	0·000230	0·0000859
629	0·0000809	0·0000302
575	0·00000326	0·00000122
556	0·000000942	0·000000352

Fig. 1 a (page 43) shows that when $\log k$ is plotted against the reciprocal of the absolute temperature an excellent straight line is obtained.

The molecular statistics of the reaction have already been discussed (page 46).

Kistiakowsky* investigated the reaction over a much wider range of concentration, from 0·02 to 7 gram molecules per litre, i.e. up to several hundred atmospheres. He found the reaction to be homogeneous, and strictly bimolecular over the whole range of concentration. At the higher pressures there is an apparent increase in the velocity constant, which seems to be due to the fact that at high concentrations the collision number is no longer proportional strictly to the square of

* *J. Amer. Chem. Soc.*, 1928, **50**, 2315.

the pressure, and a correction, depending upon the volume actually filled by the molecules, must be introduced. The correction factor is $\frac{1}{1-Nb}$, where N is the number of molecules per unit volume and b is four times the actual volume of the molecule, assumed spherical. The value of b required to give the observed change of k with pressure is in good agreement with the known size of the hydrogen iodide molecule.

The observed values of k at lower concentrations are in very good agreement with Bodenstein's values.

Kistiakowsky finds that intensive drying makes no difference to the results.

(c) The Union of Hydrogen and Bromine.

The thermal combination of hydrogen and bromine, and of hydrogen and chlorine, might be expected to be reactions analogous to the combination of hydrogen and iodine.

The formation of hydrogen bromide from its elements takes place, however, in an unexpectedly complicated manner. Bodenstein and Lind* measured the velocity at 200° to 300° C. and found that it could be expressed by the equation

$$\frac{d[\mathrm{HBr}]}{dt} = \frac{k[\mathrm{H_2}]\sqrt{[\mathrm{Br_2}]}}{m + \dfrac{[\mathrm{HBr}]}{[\mathrm{Br_2}]}},$$

m being a constant.

The interpretation of this curious result was given by Christiansen,† Polanyi,‡ and Herzfeld.§ The reaction is assumed to take place in the following steps:

$$
\begin{aligned}
&(1) && \mathrm{Br_2} = 2\mathrm{Br}, \\
&(2) && \mathrm{Br+H_2} = \mathrm{HBr+H}, \\
&(3) && \mathrm{H+Br_2} = \mathrm{HBr+Br}, \\
&(4) && \mathrm{H+HBr} = \mathrm{H_2+Br}.
\end{aligned}
$$

(1) is the ordinary thermal dissociation of bromine, which, at 200° to 300°, can only give rise to a very small number of bromine atoms. Their concentration will be proportional to the square root of the total bromine concentration: and it is, indeed, the appearance of the square root term in the velocity equation which gives the clue to this step.

* Z. physikal. Chem., 1906, **57**, 168.
† Dansk. Vid. Math. Phys. Medd., 1919, **1**, 14.
‡ Z. Elektrochem., 1920, **26**, 49.   § Ibid., 1919, **25**, 301.

Bromine atoms having been once formed, step (2) is the obvious, and indeed the only likely one to assume; it is natural also for it to be followed by (3). The assumption of step (4) is suggested by the experimental fact that hydrogen bromide retards the reaction, and must therefore be assumed to remove one of the chain-propagating atoms. But the retardation is found to be less the greater the bromine concentration: hydrogen and hydrogen bromide must therefore be in competition for the atom in question, which is thus identified as the hydrogen atom.

Expressing the fact that the rate of formation of hydrogen bromide is the sum of its rates of production in (2) and (3) less its rate of destruction in (4) we have

$$\frac{d[\text{HBr}]}{dt} = k_2[\text{Br}][\text{H}_2] + k_3[\text{H}][\text{Br}_2] - k_4[\text{H}][\text{HBr}].$$

Further, the concentration of hydrogen atoms must be constant after the first few instants of the reaction, or the rate of reaction would steadily increase. This stationary state is expressed by the equation

$$\frac{d[\text{H}]}{dt} = k_2[\text{Br}][\text{H}_2] - k_3[\text{H}][\text{Br}_2] - k_4[\text{H}][\text{HBr}] = 0.$$

Finally, we have for the bromine dissociation

$$[\text{Br}]^2 = k_1[\text{Br}_2].$$

Eliminating [H] and [Br] we obtain the experimentally found formula.

(d) The Combination of Bromine Atoms $2\text{Br} = \text{Br}_2$.

An ingenious method of finding the velocity of this reaction was employed by Bodenstein and Lütkemeyer.* The results, although approximate only, afforded the first information that had ever been obtained about the kinetics of reactions between free atoms. The method depended upon the conclusions outlined in the previous section relating to the hydrogen bromide formation.

It was based upon a comparison between the rate of hydrogen bromide formation in the dark and the rate of formation under the influence of light. The photochemical reaction proceeds in accordance with the equation

$$\frac{d[\text{HBr}]}{dt} = \frac{k\sqrt{(\text{light absorbed})}[\text{H}_2]}{m' + \dfrac{[\text{HBr}]}{[\text{Br}_2]}}.$$

* Z. physikal. Chem., 1924, **114**, 208.

The mechanism, therefore, appears to be exactly analogous to that of the thermal reaction, except that the bromine atoms are now provided in much larger numbers than before, being produced not merely by the ordinary thermal dissociation but by the reaction

$$(1)\quad Br_2 + h\nu = 2Br,$$

$h\nu$ being the quantum of light absorbed in the photochemical dissociation of the bromine. This reaction is regarded on good grounds as the primary photochemical process, and is followed as before by the series of purely thermal reactions

$$(2)\quad Br + H_2 = HBr + H,$$
$$(3)\quad H + Br_2 = HBr + Br,$$
$$(4)\quad H + HBr = H_2 + Br.$$

Simultaneously there occurs the reaction

$$(5)\quad Br + Br = Br_2.$$

These assumptions lead, by the same method of calculation as that used in the case of the thermal reaction, to the correct velocity equation. It is to be noted that since (2) is followed by either (3) or (4) the actual formation of hydrobromic acid does not use up the supply of atomic bromine, and a stationary concentration of bromine atoms is established by the balancing of the rate of their photochemical formation (1) and the rate of their thermal recombination (5).*

This stationary concentration determines the rate of hydrogen bromide formation. The photochemical reaction is about 300 times as fast as the thermal reaction at the same temperature (160° to 218° C.).

This means that in the photochemical reaction the concentration of the bromine atoms which prevails is about 300 times greater than in the dark reaction, since all other parts of the reaction mechanism

---

* An interesting point connected with the processes $Cl_2 = 2Cl$ and $Br_2 = 2Br$ arises from a comparison of the photochemical formation of hydrogen chloride and that of hydrogen bromide. The rate of the former reaction has usually been found to be proportional to the first power of the light intensity, that of the latter to the square root of the intensity. This difference is due to the fact that the chlorine atoms formed by the process $Cl_2 + h\nu = 2Cl$ are used up as quickly as formed; thus the rate of reaction is determined by the rate of dissociation of the chlorine which in turn is proportional to the light intensity. On the other hand, the bromine atoms formed by the process $Br_2 + h\nu = 2Br$ are not used up nearly so efficiently, and much recombination occurs. The rate of reaction with hydrogen is proportional to the concentration of Br atoms at any moment. Since the rate of dissociation is proportional to $[Br_2] \times$ intensity and the rate of recombination to $[Br]^2$, we have $[Br]$ proportional to $\sqrt{([Br_2] \times \text{intensity})}$. When the hydrogen-chlorine system is so carefully freed from inhibitors that few chlorine atoms are destroyed by them, recombination becomes important, and the square root law appears, as Chapman and Gibbs found.

are identical. The rate of combination is simply an indicator of the concentration of atomic bromine. Thus this concentration is found by the relation

(conc. Br at any stage of photo reaction)

$$= (\text{conc. Br in dark reaction}) \times \left[\frac{\text{speed of light reaction}}{\text{speed of dark reaction}}\right].$$

The concentration of bromine atoms in the dark reaction is known from the concentration of molecular bromine and the thermal dissociation constant of bromine; hence that prevailing at any stage of the photochemical reaction is found.

The rate of production of bromine atoms by light is estimated on the basis of Einstein's law, which requires one molecule of bromine to be dissociated for each quantum of light absorbed. In the stationary state the number of bromine atoms recombining thermally in unit time is equal to this rate of photochemical formation. Thus the number of bromine atoms which recombine per second at a known atomic concentration is found. In this way Bodenstein and Lütkemeyer found that about one collision in a thousand between bromine atoms results in combination. This number is of the right order of magnitude only, since the estimation of the number of light quanta absorbed was not very certain, and a value based only on analogy had to be assumed for the diameter of the bromine atom.

Bodenstein and Müller* attempted to employ a second method depending upon the marked retardation of the hydrogen bromide formation by iodine. The iodine was assumed to react with the atomic hydrogen and thus prevent the main reaction. If sufficient iodine were added to remove practically all the hydrogen atoms produced, the rate of hydrogen bromide formation would be reduced to the rate of thermal formation of bromine atoms from molecules. This, in conjunction with the equilibrium constant of the bromine dissociation, would give the rate of reunion of the atoms. Further investigation† showed that the retardation by iodine had a cause other than the removal of hydrogen atoms: the reaction $I_2 + Br_2 = 2IBr$ takes place, and thus diminishes the concentration of the bromine atoms.

(e) The Union of Hydrogen and Chlorine.

The thermal union of hydrogen and chlorine is a chain reaction. It appears to follow a mechanism of the same general type as that of the

---

* Z. Elektrochem., 1924, **30**, 416.   † Müller, Z. physikal. Chem., 1926, **123**, 1.

photochemical reaction, which has been much more elaborately investigated.

Although a detailed consideration of photochemical changes is really outside the province of this book, it will nevertheless be useful to summarize certain general results which have a bearing on the whole problem of chemical reaction velocity.

Only light which is absorbed by one of the reacting substances can be chemically active, but absorption, although a necessary, is not a sufficient condition for reaction. Of frequencies corresponding to absorption bands in different parts of the spectrum some may be effective and some not.

Light is absorbed by atoms or molecules in quanta of magnitude $h\nu$, where ν is the frequency of the light and h is Planck's constant.

It is clear that in a purely photochemical reaction there must be at least one quantum absorbed for each molecule which becomes activated.

For visible light the $h\nu$ is a very large quantity compared with the ordinary thermal energy of a single molecule. There is therefore a certain likelihood that the effectiveness or otherwise of a quantum of light will not, in simple cases, be profoundly influenced by minor variations in the internal state of the molecule due to purely thermal causes. If, therefore, the disturbance produced in a molecule by the absorption of the quantum of light is great enough to cause its transformation in one case, it will do so in all.

In simple instances, therefore, we should expect to find one molecule transformed for each quantum of light absorbed, provided that the light is active at all. This is Einstein's law of photochemical equivalence.

With regard to the photochemical effectiveness of light of different frequencies, we should expect that there would be a limiting frequency above which the quanta are large enough to activate the molecules and below which they are ineffective. Above this critical frequency the effect of the light would be proportional simply to the number of quanta which it contained, that is, for equal intensities would diminish slightly as the frequency increased. Below the critical frequency the light would be ineffective. It is also possible that quanta too small to be effective at low temperatures might become effective in activating molecules already partially activated by an increase of temperature.

A good example of a 'photochemical threshold' is found in the system $2NO_2 \underset{\text{dark}}{\overset{\text{light}}{\rightleftharpoons}} 2NO + O_2$. Norrish* showed that at $436\,\mu\mu$ the 'quantum

* *J. Chem. Soc.*, 1927, 761; 1929, 1158, 1604, 1611.

efficiency' was zero, while at 405 $\mu\mu$ it was 0·74 rising to 2 at shorter wave-lengths.

Deviations from Einstein's law can occur in true photochemical reactions owing to the degradation of the absorbed light energy into thermal energy as a result of collisions with other molecules which the activated molecules suffer before they have a chance to react. This makes the number of quanta absorbed greater than the number of molecules transformed. More commonly the 'quantum yield' is greater than unity, since processes of the following type take place:

$$HI + h\nu = H + I,$$
$$H + HI = H_2 + I,$$
$$I + I = I_2.$$

This gives two molecules of hydrogen iodide decomposed for each quantum absorbed. A quantum yield of two is characteristic of a very large class of reactions.

A simple relation between number of quanta and molecules transformed would be found if two or more quanta were actually needed to activate each molecule for chemical transformation. In this event, however, it is easily shown that the rate of reaction would be nearly proportional to the nth power of the light intensity, where n is the number of quanta required to be simultaneously absorbed.

No instance is known in which the rate of reaction is proportional to a power of the light intensity greater than the first. It is, indeed, very improbable that a molecule would remain in a condition where it possessed so large an excess of energy as a quantum of visible light long enough to acquire a second quantum, since all the time it would be subject to collisions which would rapidly deprive it of its first quantum. Probably all photochemical transformations are essentially one-quantum processes.

We are here chiefly concerned with the relation of photochemical to thermal changes. We have seen that thermal heats of activation commonly range from about 10,000 to about 80,000 calories. The quanta corresponding to the red lithium line and the violet mercury line amount in calories to $7·01 \times 10^{-20}$ and $1·078 \times 10^{-19}$ respectively. Allowing one quantum to a molecule, this would represent activation in a photochemical reaction to the extent of $Nh\nu$ or 42,480 calories and 65,360 calories per gram molecule.

From this we see that the absorption of visible light can lead to a high degree of activation. Ozone, for example, is decomposed by ultra-violet light of wave-length 254 $\mu\mu$, the quantum of which corresponds to 111,000 calories per gram molecule, compared with the value 29,000 for the thermal reaction.

Turning now to the combination of hydrogen and chlorine, we find a picture of considerable complexity.

The principal facts about it may be summarized as follows:

I. The reaction is provoked by the light absorbed by the chlorine.

II. There may be a long 'induction period' during which no change takes place. This was traced by Burgess and Chapman* to the presence of nitrogenous impurities which give rise to nitrogen chloride and 'inhibit' the reaction. The inhibitors are gradually destroyed by the light, and the combination starts. In their absence the induction period disappears. The inhibition has been more recently studied by Norrish and others, and the mode of action of the nitrogen chloride discussed.

III. The rate of reaction, when the phenomena of the induction period are eliminated, is normally proportional to the light intensity.

Chapman and Gibbs† later found that when the chlorine and hydrogen were very thoroughly freed from oxygen and other impurities the rate became proportional to the square root of the intensity.

IV. The Einstein law is not even approximately obeyed.‡ One quantum of light brings about the union of many thousands or even millions of molecules.

To explain this important fact Nernst§ suggested the following series of changes:

$$(1)\ \ Cl_2 + h\nu = 2Cl,$$
$$(2)\ \ Cl + H_2 = HCl + H,$$
$$(3)\ \ H + Cl_2 = HCl + Cl.$$

(1) is the only purely photochemical change; the reactions (2) and (3) proceed without the absorption of fresh quanta of light. The chlorine atom produced in (3) takes part in reaction (2) once more and a 'chain' is set up, which may lead to the union of millions of molecules for the one quantum originally absorbed. The chain can be broken by one of the reactions

$$(4)\ \ \ \ \ 2Cl = Cl_2,$$
$$(5)\ \ \ \ \ 2H = H_2,$$
$$(6)\ \ H + Cl = HCl.$$

Bodenstein and others have proposed alternative mechanisms for the chain ending; e.g.

$$(7)\ \ H + O_2 = HO_2,$$

* *J. Chem. Soc.*, 1906, **89**, 1399.   † *Nature*, 1931, **127**, 854.
‡ Cf. Bodenstein, *Z. physikal. Chem.*, 1913, **85**, 329.
§ *Z. Elektrochem.*, 1918, **24**, 335.

followed by reactions of HO_2 with HCl, H_2, or Cl_2, giving ultimately water (and sometimes oxides of chlorine as intermediates).

V. The actual kinetics of the reaction are rather complicated.

The rate is inversely proportional to the concentration of oxygen,[*] and appears to increase almost indefinitely as the gases are freed from oxygen. It is therefore necessary, in making measurements of the reaction velocity, always to work in the presence of a small but definite concentration of oxygen.

VI. The rate of combination increases at first in direct proportion to the pressure of hydrogen, when the pressure of chlorine and of oxygen is kept constant, then reaches a limit from which it very slowly declines as the pressure of hydrogen is further increased.[†]

VII. Bodenstein and Dux[‡] found that, for constant pressures of hydrogen, the rate of reaction was given by the formula

$$\frac{d[HCl]}{dt} = \frac{kI[Cl_2]^2}{[O_2]},$$

where I is the intensity of the light and k a constant, whilst Chapman and Whiston[§] found it to be more nearly expressed by the formula

$$\frac{d[HCl]}{dt} = \frac{kI[Cl_2]}{[O_2]}.$$

VIII. M. C. C. Chapman[||] submitted the matter to a careful re-investigation, and found that the rate of combination was proportional to the first power of the concentration of the chlorine when the proportion of hydrogen present was small, and proportional to the square of the concentration of the chlorine when the proportion of hydrogen present was large.

Another important result was that as the pressure of hydrogen becomes smaller the rate of reaction becomes less and less dependent on the oxygen concentration.

The results are summarized in the formula

$$\frac{d[HCl]}{dt} = \frac{k_1[H_2][Cl_2]^2}{k_3[H_2]^{2-x}[O_2]+[Cl_2]},$$

where x is a fraction less than 0.5.

IX. Thon,[**] in a critical survey of the problem, questioned the reality

 * Bodenstein and Dux, Z. physikal. Chem., 1913, **85**, 297. Chapman and Macmahon, J. Chem. Soc., 1909, **95**, 959.

 † Chapman and Underhill, J. Chem. Soc., 1913, **103**, 496.

 ‡ Z. physikal. Chem., 1913, **85**, 297.

 § J. Chem. Soc., 1919, **115**, 1264. || Ibid., 1923, **123**, 3062.

 ** 'Die Chlorknallgasreaktion', Fortschritte der Chemie, Physik und physikalischen Chemie, Band 18, Heft 11 (Berlin 1926).

of the slight retardation caused by excess of hydrogen in Chapman's experiments, and suggested the equation

$$\frac{d[\text{HCl}]}{dt} = \frac{k[\text{Cl}_2]^2[\text{H}_2]}{k'[\text{H}_2][\text{O}_2] + k''[\text{Cl}_2]}.$$

The apparently divergent results of different investigators can, on the whole, be regarded as special cases of this general equation. It is clear, for example, that with different relative proportions of chlorine and hydrogen the rate could be nearly proportional either to $[\text{Cl}_2]^2$ or to $[\text{Cl}_2]$.

X. Whatever be the exact mechanism of the chain process set up in mixtures of hydrogen and chlorine by illumination, it is evident that the wall of the containing vessel might play an important part in facilitating the removal from the system of some atom, radical, or molecule upon which the propagation of the chain depends.

Chapman and Grigg* have indeed shown that in light of the same intensity the rate of combination of hydrogen and chlorine is less in capillary tubes than in tubes of wider diameter.

XI. Very complete desiccation has been stated to prevent the combination of hydrogen and chlorine under the influence of light of the visible region. Coehn and Jung† stated that there was no combination in systems where the pressure of water vapour was estimated to be 10^{-7} mm. Hg, but that the reaction took place rapidly when the pressure was 10^{-5} mm. Bodenstein and Dux‡ had found that variation of the pressure of water vapour between 10 mm. and 10^{-3} mm. had no effect on the combination.

In ultra-violet light, on the other hand, Coehn and Jung found that the thoroughly dried mixture combined as well as the moist mixture.

Kistiakowsky has shown that when light is absorbed by intensively dried chlorine no appreciable part of it is re-emitted by fluorescence. Since, moreover, the total absorption is unaffected, it seems impossible that the water can play any part in the dissociation of chlorine molecules. Its role, if any, in the hydrogen chlorine combination must be at some later stage of the chains.

XII. Norrish has shown that hydrogen chloride retards the reaction.

The general lines of the theoretical interpretation of these facts are clear enough. The divergent results which have been found, and the varying views held about the kinetic details, almost certainly arose from differences in experimental conditions which altered the balance of the various chain-breaking processes.

* J. Chem. Soc., 1928, 3233.
† Z. physikal. Chem., 1924, 110, 705.   ‡ loc. cit., supra.

Taking the simple Nernst chain as a basis, there are possibilities (4), (5), (6), and (7) for the chain ending: and even then the alternatives that the chains are ended chiefly by recombination of atoms in the gas or by their diffusion to the wall. In the latter event the rate will be a function of the diffusion coefficients which depend in a complex way upon all the concentrations.

Every possibility leads to a different equation for the reaction rate. It was only after the study of chain processes in combustion reactions that these factors became clear, so that the older discussions of the hydrogen-chlorine reaction are naturally full of cross-purposes.

Assuming the Nernst chain and process (7) in the gas phase as the ending mechanism, the rate of combination comes out to be inversely proportional to $[O_2]$, independent of $[H_2]$, and proportional to $[Cl_2]$ times the absorbed light. The latter, according to the extinction coefficient, may be proportional to the chlorine pressure or independent of it. This simplest scheme thus reproduces in a rough form many of the kinetic results found by one or other of the observers, and if we allow for the probable embroideries on it due to other chain-breaking mechanisms, we see that there is no great mystery left about the reaction. Numerous modifications* of the detailed mechanism have been suggested, involving OH, ClO_2, Cl_3, and H_2O.

(f) The Thermal Decomposition of Chlorine Monoxide.

Although contact with organic matter, or local overheating, readily initiates explosion waves in chlorine monoxide, the slow decomposition can conveniently be observed between about 60° and 140° C.†

The change is homogeneous, uninfluenced by the glass walls of the containing vessel or by glass wool.

If the change took place in the one simple stage $2Cl_2O = 2Cl_2+O_2$ the increase in pressure at any time would be a direct measure of the extent to which the reaction had progressed. When the pressure increase is plotted against time the curve shows that the reaction apparently accelerates as it proceeds, as though the chlorine or the oxygen which are produced had an autocatalytic effect. Experiments in which excess of chlorine or of oxygen is present initially show, however, that these gases exert no influence on the course of the reaction. The acceleration is not, therefore, due to autocatalysis, but is attributable to the occurrence of the change in consecutive stages of which

---

* See, e.g. Franck and Bodenstein, *Trans. Faraday Soc.*, 1931, **27**, 413.

† Hinshelwood and Prichard, *J. Chem. Soc.*, 1923, **123**, 2730; Hinshelwood and Hughes, ibid., 1924, **125**, 1841.

the first is not accompanied by so marked a pressure change as the subsequent ones. There is chemical as well as kinetic evidence for the existence of these consecutive reactions, which possibly involve the formation of several different oxides of chlorine.

The rate of reaction is influenced by pressure in such a way as to indicate that each stage in the complex process is bimolecular, for the time taken to reach any given stage of the reaction is inversely as the initial pressure of chlorine monoxide, and the curves obtained at different initial pressures become superposable over their whole course if the time scales are altered so as to make them coincide at one point.

Since there are consecutive reactions at least two values of k must be involved, which are difficult to disentangle by mathematical means. The difficulty is, however, not insurmountable. This is due to the exponential relation between k and E. Since the various stages of the reaction are not sharply defined, the separate values of k are obviously of the same order of magnitude. Moreover, since each k is principally determined by the corresponding value of $e^{-E/RT}$, values of k which lie fairly close together should correspond to values of E which are practically identical. It might therefore be expected that E would show little or no variation at different stages of the reaction, and experiment confirms this expectation. The influence of temperature is found to be uniform, and thus E to be nearly constant, throughout the reaction.

Plotting against the reciprocal of the absolute temperature the logarithm of the velocity of reaction for the ranges 20% to 40%, 40% to 60%, and 60% to 80%, parallel straight lines are obtained, giving for E a uniform value of 21,000 calories.

From the nature of the relation between k and E, it might now be permissible to take an average of k for the whole reaction and to investigate the relation between this and the constant value of E. Substitution of such an average value of k in the simple equation for reaction rates given on page 46 leads to a value of E equal to 22,000 calories. This agrees well with the value 21,000 found from the temperature coefficient. In this calculation the molecular diameter of the chlorine monoxide molecule is taken 4.8×10^{-8} cm. This procedure is based upon the idea that there are no long reaction chains.

The decomposition of chlorine monoxide was later studied by Beaver and Stieger,* whose experimental results are almost the same as those which have just been described. They observed that an explosion—

* Z. physikal. Chem., B, 1931, **12**, 93.

probably of the intermediate oxide—frequently occurs towards the end of the reaction, and for this reason prefer to classify the decomposition as a chain reaction. Whether this view is adopted or not is really a question of nomenclature. The early work showed the existence of *consecutive* reactions: in a chain reaction the cycle of consecutive changes should repeat itself a large number of times. There is no evidence that this happens in the chlorine monoxide decomposition. In the photo-chemical decomposition the 'quantum yield' is two only. This argues against the existence of 'chains'; but the mechanism may be quite different, so that the argument is not conclusive. Nevertheless there is no positive evidence for the existence of long chains.

(g) *Other Reactions of the Halogens and their Oxides.*

The relative ease with which halogens dissociate into atoms, and, especially with chlorine, the numerous possibilities for the formation of oxides which are very reactive, give rise to an almost endless variety of reactions. The unravelling of the mechanism of these in detail is a matter of great complexity, since at almost every step alternative hypotheses are often possible.

Sometimes, however, *relatively* simple mechanisms prevail, as, prob-ably, in the decompositions of Cl_2O, F_2O, F_2O_2.

The methods of investigation include such as the following: the com-parison of thermal reactions with photochemical changes where some information about the primary process may be available from spectro-scopic evidence: isolation of intermediate products, e.g. formation of Cl_2O_6 suggests existence of ClO_3 in a chain: employment of knowledge of heats of formation in deciding whether a proposed step in a chain of processes is thermochemically possible or not. In the schemes which have been proposed for the mechanism of various reactions of chlorine, Cl, ClO, ClO_2, ClO_3 have all been postulated as intermediates.

As an example we may consider the suggestion of Bodenstein, Padelt, and Schumacher* for the mechanism of the thermal reaction between chlorine and ozone:

$$(1) \qquad Cl_2 + O_3 = ClO + ClO_2$$
$$(2) \qquad ClO_2 + O_3 = ClO_3 + O_2$$
$$(3) \qquad ClO_3 + O_3 = ClO_2 + 2O_2$$
$$(4) \quad ClO_3 + ClO_3 = Cl_2 + 3O_2$$
$$(5) \qquad ClO + ClO = Cl_2 + O_2$$
$$(6) \qquad ClO + O_3 = Cl + 2O_2.$$

* *Z. physikal. Chem.*, B, 1929, **5**, 209.

A condition establishes itself, in this case after an induction period, where the rates of formation and destruction of the intermediate products balance.

Thus

$$\frac{d[ClO_3]}{dt} = k_2[ClO_2][O_3] - k_3[ClO_3][O_3] - k_4[ClO_3]^2 = 0,$$

$$\frac{d[ClO_2]}{dt} = -k_2[ClO_2][O_3] + k_3[ClO_3][O_3] + k_1[Cl_2][O_3] = 0.$$

Solving these equations, and neglecting $k_4[ClO_3]^2$ in comparison with $k_3[ClO_3][O_3]$, one finds

$$-\frac{d[O_3]}{dt} = k_1[Cl_2][O_3] + k_2[ClO_2][O_3] + k_3[ClO_3][O_3],$$

where

$$[ClO_2] = \frac{k_3}{k_2}\sqrt{\left(\frac{k_1}{k_4}[Cl_2][O_3]\right)}.$$

Neglecting the first term, as small compared with the others, the rate of reaction comes to

$$-\frac{d[O_3]}{dt} = 2k_3\sqrt{\left(\frac{k_1}{k_4}\right)}[Cl_2]^{\frac{1}{2}}[O_3]^{\frac{3}{2}},$$

which corresponds to the experimental result approximately.

In constructing specific theories an element of doubt is very often introduced by the necessity for making *ad hoc* assumptions about the relative values of the various constants, for the purpose of simplifying the formulae: unless this is done, however, the equations are usually too unwieldy to handle. It may be remarked that the complexity of the formulae to which the theory leads is reflected in a corresponding complexity of the experimental facts: under one set of circumstances the rate of a given reaction may vary as the square root of the concentration of one of the reactants, under other circumstances as the three-halves power, and so on. While there may be much uncertainty about particular theories, there is no doubt about the general truth that the chemistry of the halogens depends partly upon chain reactions of considerable complexity and partly upon more simple direct processes.*

* Compare *inter alia*: 'Decomposition of chlorine dioxide': Schumacher and Stieger, *Z. physikal. Chem.*, B, 1930, 7, 363; Bowen and Cheung, *J. Chem. Soc.*, 1932, 1200; 'Reaction between bromine and ozone', Lewis and Schumacher, *Z. physikal. Chem.*, B, 1930, 6, 423; 'Decomposition of nitrogen trichloride', Griffiths and Norrish, *Proc. Roy. Soc.*, A, 1931, 135, 69; 'Decomposition of F_2O_2', Schumacher and Frisch, *Z. physikal. Chem.*, B, 1937, 37, 1; 'Decomposition of F_2O', Schumacher and Koblitz, *Z. physikal. Chem.*, B, 1934, 25, 283.

When we should speak of a chain, and when of ordinary 'consecutive reactions', is doubtless only a matter of terminology. It is, of course, wrong to assume that all reactions depending on a series of consecutive changes involve long chains starting from one initial activation process. It might be an advantage only to speak of chain reactions in cases where the series of changes is known to be repeated a number of times without fresh initial activation. The quantum yield in the analogous photochemical reaction may sometimes be a guide here.

Further Examples of Atomic Reactions

(a) *Thermal Transformation of Para-Hydrogen.*[*]

This is an interesting example of the atom-molecule type of reaction:

$$A_2 = A + A$$
$$A + B_2 = AB + B.$$

The conversion of para-hydrogen into ortho-hydrogen can take place as a homogeneous reaction in the region of 600° C. A. Farkas has found the order of reaction to be 1·5. This suggests that the mechanism involves a collision between a molecule of para-hydrogen and an atom of hydrogen formed by the thermal dissociation of another molecule. The concentration of atoms will, by the law of mass action, be proportional to the square root of the concentration of molecular hydrogen, as long as the dissociation is small. The product of the concentrations of molecular and atomic hydrogen is thus proportional to the three-halves power of the total concentration.

(b) *The Interaction of Alkali Metal Vapours with Halogens and Halogen Compounds.*

When the vapour of alkali metals is mixed at low pressures, of the order 10^{-3} mm., with certain halogen compounds, a cold, highly diluted flame is produced. A deposit of alkali halide is formed on the wall of the tube in which the reaction takes place, and from the distribution of this deposit and the velocity of the gas stream the partial pressures of the reacting substances and the reaction velocity can be inferred. A number of investigations with various modifications of this method have been carried out by Polanyi and others,[†] and a careful analysis and interpretation of the results has yielded much interesting and valuable information about the speed of the chemical reactions involved.

[*] Farkas, *Light and Heavy Hydrogen*, Cambridge, 1935 (Chapter IV).
[†] Beutler and Polanyi, *Z. physikal. Chem.*, B, 1928, **1**, 3; Bogdandy and Polanyi, ibid., B, 1928, **1**, 21; Polanyi and Schay, ibid., B, 1928, **1**, 30; Ootuka and Schay, ibid., B, 1928, **1**, 62, 68.

Two types of reaction may occur. The first type is exemplified by the action of sodium or potassium vapour with chlorine, bromine, iodine, cyanogen chloride, and cyanogen bromide. Taking sodium and chlorine as an example, it is found that the primary reaction is $Na+Cl_2 = NaCl+Cl$. In this primary reaction it appears that every collision is effective in leading to chemical change. Indeed, it appeared probable that in all the primary reactions of this type each collision is effective, and Polanyi suggested that wherever an atom can undergo an exothermic reaction with a molecule the collisions will all be effective. This amounts to saying that in such reactions no activation is required.

Most of the chlorine atoms formed in the primary process appear to unite with sodium atoms at the wall of the vessel. This process is not accompanied by the emission of any light. Some chlorine atoms, however, react in the gas with sodium, but according to the equation

$$Na_2+Cl = NaCl+Na;$$

the NaCl molecules thus formed are activated, and on collision with Na atoms stimulate them to light emission.

An increase in the temperature of the reaction zone weakens the light emission, as a result of the dissociation of the sodium molecules, and this weakening can be used to determine the heat of dissociation of the sodium molecule (the value obtained is in approximate agreement with an independently determined value). Increase in the pressure of the sodium vapour increases the light emission. Both of these facts support the view that chlorine atoms react in the gas phase with molecular rather than atomic sodium.

While every collision between Na and Cl_2 appears to be effective in the gas, not more than one collision in 10,000 between Na and Cl in the gas phase appears to lead to the formation of a sodium chloride molecule.

In the second type of reaction sodium or potassium vapour reacts with the vapour of such compounds as mercuric chloride or bromide.

In these reactions heating the reaction zone does not diminish the light emission, and this increases much less rapidly with the pressure of the alkali metal than in the first type of reaction. Thus the molecules of the alkali metal apparently do not play the same important part. The primary reaction with sodium and mercuric chloride is

$$Na+HgCl_2 = NaCl+HgCl,$$

followed by $$HgCl+Na = Hg+NaCl$$

in the gas.

One of the most interesting results of these studies is the establishment of the fact that certain reactions between atoms and molecules take place, without activation, at every collision. This result is not, however, an absolutely general one.* In the reactions between sodium vapour and the methyl halides the activation energy is nil for the iodide and rises regularly through the bromide and chloride to the fluoride. There is also, it is interesting to note, an appreciable 'inertia' associated with the reaction between sodium vapour and cyanogen, but since this is independent of temperature it must depend upon some kind of 'orientation' factor rather than upon the necessity for activation.

Decomposition Reactions of Molecules of Varying Degrees of Complexity

We shall now pass on to the consideration of some examples of decomposition reactions. The mechanism of these is not always fully established, but it seems clear that either the Lindemann mechanism applies, or that they are chain reactions: and, indeed, some of them are probably partly chain processes and partly dependent upon the direct molecular transformation.

For the latter, we have activation by collision, time-lag, internal redistribution of energy, and then chemical transformation. The more rapidly the internal redistribution occurs the greater is the transformation probability, and, in accordance with the theory given in an earlier chapter, the higher the pressure up to which the reaction will remain predominantly of the first order. The simpler the molecule the easier the redistribution, so that, other things being equal, the reaction order at a given pressure, such as atmospheric pressure, should be more nearly the second for molecules of simple structure and more nearly the first for molecules of complex structure. The following are some typical examples:

Reaction more nearly of the second order at atmospheric pressure: decomposition of

$$HI, \ O_3, \ Cl_2O, \ N_2O, \ NO_2Cl,\dagger \ NO_2,\ddagger \ CH_3CHO.$$

Reaction more nearly of the first order at atmospheric pressure: decomposition or isomeric change of

$$N_2O_5, \ CH_3COCH_3, \ C_2H_5CHO, \ C_2H_5OC_2H_5, \ CH_3N{=}NCH_3,$$
$$C_{10}H_{16}, \ Ge(C_2H_5)_4.\S$$

---

* von Hartel and Polanyi, *Z. physikal. Chem.*, B, 1930, **11**, 97; von Hartel, Meer, and Polanyi, ibid., 1932, **19**, 139.

† Schumacher and Sprenger, *Z. physikal. Chem.*, B, 1931, **12**, 115.

‡ Bodenstein and Ramstetter, *Z. physikal. Chem.*, 1922, **100**, 68.

§ Geddes and Mack, *J. Amer. Chem. Soc.*, 1930, **52**, 4372.

Despite all the complexities of the situation, there does seem to be a general conformity here with the kind of behaviour which would be expected from theoretical reasoning.

If we have a chain reaction, we must distinguish type (1) and type (2) of the preceding chapter: and if we have molecules of an intermediate degree of complexity, such as acetaldehyde, we must consider the possibility of the kinetically composite type of mechanism discussed on page 95.

Evidently, therefore, there is room for a considerable variety of behaviour.

We shall start with the discussion of a few of the decompositions of more complex molecules. These have played an interesting part in the history of the subject since they first revealed the phenomenon of the transition from first to second order with change of pressure (propionic aldehyde, 1926).

(a) The Decomposition of Nitrogen Pentoxide.

In 1925 the only known gaseous first-order reaction was the decomposition of nitrogen pentoxide. The result of the decomposition is expressed by the equation

$$2N_2O_5 = 2N_2O_4 + O_2.$$

Since the reaction is unimolecular, the primary change cannot be expressed by this equation but must take place by a mechanism such as the following:

$$N_2O_5 = N_2O_3 + O_2.$$

The nitrogen trioxide then decomposes almost instantaneously into nitric oxide and nitrogen peroxide

$$N_2O_3 = NO + NO_2.$$

Nitrogen peroxide has no influence on the thermal decomposition of nitrogen pentoxide, but an almost instantaneous reaction occurs between nitric oxide and the pentoxide[*]

$$NO + N_2O_5 = 3NO_2.$$

Thus each primary act of chemical change results in the decomposition of two molecules of the pentoxide, a fact which has to be taken into account in dealing with the molecular statistics of the reaction.

According to Schumacher and Sprenger,[†] an oxide NO_3 is produced when nitrogen pentoxide reacts with ozone, but this does not appear to play any part in the thermal decomposition.

[*] Busse and Daniels, *J. Amer. Chem. Soc.*, 1927, **49**, 1257.
[†] *Z. physikal. Chem.*, A, 1928, **136**, 77; ibid., A, 1928, **140**, 281.

Daniels and Johnston* investigated the kinetics of the reaction, using an all-glass manometer of special construction.

They found the change to be completely homogeneous, applying the test of the addition of glass wool to the reaction vessel. It proceeds with conveniently measurable velocity at ordinary temperature. In calculating velocity constants corrections have to be applied for the changing dissociation of the N_2O_4 as its concentration alters.

The fraction of the total nitrogen pentoxide which is transformed in unit time is constant and independent of the initial concentration for ordinary variations of pressure. Satisfactory first-order constants are obtained.

The following table gives the velocity constants at different temperatures, and the value of the heat of activation:

Temperature °C.	k (Time in minutes)	Heat of activation
65	0·292	
55	0·0900	25,830
45	0·0299	22,750
35	0·00808	25,370
25	0·00203	25,100
0	0·0000472	24,240
		Mean, 24,700 calories.

The velocity constants, with the time expressed in seconds, are given by the formula†

$$\ln k = 31\cdot45 - \frac{24,700}{RT}.$$

At an early stage nitrogen pentoxide was the subject of tests of the Trautz-Lewis-Perrin radiation theory of chemical reactions.

Taking the value for the heat of activation, and calculating the frequency which corresponds to a quantum of radiation of this size, it was predicted that light of wave-length $1\cdot16\,\mu$ should be effective in decomposing nitrogen pentoxide. The amount of light of this wave-length present in the ordinary thermal radiation in an enclosure at 0° to 65° C. is very small, so that, if the theory was applicable, illumination of the system from outside with light of this kind should have had all the effects on the reaction velocity of a great increase of temperature. The short waves appear in thermal radiation with greater and greater relative intensity as temperature increases, and if chemical change is provoked by more or less monochromatic radiation, increase in the intensity of this one particular frequency is chemically equivalent to raising the temperature of the whole system to the point where the

* J. Amer. Chem. Soc., 1921, 43, 53.   † Kassel, ibid., 1928, 50, 1344.

natural thermal intensity of this would be equal to the artificially produced intensity.

Exposure of a cell containing nitrogen pentoxide to strong sunlight, filtered through iodine solution, which is transparent to waves of length $1 \cdot 16 \mu$ but opaque to visible light, produced no detectable acceleration of the reaction.

It was found, on the other hand, that nitrogen pentoxide is decomposed under the influence of blue light, but only when some nitrogen dioxide is present,* an example of the phenomenon of photocatalysis.

Further tests of the influence of infra-red radiation on the reaction velocity were made by Rice, Urey, and Washburne,† who exposed a 'molecular beam' of nitrogen pentoxide to black-body radiation of high temperature with a negative result, and by Kassel,‡ who also found that radiation of wave-length less than 5μ does not increase the reaction rate even at low pressures, where its effect relative to that of collisions might have been expected to be greater than at atmospheric pressure.

In the earlier experiments on the decomposition the nitrogen pentoxide had never been free from some nitrogen dioxide, since in the sealing off of the apparatus a certain amount of decomposition had been inevitable. Daniels, Wulf, and Karrer§ attempted to repeat some of the previous work in the presence of ozone, which ensures the complete absence of lower oxides since it oxidizes them instantaneously to the pentoxide. In the decomposition of the pentoxide, therefore, there should be a period of induction during which the decomposition products are re-oxidized by the ozone. When all the ozone is used up brown fumes should appear and the decomposition of the pentoxide should go forward in the normal way. It appeared, however, that when the lower oxides were removed in this way the decomposition did not take place at all. This led to the conclusion that the reaction was not, after all, a simple unimolecular decomposition but a change depending on collisions between molecules of nitrogen pentoxide and molecules of nitrogen dioxide.

The matter was then reinvestigated by Hirst,‖ who repeated the experiments of Daniels, Wulf, and Karrer on the decomposition in presence of ozone and failed to confirm their result. On the other hand, the original work of Daniels and Johnston was confirmed.

* Daniels and Johnston, *J. Amer. Chem. Soc.*, 1921, **43**, 72.
† *J. Amer. Chem. Soc.*, 1928, **50**, 2402.
‡ Ibid., 1929, **51**, 54.
§ Ibid., 1922, **44**, 2402.
‖ *J. Chem. Soc.*, 1925, **127**, 657.

Later White and Tolman* again showed that when nitrogen pentoxide is allowed to decompose in presence of ozone, as soon as the ozone is used up the pure nitrogen pentoxide left decomposes at the normal rate found by Daniels and Johnston in their first experiments.

Thus it seems most probable that the isolated result of Daniels, Wulf, and Karrer was due to error rather than a real anomaly in the reaction.

With regard to the influence of impurities and accidental catalysts in general on the rate of reaction, it may be said to be of little account, and there can be no doubt that what is measured is the rate of the uncatalysed decomposition. The reaction has now been investigated under a great variety of circumstances by observers in different parts of the world, and with material of varying origin. The results are all in agreement. Hirst† found a velocity constant of $7 \cdot 11 \times 10^{-3}$ at $35 \cdot 4°$ compared with the value $7 \cdot 71 \times 10^{-3}$ calculated for this temperature from the data of Daniels and Johnston. Some results of White and Tolman‡ can be compared with those of Daniels and Johnston over a range of temperatures:

Temperature	20° C.	25°	35°	40°
$k \times 10^5$ (W. and T.)	103	219	837	1480
$k \times 10^5$ (D. and J.)	117	203	808	1510

Rice and Getz§ made a very complete study of the matter from this point of view. At 65° C. they found $k = 0 \cdot 286$, compared with the value $0 \cdot 292$ of Daniels and Johnston. In order to test the possibility that the reaction might depend on catalysis by dust, they compared the velocity constants for filtered and unfiltered nitrogen pentoxide and for gas which had been passed through an electrical dust precipitator. In some experiments the gas was dried with phosphorus pentoxide, in others not. In some it was prepared by the dehydration of nitric acid with phosphorus pentoxide and in others by the action of chlorine on silver nitrate. Nitric acid was found to have no catalytic effect on the decomposition. Some of the principal results are summarized below, all data referring to 65° C.

	k
'Ordinary' experiments	$0 \cdot 286$
Gas filtered through blue asbestos . .	$0 \cdot 284$
Gas passed through electrical precipitator .	$0 \cdot 278$
P_2O_5 in reaction vessel	$0 \cdot 278$
N_2O_5 made from $AgNO_3$ and chlorine .	$0 \cdot 291$

* J. Amer. Chem. Soc., 1925, **47**, 1240.   † J. Chem. Soc., 1925, **127**, 657.
‡ Loc. cit.   § J. Physical Chem., 1927, **31**, 1572.

It is of considerable interest that Lueck* found the rate of decomposition in solution in carbon tetrachloride and in chloroform to be practically the same as in the gaseous state.

Busse and Daniels† have, moreover, found that hydrogen, carbon monoxide, bromine, and chlorine are without influence on the reaction. Certain organic vapours, which are themselves attacked by nitrogen pentoxide, bring about rapid decomposition. Hirst found that argon exerted no influence, while Hunt and Daniels showed that the presence of a large excess of nitrogen did not alter the rate of reaction at all.

The rate of decomposition at low pressures is of special theoretical interest. Hunt and Daniels‡ showed that the first-order character of the reaction was preserved down to quite low partial pressures of nitrogen pentoxide. Hirst and Rideal§ found, on the other hand, that the velocity constant, so far from decreasing at low pressures, actually increased, but Hibben‖ again found a normal velocity constant between 0·2 and 0·002 mm. These discordant results seemed to suggest that at the low pressures interference by surface reactions must be more or less serious. Sprenger** then reported that when nitrogen pentoxide is admitted to a vessel at low pressure the reaction begins at the normal rate and then stops completely, even though undecomposed nitrogen pentoxide is demonstrably present. He regarded this as evidence for some kind of chain mechanism, but later experiments seemed to show that the whole phenomenon was not a real one. The most recent work, and a careful analysis of possible experimental errors by Hibben, seem to establish now that there really is a definite falling off in the velocity constant in the neighbourhood of about 0·06 mm.†† Even so there remains an uncertainty to which Daniels has called attention. At higher pressures the second stage $NO + N_2O_5 = 3NO_2$ can be regarded as instantaneous. At low pressures this need no longer be true. Slowness of the second stage could lead to an apparent fall in k, as ordinarily measured. As has been pointed out already, there are difficulties about accounting for the absolute activation rate according to the collision theory. This would suggest the existence of a chain reaction. But of such a mechanism there appears to be no definite positive evidence.

* J. Amer. Chem. Soc., 1922, **44,** 757.   † Ibid., 1927, **49,** 1257.
‡ Ibid., 1925, **47,** 1602.
§ Proc. Roy. Soc., A, 1925, **109,** 526.
‖ Proc. Nat. Acad. Sci., 1927, **13,** 626.
** Z. physikal. Chem., 1928, **136,** 49.
†† H. C. Ramsperger and R. C. Tolman, Proc. Nat. Acad. Sci., 1930, **16,** 6; H. J. Schumacher and G. Sprenger, ibid., p. 129; J. H. Hibben, J. Physical Chem., 1930, **34,** 1387; J. H. Hodges and E. F. Linhorst, Proc. Nat. Acad. Sci., 1931, **17,** 28.

(b) The Decomposition of Azomethane and Homologues.

Ramsperger* found that between 278·6° and 327·4° C. azomethane decomposes principally in accordance with the equation

$$CH_3N : NCH_3 = N_2 + C_2H_6.$$

The reaction is homogeneous and of the first order, with a heat of activation of 51,200 calories.

The velocity constants fall with the pressure when this is reduced below a certain limit. Thus at 290° C. k at 0·259 mm. is one-fourth of the high-pressure value at 707·9 mm. At higher temperatures the falling off is more marked. Thus over the same range of pressure at 330° C. the constant falls to one-tenth. As the reaction proceeds the constant does not drop, as would be expected from the changing partial pressure of azomethane, indicating that the reaction products exert an influence in preventing the falling off. The value of the constant in the region of higher pressures is given by

$$\ln k = 36·73 - \frac{51,200}{RT}.$$

Azoisopropane† has also been studied. The principal chemical change involved in this decomposition may be expressed by the equation

$$C_3H_7N : NC_3H_7 = N_2 + C_6H_{14}.$$

The change $\quad C_3H_7N : NC_3H_7 = N_2 + C_3H_6 + C_3H_8$

is also thought to occur to the extent of about 15 per cent.

The reaction is homogeneous and of the first order between the initial pressures of 46 mm. and 0·25 mm., in the temperature range 250° to 290° C. The velocity constant does not change over this range of pressures. The falling off in the value of the velocity constant, if it occurs as would be expected from analogy with the decomposition of azomethane, must begin, therefore, at a pressure lower than 0·25 mm. The heat of activation is 40,900 calories, and the velocity constants are given by the expression

$$k = 5·6 \times 10^{13} \times e^{-40,900/RT},$$

or $\quad\quad \ln k = 31·65 - \frac{40,900}{RT}.$

The course of the curve showing k against pressure for these reactions accords with the theory that the transformation probability increases

* J. Amer. Chem. Soc., 1927, **49**, 912, 1495.

† Ramsperger, J. Amer. Chem. Soc., 1928, **50**, 714.

steadily with the excess energy in the molecule. But the question arises how far the results are influenced by the presence of chains.

By the application of the mirror removal method, and by the study of the catalytic action which azomethane can exert on other substances, such as acetaldehyde, it has been made probable that free radicals are formed when azomethane decomposes. These must enter into secondary reactions. But from the insensitiveness of azomethane itself to photo-chemically generated free radicals, and from the absence of the surface effects so prominent in reactions with long chains (see Chapter VIII), it can be inferred that the decomposition is probably not a true chain reaction. The composition of the reaction products, however, changes somewhat as the reaction proceeds, so that it may be unsafe to make deductions of too detailed a nature from the (k, p) curves. The broad lines of the existing interpretation are nevertheless probably correct.

(c) *The Thermal Decomposition of Acetone.*

The decomposition of gaseous acetone at about 500° is a homogeneous reaction. The course is represented by the equations:

$$(a) \quad CH_3COCH_3 = CH_2 : CO + CH_4,$$

$$(b) \qquad CH_2 : CO = \text{further products.}$$

The ketene decomposes rapidly, giving carbon monoxide, ethylene, and other products. If the final stages are regarded as very fast in comparison with the initial process, then measurements of the rate of pressure increase can be used to follow the progress of the reaction. On this basis the reaction was shown to be of the first order over a considerable pressure range,[*] the velocity constant being expressed by the formula

$$\ln k = 34 \cdot 95 - \frac{68,500}{RT}.$$

This is an approximation only, since the rate of decomposition of the intermediate ketene is not immeasurably fast. The ketene has been shown to accumulate in the system, its concentration reaching a maximum and then falling again, in the manner required by the theory of consecutive reactions. To obtain more accurate results for the rate of the primary decomposition, Winkler and Hinshelwood[†] followed the decomposition by direct analysis of the residual acetone at each stage,

---

[*] Hinshelwood and Hutchison, *Proc. Roy. Soc.*, A, 1926, **111**, 245.
[†] Ibid., A, 1935, **149**, 340.

the iodoform method being employed. For the first-order constants, they found

$$\ln k = 34 \cdot 34 - \frac{68,000}{RT}.$$

Thus the original approximate treatment led to results which were not far in error, as indeed would be expected, since the ketene decomposes several times as fast as the acetone.

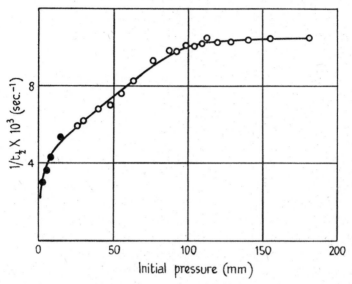

FIG. 10. Influence of initial pressure on time of half-change of acetone at 602° C.

The reaction order is shown by the following figures:

Initial pressure mm.	Time of half-change seconds
311	89
232	90
212	96
155	95
113	95
99	99

At low pressures the first-order constant falls off. In Fig. 10 are shown the values of $1/t_{\frac{1}{2}}$, which are proportional to k, plotted against the initial pressure. The form of the curve does not correspond to any of the simple theories of the dependence of k upon pressure, but gives a clear indication of being composite, possibly for reasons similar to those discussed on page 95.

The question of reaction chains arises: Rice and Herzfeld suggested a mechanism, in which the primary decomposition yields CH_3 and

CH_3CO, after which there is a chain very similar to that proposed for ether. Now small quantities of nitric oxide reduce the rate of reaction of dimethyl ether 15 times and of diethyl ether 3 to 4 times. These reactions take place in the same temperature range as the acetone decomposition and also involve methyl or similar radicals as the principal agents. If, therefore, the acetone reaction is a chain reaction it should presumably be subject to inhibition by nitric oxide, unless there is a positive catalytic effect of the nitric oxide so great as to mask any inhibition. Actually there is neither appreciable inhibition nor, for moderate additions, appreciable catalysis.

Pressure of nitric oxide mm.	Relative reaction rate
0	1·00
0·05	1·02
0·10	1·12
0·29	0·95
5·6	1·16
15	0·94

These numbers should be contrasted with the results for the ethers given in the following section. They seem to be a clear indication that chains make no appreciable contribution to the reaction at temperatures where rate measurements are usually made. A similar conclusion is reached from the negative results of attempts to speed up the reaction by the introduction of free radicals from without; though, incidentally, it may be observed that a positive result of such experiments would not prove that an appreciable proportion of the decomposing molecules yielded radicals under the normal conditions of the rate measurements. (The observation of Allen,* that at considerably lower temperatures the rate of pressure change develops an induction period, therefore seems much more likely to be due to spurious secondary causes, such as the intrusion of condensation reactions, which always accompany these organic decomposition reactions, and which may introduce serious errors unless they are very carefully controlled. At the higher temperatures, where most of the velocity measurements have been made, there is no sign of this induction period: nor would it be easy to explain one in terms of the time taken for the radicals to attain their stationary concentration: this should be attained very rapidly indeed.)

On the whole, therefore, the acetone decomposition is probably to be regarded as an example of a unimolecular reaction, in which chain processes play very little part, where the pressure dependence in general

* *J. Amer. Chem. Soc.*, 1936, **58**, 1052.

follows the predictions of the collisional activation theory, and where a large number of internal degrees of freedom must contribute to the activation process. The detailed analysis of the low-pressure part of the (k, p) curve is doubtful, but there are distinct signs of composite nature in the kinetic mechanism.

(d) The Thermal Decomposition of the Ethers.

In these reactions there seems to be a contribution from a chain process and from a non-chain reaction occurring simultaneously. It is probable that the non-chain parts are typical examples of unimolecular reactions with collisional activation, while the chain parts are examples of type (2) as discussed on page 90.

Diethyl ether* will be considered first, as a typical example.

The first stage of the decomposition gives acetaldehyde and ethane, some of the latter breaking down into ethylene and hydrogen. The acetaldehyde then decomposes, more rapidly than the ether, into methane and hydrogen.

$$C_2H_5OC_2H_5 = CH_3CHO + C_2H_6,$$
$$CH_3CHO = CH_4 + CO.$$

These equations predict a pressure increase of 200%. That observed is 188% only, a certain amount of condensed products being formed. A side reaction gives some formaldehyde in the first stage.

The earlier measurements were based upon the assumption that the aldehydes decomposed so much faster than the ether that the rate of pressure increase gave the rate of the first stage. This is a rather rough approximation. Later results have been corrected for the accumulation of aldehyde, which increases up to a maximum and then disappears again; the essential conclusions have, however, not been changed by these corrections.

Addition of a little nitric oxide reduces the rate to a well-defined limit as shown in Fig. 11. This may be taken to indicate the presence of radical chains.

Fig. 12 shows that the dependence of the reaction rate upon the ether pressure is nearly the same for the inhibited reaction as for the uninhibited reaction. If we accept the hypothesis that the nitric oxide suppresses all the chains, this result means that the average chain-

---

* Hinshelwood, *Proc. Roy. Soc.*, A, 1927, **114**, 84; Staveley and Hinshelwood, ibid., A, 1936, **154**, 335; Davoud and Hinshelwood, ibid., A, 1939, **171**, 39; Hinshelwood and Staveley, *J. Chem. Soc.*, 1936, 818; Fletcher and Rollefson, *J. Amer. Chem. Soc.*, 1936, **58**, 2129.

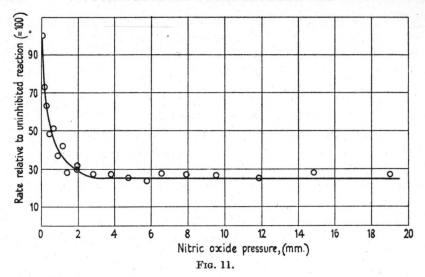

FIG. 11.

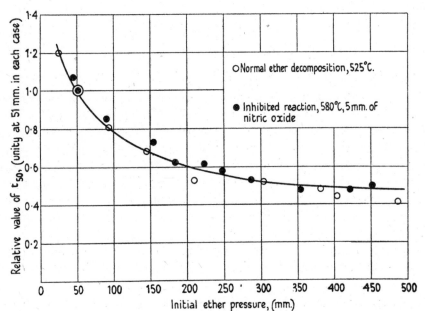

FIG. 12. Variation of t_{50} of the inhibited reaction with initial ether pressure; comparison with normal reaction.

length is practically independent of pressure. Therefore earlier conclusions about the kinetics, which ignored the existence of the chains, would to a considerable extent hold good for the non-chain part of the reaction also.

The residual reaction in presence of nitric oxide shows the usual pressure dependence: $t_\frac{1}{2}$ lengthens out considerably as the pressure drops below about 150 mm. At higher pressures it tends to a nearly steady value. In other words, the reaction is very nearly of the first order. The addition of hydrogen at lower partial pressures of ether restores the rate to what it would be at higher partial pressures as shown in Fig. 13. It appears that the function of the hydrogen is to

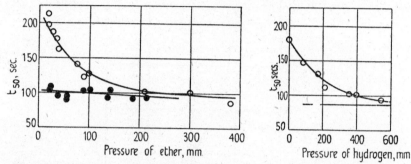

Fig. 13. (Left) Decomposition of ethyl ether at 580°. Influence of hydrogen for different partial pressures of ether. Reaction inhibited by 5 mm. of nitric oxide. Open circles—no hydrogen present: shaded circles—c. 400 mm. of hydrogen present. This figure should be compared with that for the uninhibited reaction (Fig. 1 of *Proc. Roy. Soc.*, A, 1927, **114**, 84).

(Right) Influence of various pressures of hydrogen on NO-inhibited reaction of ethyl ether at 580°. Initial ether pressure c. 35 mm. Horizontal line shows value for 387 mm. of ether without hydrogen.

maintain the Maxwell-Boltzmann distribution at pressures where this would normally begin to fail.

The first-order velocity constant of the total reaction (chain plus non-chain) shows a continued very slow increase up to pressures of several hundred atmospheres.* This may or may not be true of the reaction inhibited by nitric oxide. But in any case it is evidence for a certain kinetic complexity in the reaction possibly due to the causes referred to on page 95. This fact does not invalidate general conclusions based upon the study of the reaction at normal pressures, for from Fig. 13 it is clear that *some process predominant in the low-pressure range reaches a limiting rate* at several hundred millimetres. At several hundred atmospheres other mechanisms may very well predominate.

With the other ethers the results are generally similar.† The proportion of chain reaction, as measured by the nitric oxide method, falls steadily as the number of carbon atoms increases (Fig. 14).

* Steacie and Solomon, *J. Chem. Physics*, 1934, **2**, 503.
† Staveley and Hinshelwood, *Proc. Roy. Soc.*, A, 1937, **159**, 192.

The first-order character of the reaction is maintained to lower pressures the more complex the ether, as would be indicated by the theory developed in the preceding chapter.

The activation energies of the non-chain parts of the reaction are given in the table below, together with n, the number of square terms

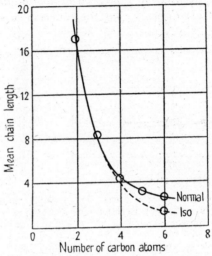

Fig. 14. Variation of mean chain-length with structure of ether.

contributing to the activation energy (calculated according to the simple approximate method given on page 81).

Ether	Mean chain-length at 540° C.	E for inhibited reaction	E for uninhibited reaction	n
Dimethyl	17·0	62,000	58,500	10
Methyl ethyl	8·4	62,000	54,500	10
Diethyl	4·4	67,000	53,000	18
Ethyl propyl	3·2	..	..	..
Dipropyl	2·7	60,500	..	17
Di-isopropyl	1·4	65,500	63,000	> 24

Since the total reactions show the same pressure dependence as the non-chain part, both being nearly of the first order over a considerable range of pressure, the chain part must be of type (2), considered on page 90, for the case of diethyl ether.

One essential condition for this type of behaviour is that a heavy radical, which for diethyl ether will be $CH_2 . OC_2H_5$ or $CH_3CH . O . C_2H_5$,* should only propagate the chain after suffering a thermal decomposi-

* As to which, see Rice and Teller, J. Chem. Physics, 1938, 6, 489.

tion of its own. Methyl or ethyl radicals will react very rapidly with ether, generating the heavier type of radicals: the latter do not decompose at once. Therefore, in the steady state, there will be far more heavy radicals present than methyl or ethyl radicals. Consequently it will be predominantly the heavy radicals which the nitric oxide will attack. Let us now contrast this state of affairs with the decomposition of ethane, where the chains are propagated in a manner involving no intermediate unstable radicals. Here the nitric oxide competes for the radicals with the ethane itself, and, for a given degree of inhibition, more nitric oxide is needed the higher the ethane pressure, as shown in Fig. 15. On the other hand, as shown in Fig. 16, the inhibition of the ether reaction by the nitric oxide is seen to be independent of the ether pressure. This means that the inhibiting process must be competing with one which does not itself depend upon the pressure, and this must be the unimolecular decomposition of the radical with which the nitric oxide combines, i.e. probably the radical $CH_2OC_2H_5$ or $CH_3CH.O.C_2H_5$. Quantitative treatments of these processes have been given* which, on the whole, make all the above interpretations rather probable ones.

Some Reactions of Intermediate Type

We now pass to the consideration of some reactions, of which the following statements appear to be, generally speaking, true.

(a) The activation rates for the part of the reaction which predominates at atmospheric pressure is nearly equal to the collision number $\times e^{-E/RT}$.

(b) The kinetic mechanism appears to be composite.

(c) The mean value of the activation energy shows a certain variation with pressure, as though processes with different values of E, and correspondingly different transformation probabilities, contributed in varying proportions in different pressure ranges.

(a) The Thermal Decomposition of Nitrous Oxide.

The reaction is $2N_2O = 2N_2+O_2$

with simultaneous formation of a very small percentage of nitric oxide (which has a catalytic action).

Hinshelwood and Burk† measured the rate of reaction in a silica bulb by observing the pressure increase accompanying the change; over the

* Staveley, *Proc. Roy. Soc.*, A, 1937, **159**, 192; Hobbs, ibid., A, 1938, **167**, 456; Hobbs and Hinshelwood, ibid., A, 1938, **167**, 439.
† *Proc. Roy. Soc.*, A, 1924, **106**, 284.

range of temperature 565° to 852° C. the reaction was homogeneous, since, even with the silica reaction vessel filled to the extent of two-thirds with coarse silica powder, no measurable increase in reaction

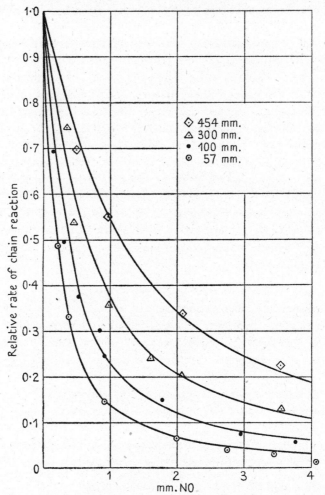

FIG. 15. Inhibition of thermal decomposition of ethane. (Continuous lines are those given by theoretical formula.)

velocity was observable. Variation of the initial pressure of the nitrous oxide up to about one atmosphere showed the reaction to be more nearly of the second than of any other order, proving that the activation process was collisional, and not one depending upon the absorption of radiation by isolated molecules—a possibility then considered. For a first-order reaction the plot of the reciprocal of the half-reaction time against pressure is a line parallel to the pressure axis, while for a second-order reaction it is a line inclined to the axis and passing through the origin. In a series of investigations* it has come to light that the form

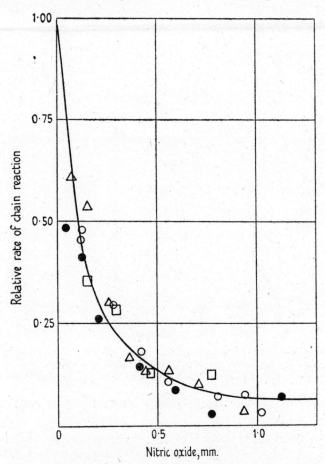

FIG. 16. Showing that the course of the 'inhibition curve' is independent of the pressure of diethyl ether. □ 51 mm. of ether; ○ 103 mm.
of ether; ● 200 mm. of ether; △ 400 mm. of ether.

of this curve for nitrous oxide is really rather complex and may be divided into the following parts: (a) an initial steep increase, starting from the origin, which between 50 and 100 mm. becomes shallower and

* Hunter, *Proc. Roy. Soc.*, A, 1934, **144**, 386; Lewis and Hinshelwood, *Proc. Roy. Soc.*, A, 1938, **168**, 441; Musgrave and Hinshelwood, *Proc. Roy. Soc.*, A, 1932, **135**, 23; Volmer and Bogdan, *Z. phys. Chem.*, B, 1933, **21**, 257; Volmer and Froelich, *Z. phys. Chem.*, B, 1932, **19**, 85; Volmer and Kummerow, *Z. phys. Chem.*, B, 1930, **9**, 141; Volmer and Nagasako, *Z. phys. Chem.*, B, 1930, **10**, 414.

passes into (*b*) an almost linear curve continuing up to several atmospheres, when it gradually bends again passing into (*c*) an almost straight line of still smaller slope, which continues up to 20–30 atmospheres, when it bends round and becomes nearly parallel to the pressure axis, as for a reaction of the first order.

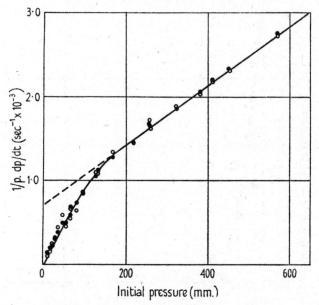

Initial pressure (mm.)

FIG. 17. Influence of pressure on reaction rate at 747° C., showing similarity of curves derived from half-times and initial rates respectively.   Circles = $1/p \cdot dp/dt$; black dots = $1/t_{\frac{1}{2}} \times$ constant.

The low-pressure and high-pressure ranges are shown separately in Figs. 17 and 18.

There is little probability that the whole range can be represented by any expression with a single set of constants, for example, one making the rate proportional to $[N_2O]^{\frac{3}{2}}$.

Various interpretations have been suggested: (1) The curve results from the superposition of three unimolecular reactions, each of the second order at low pressures and of the first order at higher pressures (typical of reactions in which activation is by collision and is followed by transformation of isolated molecules). The three components represent different activation modes with different transformation probabilities of the activated molecules. (2) The curve is not really composite in form, but represents a single unimolecular reaction, the transformation probability of the molecules being a continuous function of the excess energy they contain. This view was supported by Volmer who, however, was not aware of the existence of region (c) of the curve, and believed that the portion (b) became parallel to the axis above about 10 atmospheres. He did not admit the distinctness of portion (a) but plotted the reciprocal of the velocity constant against the reciprocal of the pressure so that points corresponding to low pressures were spread

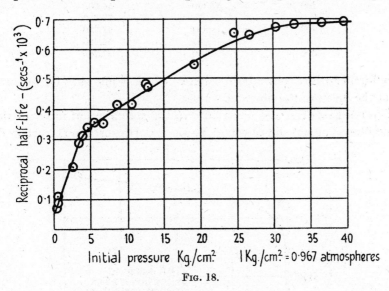

Fɪɢ. 18.

out into an indefinite sweep which masked the normal composite appearance of the curve. (3) The third interpretation is that the changes of slope shown by the curve are not so much due to changes from one integral reaction order to another as to the existence of fractional orders, such as the order 3/2 which arises in certain circumstances when the mechanism depends upon the intervention of atoms or radicals. Limited stretches of the nitrous oxide curve could be represented approximately by the equation of a reaction of the 3/2 order: and, although this would not apply over the whole range, nevertheless, if we assume that the curve is complex, we should not neglect the possibility that *one* of the components is of this type.

A certain trend of the mean activation energy with pressure is observable. The table overleaf refers to lower pressures. Fig. 19 shows the trend over a wide range of pressures.

From the observed rate at atmospheric pressure, and the equation

$$\text{number of molecules reacting} = Ze^{-E/RT},$$

Pressure mm.	E (from values of half-time)	E (from values of initial rate)
25	54,500	47,700
50	56,200	51,000
75	56,600	53,400
100	57,100	55,300
150	57,600	57,100
200	57,700	57,700
300	58,000	57,700
400	58,300	57,700
500	58,600	57,700
600	58,700	57,700

E is found to be about 55,000 calories, which is not very far removed from the mean of the observed values.

Foreign gases can also contribute to the activation of nitrous oxide molecules (Volmer and Bogdan; Lewis and Hinshelwood), carbon di-

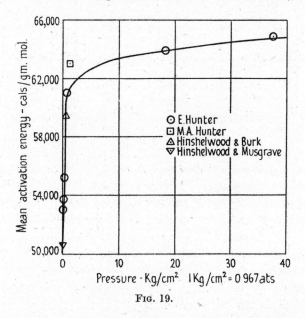

FIG. 19.

oxide being nearly as effective as nitrous oxide itself. The influence of foreign gases gives further indications that the pressure-rate curve is composite.

Halogens* have a very striking catalytic effect on the decomposition which is probably due to the transitory intermediate formation of halogen oxides from nitrous oxide and free atoms of halogen.

* *Proc. Roy. Soc.*, A, 1932, **137**, 25.

(b) Thermal Decomposition of Acetaldehyde and Other Aldehydes.*

The decomposition of acetaldehyde at temperatures in the neighbourhood of 500° takes place almost quantitatively according to the equation

$$CH_3CHO = CH_4 + CO,$$

the pressure change being an accurate measure of the amount decomposed, as shown by the two lines in Fig. 20, one of which shows the

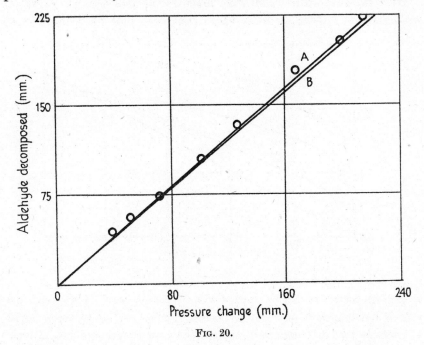

FIG. 20.

decomposition inferred from the pressure change and the other that determined by direct analysis with bisulphite and iodine.

Under certain experimental conditions, for example, if the vapour is kept for an appreciable time at lower temperatures, complex condensation reactions obscure the simpler results. Such reactions were absent in the experiments upon which the following observations are based.

The radical chain mechanism given on page 89 explains very satisfactorily the photochemically induced reaction which takes place at 300°–400° C. It seems, however, not to apply to the thermal reaction at 500°–600° C, which shows no trace of inhibition by nitric oxide. The following figures show the absence of such inhibition, and also show

* Hinshelwood and Hutchison, *Proc. Roy. Soc.*, A, 1926, **111**, 380; Fletcher and Hinshelwood, ibid., A, 1933, **141**, 41; Letort, see below.

that such inhibition is unlikely to be masked by the positive catalytic effect which large amounts of nitric oxide exert.

| NO mm. | . | . | . | 0 | 0·11 | 0·53 | 1·0 | 5·5 |
| $t_{\frac{1}{2}}$ (sec.) | . | . | . | 173 | 174 | 172 | 165 | 132 |

These numbers should be contrasted with the results shown in Fig. 11.

Over the range 0 to 1,000 mm. pressure the rate-pressure curve for acetaldehyde follows a course which resembles that for nitrous oxide

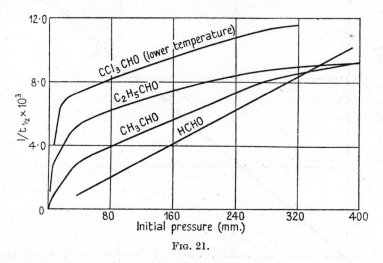

FIG. 21.

in general form. It can be approximately represented by the equation $rate = k[\text{aldehyde}]^{\frac{3}{2}}$, but only by ignoring parts of the pressure range. If there is no chain reaction, then this curve would seem to provide evidence for a kinetically composite mechanism.

A natural enough interpretation of the composite form of the curve would be that there are different types of activated acetaldehyde molecules, corresponding to localization of the activation energy in different parts of the molecule, that these have characteristically different transformation probabilities, and that one type does not readily change into another in the absence of collisions (page 95).

This view certainly explains the very characteristic gradation in the form of the rate-pressure curves as we pass from the simplest aldehyde (formaldehyde) up the homologous series.* This is shown in Fig. 21.

Some prefer, however, not to regard the evidence against radical

* Hinshelwood, Fletcher, Verhoek, and Winkler, *Proc. Roy. Soc.*, A, 1934, **146**, 327.

chains as valid: to take the rate as nearly enough proportional to the 3/2 power of the pressure, and to assume a chain mechanism.*

With formaldehyde and acetaldehyde at about 500 mm. the rate is close to that calculated from $Ze^{-E/RT}$. With propionic aldehyde, a more complex activation mechanism predominates at this pressure, where the reaction is already of the first order. With propionic aldehyde, the nitric oxide method reveals the presence of some chain reaction, which, however, seems to be confined to those modes of reaction most in evidence at the lower pressures.

* See especially Letort, *J. Chim. phys.*, 1937, **34**, 206, 265, 355.

Notes added July 1945

Thermal decomposition of acetone. The application of the propylene inhibition method (see note, p. 97) has now provided positive evidence for the occurrence of radical chains in this reaction.†

Thermal decomposition of ethers. The application of the propylene inhibition method has confirmed the results obtained by the nitric oxide method. There is a characteristic difference in the ease with which the various types of radical involved combine with nitric oxide and propylene respectively.‡

Thermal decomposition of acetaldehyde. Interesting and to some extent conflicting evidence on this reaction has accumulated. Alexander and Lambert by measurements on the dispersion of sound in acetaldehyde vapour (p. 84) found evidence§ for different possible modes of activation (cf. p. 96). Morris found that by the thermal decomposition of mixtures of acetaldehyde and deutero-acetaldehyde only pure CH_4 and CD_4 were produced:‖ infra-red spectroscopy failed to detect any of the mixed products which would be formed in radical-chain reactions. These two investigations lent support to the view that the thermal reaction does not take place by way of chains. By applying the method of propylene-inhibition (p. 97) Smith and Hinshelwood found positive evidence for a distinct proportion of radical-chain reaction.¶ Later Morris showed that acetaldehyde which contains traces of oxygen does in fact yield the mixed products when decomposed simultaneously with the deutero compound.** He adopts the view that pure aldehyde decomposes thermally without chains, and that the later are due to traces of impurity in normal specimens.

† Smith and Hinshelwood, *Proc. Roy. Soc.*, A, 1944, **183**, 33.
‡ Smith and Hinshelwood, ibid., 1942, **180**, 237.
§ Alexander and Lambert, ibid., A, 1942, **179**, 499.
‖ Morris, *J. Amer. Chem. Soc.* 1941, **63**, 2535.
¶ Smith and Hinshelwood, *Proc. Roy. Soc.*, A, 1942, **180**, 237.
** Morris, *J. Amer. Chem. Soc.*, 1944, **66**, 584.

VI

TERMOLECULAR REACTIONS

IF, in bimolecular reactions, any considerable proportion of the collisions taking place at atmospheric pressure led to reaction, the velocity of transformation would be too great to be measured experimentally. Indeed, in many reactions proceeding at conveniently measurable rates about one collision in 10^{10} to 10^{12} is effective. The value of E/RT in these instances is 25 to 30. Reactions with much smaller values than this will appear almost instantaneous.

With termolecular reactions the position is quite different. An appropriate ternary collision is an event of such rarity that, if in addition to a molecular encounter considerable activation is required, the velocity of reaction will be negligibly small. Conversely, it may be expected that if any termolecular gaseous reactions are observed to take place with measurable speed at ordinary pressures, they must be associated with a very small heat of activation. These theoretical expectations are confirmed by experiment.

With regard to the probability of ternary collisions in gases, Trautz[*] suggested that it was so small as to render true termolecular reactions impossible. Bodenstein, however, showed that the combination of nitric oxide and oxygen $2NO + O_2 = 2NO_2$ is a homogeneous change which is kinetically of the third order, and the same appears to apply to the combination of nitric oxide with chlorine[†] and with bromine[‡] and to the reaction between nitric oxide and hydrogen.[§]

$$2NO + Cl_2 = 2NOCl,$$
$$2NO + Br_2 = 2NOBr,$$
$$2NO + H_2 = N_2O + H_2O$$
$$(\text{or } N_2 + H_2O_2).$$

What are virtually termolecular reactions occur in the recombination of atoms in triple collisions.

Bodenstein, in the course of a comprehensive study of the formation and decomposition of the higher oxides of nitrogen,[‖] showed, in con-

---

[*] Trautz, *Z. Elektrochem.*, 1916, **22**, 104.

[†] Trautz, *Z. anorg. Chem.*, 1914, **88**, 285.

[‡] Trautz and Dalal, ibid., 1918, **102**, 149.

[§] Hinshelwood and Green, *J. Chem. Soc.*, 1926, 730; Mitchell and Hinshelwood, ibid., 1936, 378.

[‖] *Z. physikal. Chem.*, 1922 **100**, 68.

junction with Lindner, that the reaction between nitric oxide and oxygen proceeds in accordance with the equation

$$\frac{d[NO_2]}{dt} = k[NO]^2[O_2].$$

The velocity was measured manometrically, definite quantities of nitric oxide and oxygen being allowed to stream into a vacuous vessel, which was provided with a bromnaphthalene manometer, protected from the oxides of nitrogen by an air-buffer.

The remarkable fact about the velocity of reaction was the negative temperature coefficient. The following figures are taken from Bodenstein's paper, and illustrate the way in which the rate of reaction decreases as the temperature rises:

T (abs.)	$k \times 10^{-6}$
273	2·09
333	1·33
470	0·80
564	0·68
662	0·61

The temperature coefficient, expressed as the relative increase in velocity for a ten-degree rise in temperature, k_{t+10}/k_t, changes gradually from 0·912 to 0·997 with rising temperature.

A comparison between this and the usual temperature coefficient of a two- to threefold increase for ten degrees shows the expectation of a very low heat of activation to be realized.

But the existence of a very low heat of activation would mean a temperature coefficient of just over unity. It would not account for an actual inversion of the normal effect. The depression of the coefficient below unity was due, according to Bodenstein, to another factor. This was a diminished 'duration of collisions' at higher temperatures, which lessened the chance of ternary collisions. Owing to the increasing molecular speeds, there was less and less chance, at greater temperatures, that two molecules should still be 'within range of each other' when a third one approached. There is, as a matter of fact, nothing in the simple kinetic theory of collisions between ideal molecules which would give this result, but possibly collisions between molecules of nitric oxide result in a temporary association to a complex, the life of which diminishes with increasing temperature. It is to be noted that the velocity of reaction falls off only very slowly, so that the diminishing frequency of the right kind of collision might account for the retrogression without undue strain.

With regard to the molecular statistics of the reaction, at $0°$ C., and $\frac{1}{3}$ atmosphere pressure of oxygen and $\frac{2}{3}$ atmosphere of nitric oxide, the number of molecules reacting in one second is 7×10^{19} per c.c. It is now necessary to find whether the number of ternary collisions is sufficient to account for this rate of reaction.

Bodenstein made a preliminary rough calculation in the following way.[*] The chance that an oxygen molecule hits a nitric oxide molecule actually in collision with one of its own kind bears the same ratio to the chance that it hits a single nitric oxide molecule as the molecular diameter bears to the mean free path. This gives the ratio of ternary to binary collisions as $10^{-8}/10^{-5}$ or 1 to 1,000. The number of collisions between oxygen and nitric oxide molecules under the experimental conditions is 3×10^{28}. Thus there would be about 3×10^{25} ternary collisions to provide for 7×10^{19} cases of transformation.

In ternary collisions it is probable that the orientation of the molecules at the moment of impact is much more important than in bimolecular processes, so that it is probably necessary to reduce the number of collisions likely to lead to reaction to 3×10^{24}. In this way the ratio of the number of molecules reacting to the number suffering collisions of suitable orientation is found to be about 10^{-4} to 10^{-5}.

Now if we write, in the usual way, $e^{-E/RT} = 10^{-4}$ or 10^{-5}, we find a value for the heat of activation of a few thousand calories only. Thus a very small temperature coefficient is to be expected.

Nevertheless, it is interesting that other factors should actually invert the small positive effect which might have been expected.

Two other termolecular reactions, namely, the formation of nitrosyl chloride and nitrosyl bromide, have in fact small positive coefficients, but very little above unity.

Trautz and Schueter[†] showed that the whole matter could be envisaged from a formally different point of view. The termolecular reaction between nitric oxide and chlorine is assumed to proceed in the following two stages:

$$NO + Cl_2 \rightleftharpoons NOCl_2,$$
$$NOCl_2 + NO = 2NOCl.$$

The concentration of $NOCl_2$ is always small, the equilibrium in the first reaction being well on the side of dissociation. In this equilibrium

$$[NOCl_2] = k[NO][Cl_2].$$

[*] For a detailed consideration of triple collisions, cf. Steiner, *Z. physikal. Chem.*, B, 1932, **15**, 249.

[†] *Z. anorg. Chem.*, 1924, **136**, 1.

The rate of formation of NOCl in the second reaction is proportional to $[NOCl_2][NO]$ and therefore to $[NO]^2[Cl_2]$. If the speed of the second reaction determines the measured speed of the whole change, then the reaction is purely termolecular in the kinetic sense.

The increasing dissociation of the intermediate compound with rising temperature accounts for the low temperature coefficient of the resultant velocity.

The decrease in rate resulting from the diminishing concentration of this compound might indeed be greater than the normal increase with temperature in the rate of the second reaction, and the temperature coefficient would then actually be negative as in the example of the nitric oxide oxidation.

It is a rather striking fact that all the four termolecular reactions which are known involve the participation of two molecules of nitric oxide. This may be simply a coincidence, but it more probably indicates that collisions between two molecules of nitric oxide, even if they do not result in the formation of N_2O_2, have a rather more 'inelastic' character and a longer duration than most molecular impacts.

A treatment of the reaction between nitric oxide and oxygen, based upon the view that N_2O_2 is an intermediate, has been worked out by Bodenstein.*

The reaction between nitric oxide and hydrogen is interesting because it takes place at much higher temperatures than the other three termolecular reactions. Its speed at $1,100°$ abs. is more or less comparable with that of the oxidation of nitric oxide at the ordinary temperature. The reaction takes place roughly according to the equation

$$-\frac{d[NO]}{dt} = k[NO]^2[H_2],$$

which shows that the primary reaction is between two molecules of nitric oxide and one of hydrogen. The subsequent decomposition of the nitrous oxide or hydrogen peroxide thus formed is very rapid in comparison.

The molecular statistics of this reaction are of some interest. The heat of activation, as measured directly from the temperature coefficient, is 47,000 calories.

A bimolecular reaction which would proceed with comparable velocity at the same temperature as this reaction would have a heat of activation of about 60,000 calories. Now termolecular collisions are

* Report of Vth Solvay Council, 1935, p. 1.

about 1,000 times less frequent than bimolecular collisions at atmospheric pressure. Thus, if we have a bimolecular reaction and a termolecular reaction with equal heats of activation, the rate of the latter should be at least 1,000 times smaller than that of the former at the same temperature. It will probably be more nearly 10,000 times slower, since a larger proportion of the ternary collisions are likely to be ineffective on account of unfavourable orientation of the molecules during impact. Conversely, if a termolecular reaction and a bimolecular reaction are to take place at equal rates at the same temperature, then the heat of activation of the termolecular reaction would need to be the smaller by an amount ΔE, such that $e^{\Delta E/RT} = 1,000$ to $10,000$. Thus, other things being equal, the heats of activation of termolecular reactions ought to be about 5,000 calories less at the ordinary temperature, and about 15,000 calories less at $1,000°$ abs., than those of second-order reactions. The value 47,000 calories in the light of this appears quite a natural one.

A closer study of the reaction* shows that a more accurate expression for the reaction rate is given by

$$-\frac{d[NO]}{dt} = k_1[NO]^2[H_2] + \frac{k_2[NO]^2[H_2]}{1+a[NO]} + \frac{k_3[NO]^2[H_2]}{1+b[H_2]},$$

where a and b are constants.

This can be interpreted by supposing that binary collision complexes $(2NO)$ and $(NO.H_2)$ are formed, and that these have definite 'lives'. Reaction occurs between the pair $(2NO)$ and H_2 or between the pair $(NO.H_2)$ and NO, it being necessary for the third partner to arrive during the life of the binary complex. Calculations based upon this idea lead to a formula of the above type.

The whole question of termolecular reactions, and the problem whether they involve binary intermediate compounds, assume a logically simpler aspect if we realize that a binary collision must be regarded as possessing a certain duration, whether an association compound is formed or not. The duration may be difficult to define in precise quantitative terms, but it is obviously a function of the structure of the molecules and of the forces acting between them.

Ternary collisions play an important part in the recombination of free atoms, and in some cases seem to be of a high degree of efficiency. The complexity introduced by varying collision times is shown by the fact that in a reaction where A' combines with A'', not only must

* Mitchell and Hinshelwood, *J. Chem. Soc.*, 1936, 378.

encounters in the order $A'A''$ meeting X be taken into consideration but also* those in the order $A'X$ meeting A''. The characteristic time relations for the two types will naturally be different. A similar state of affairs appears to exist in the reaction between nitric oxide and hydrogen. For example, if the pair NO.NO persists so long that it is certain to meet hydrogen before resolution, the rate of reaction becomes independent of the hydrogen pressure, but, if its life is very short compared with the time between collisions, then the rate is directly proportional to the hydrogen pressure.

The combination of free radicals seems to be a process of the third order only when the structure of the radical is rather simple. With complex structures the kinetic energy of approach and the heat of union wander off into internal degrees of freedom and would only find their way back after a relatively long time into the coordinate corresponding to separation of the two radicals. But before this happens there will probably have been many collisions of the associated pair with something else. And it does not matter how many as long as there has been one at all. The rate of combination only becomes proportional to the concentration of molecules capable of providing the third partner when the life of the binary complex is not long compared with the time between collisions. This state of affairs is more completely realized the simpler the combining pair.†

Hydrogen atoms combine in a third-order process: the same applies to the recombination of nitrogen atoms which seems to play some part in the decay of active nitrogen. The recombination of two methyl radicals seems, however, to be a second-order process, which means that the life of the association complex is much longer than that of a pair of atoms. The evidence for this is derived from the study of the photolysis of acetaldehyde, the kinetics of which are completely accounted for by the assumption of the binary recombination process but would not admit the ternary process. The recombination of hydroxyl radicals, in activated steam, appears to depend upon ternary collisions in which the duration of the binary encounters of two hydroxyl radicals is rather long.‡

* Rabinovitsch, *Trans. Faraday Soc.*, 1937, **33**, 283.
† Cf. Kimball, *J. Chem. Phys.*, 1937, **5**, 310.
‡ Oldenberg and Rieke, ibid., 1939, **7**, 485.

VII

CHAIN REACTIONS SHOWING SPECIAL CHARACTERISTICS

THE significance of the process called activation has been abundantly illustrated in previous chapters. Ordinarily it is governed by the energy distribution laws prevailing in a system in thermodynamic equilibrium, but in exothermic reactions a special mechanism becomes possible, in which the energy set free is communicated to molecules which it immediately activates, a reaction chain being thereby established. As a special, and, as it has proved, very important case, the original activation may have proceeded to the limit of resolution into free atoms or radicals: and the chain consists in the repeated regeneration of these at each stage.

The idea of chain reactions originated in two ways, both of which have been referred to in the foregoing pages. In one form it was introduced to explain the enormous deviation of the hydrogen chlorine combination from Einstein's law; and chain reactions are now generally recognized to occur wherever many molecules are transformed per quantum absorbed in a photochemical change. In a different connexion the idea was used by Christiansen and Kramers to remove the difficulty then felt about accounting for the rate of activation, which was apparently too great to be explained except by a chain mechanism. We have now to consider some special characteristics of the chain mechanism.

The Theory of Negative Catalysis.

The explanation of negative catalysis in terms of the chain reaction mechanism was given by Christiansen.†

There is no particular difficulty in understanding how a small trace of some foreign substance can accelerate a chemical reaction to a very marked extent: the molecules resort one after another to the catalyst where they undergo an extremely rapid change. But there is much more mystery about the converse process, known as negative catalysis, whereby a small trace of some substance may almost entirely inhibit a reaction which in the absence of the negative catalyst would be taking place quite rapidly. Molecules are known to exert appreciable forces only at distances which are not much greater than their own diameters;

* Cf. Semenov, *Chemical Kinetics and Chain Reactions*, Oxford, 1935.
† *J. Physical Chem.*, 1924, **28**, 145.

if, therefore, the negative catalyst is present in small concentration only, most of the molecules will be quite outside the range of its influence, and there is at first sight no reason why they should not be undergoing their normal reactions.

One suggestion made was that all reactions subject to the influence of negative catalysts were in reality reactions already catalysed by a trace of some other substance present in small enough amount to be more or less completely removed even by the small quantity of negative catalyst added. Examples of this kind of action are known: and indeed the 'poisoning' of a catalytic surface in a heterogeneous reaction is something of the kind. Nevertheless, examples of inhibition are known which are not explicable in this way.

If a reaction takes place by a chain mechanism, and if a molecule of the negative catalyst combines with or deactivates one of the atoms or molecules participating in the propagation of the chain, then not only is this one atom or molecule put out of action, but, virtually, all those which would normally have reacted in the rest of the chain. Since the chain might have been a very long one, it is evident that one molecule of the negative catalyst may thus stop the reaction of hundreds or thousands of molecules.

The most direct evidence that negative catalysis sometimes works in this way in ordinary thermal reactions, and, therefore, incidentally, that the chain mechanism can operate in such reactions, was found by Bäckström.* In the photochemical oxidation of benzaldehyde, heptaldehyde, and of solutions of sodium sulphite, there are very large numbers of molecules transformed for each quantum of light absorbed, amounting respectively to 10,000, 15,000, and 50,000 for the three reactions. Such deviations from Einstein's law show that the light probably sets up chain reactions. These photochemical changes are markedly subject to the action of inhibitors, which presumably cut short the chains. Bäckström established the important fact that the corresponding reactions which take place in the dark are subject to the influence of the same inhibitors in an almost exactly parallel way. Thus it would appear that chain processes occur in the ordinary thermal reactions, and that the inhibitors act in the manner supposed by Christiansen's theory.

The results obtained for the oxidation of sodium sulphite solutions containing various alcohols as inhibitors are particularly instructive.

* J. Amer. Chem. Soc., 1927, **49**, 1460; Medd. K. Vetenskapsakad. Nobel-Inst., 1927, **6**, Numbers 15 and 16; Trans. Faraday Soc., 1928, **24**, 601.

The rate of reaction depends upon the concentration of the inhibitor, C, in the following way:

$$\text{rate of dark reaction} = k_1/(kC+k_2),$$
$$\text{rate of photochemical reaction} = k_3 k_1/(kC+k_2),$$

k_1, k_2, k_3, and k being constants, the latter depending on the nature of the alcohol.

The alcohols themselves are gradually oxidized; thus the mechanism of the inhibition seems to be that at some link of the sulphite oxidation chain an alcohol molecule is oxidized instead of a sulphite ion, and the chain is thereby interrupted. The exact mechanism of the normal uninterrupted chain is not exactly known: nor is it relevant to the discussion. By measurements of the rate of oxidation of the inhibitor the chain-length can be found: the calculation is based upon the following considerations. Chains are broken in two ways: by the alcohol, and in some way which prevents them from reaching an infinite length when there is no alcohol present. This is represented by the two terms kC and k_2 in the above equations. When the inhibition is considerable it may be taken that all the chains are broken by alcohol molecules: this stage is marked by the fact that kC is large compared with k_2 and thus the rate is inversely proportional to the concentration of the inhibitor. Thus measurement of the number of alcohol molecules oxidized gives the number of chains broken in unit time: this must equal the number started. Dividing the total number of molecules of sulphite oxidized by the number of chains gives the number of links in each chain. Another way of finding the chain-length is by measurement of the quantum efficiency of the photochemical reaction under the same conditions of concentration: for, although the light increases the number of chains starting, it does not alter their length provided that the alcohol concentration is in the region where all the chains are broken by the inhibitor molecules. Bäckström found good agreement between the chain-lengths determined in these two ways.*

Although the reactions just described are not gaseous reactions they have been dealt with in some detail because the processes which they illustrate play an important part in gas reactions also. The action of 'anti-knocks' may be interpreted as a phenomenon of negative catalysis of a chain reaction. There is evidence to show that in the combustion of hydrocarbons bodies of a peroxide character are formed, and that these act as centres from which chains are propagated.† Metallic anti-

* See also Bäckström, Z. physikal. Chem., B, 1934, 25, 99, 122.
† Egerton and Gates, J. Inst. Petroleum Tech., 1927, 13, 281.

knocks, such as lead tetra-ethyl, are supposed to give rise to peroxides themselves, which react with and destroy the fuel peroxides and thus interrupt the chains. Further examples of this kind of action will arise in a later section dealing with the union of hydrogen and oxygen.

Quantitative Treatment of Reaction Chains.

To write down the differential equation for the rate of a chain reaction we employ the law of mass action, but the simple application of this involves the concentration of the transitorily formed atoms, radicals, or activated molecules which propagate the chain, and as this concentration is unknown the equation written down would be useless unless some other relations are established by means of which the unknown quantities can be eliminated. These relations are provided by the condition that the chains shall be stable, or the condition of the system 'stationary'. This means that the number of chains starting in unit time must be equal to the number finishing, as long as the concentrations of the reacting substances are thought of as constant. If we imagine a system at the very instant when a chain reaction starts in it, it is evident that for a fraction of a second the reaction velocity will increase as the chains develop, but in an extremely short space of time will reach a 'stationary' value where the number of new active particles formed in time dt is equal to the number disappearing. This 'stationary' value only remains constant, of course, so long as the concentrations of the primary reacting substances do not change appreciably—a condition which is, however, automatically provided for when we establish a *differential* equation for the reaction velocity. Some examples follow.

(a) The best example to consider first is that treated by Christiansen and Kramers.* Here we have a single reacting gas, undergoing, for example, thermal decomposition. The molecules are activated by collision in the first instance, but the product of reaction is able to activate fresh molecules of the initial substance in giving up its excess energy; moreover, each molecule of the product is supposed to activate, on the average, α molecules in the process of relapsing to the normal condition. In the original treatment the chain was imagined to consist in the handing on of energy. The arguments apply, *mutatis mutandis*, to the regeneration of fresh atoms or radicals. This can be taken as understood throughout in the following.

Let n be the concentration of normal, unactivated molecules of the

* Z. physikal. Chem., 1923, **104**, 451.

reacting gas, a that of activated molecules of the reacting gas, and a' that of activated molecules of the product. The condition for a stable chain is that

$$\frac{da}{dt} = 0 \quad \text{and} \quad \frac{da'}{dt} = 0.$$

Thus we have

$$\frac{da'}{dt} = \qquad Aa \qquad - \qquad Z_1 na' \qquad = 0$$

Rate of spontaneous change of activated reactant into activated product. A is a constant.	Loss of activated product molecules by collision with normal molecules, which *may* be activated themselves in the process. Z_1 is a constant.
(1)	(2)

$$\frac{da}{dt} = Kn^2 \quad + \quad \alpha Z_1 na' \quad - \quad Aa \quad - \quad Z_2 na = 0$$

Production of activated molecules of reactant by collision among themselves, i.e. independently of the chain process.	Corresponding to process (2) of the above equation.	Corresponding to process (1) above.	Rate of deactivation of active molecules of reactant by collision with normal molecules. Z_2 is a constant.

The first and last terms of the second equation would naturally balance for thermodynamic reasons if no chemical reaction were going on. Z_1 and Z_2 depend upon the molecular speeds and diameters.

From the first equation

$$a' = \frac{Aa}{Z_1 n};$$

substituting in the second

$$Kn^2 + \alpha Aa - Aa - Z_2 na = 0,$$

whence

$$a = \frac{Kn^2}{Z_2 n + A(1-\alpha)}.$$

$$\text{Rate of reaction} = Aa = \frac{AKn^2}{Z_2 n + A(1-\alpha)}.$$

If every activated molecule of product activates just one molecule of reactant, then $\alpha = 1$ and the rate reduces to $\dfrac{AK}{Z_2}n$.

Under these conditions the rate varies as the first power of n, although the reaction really depends upon collisions, a result which we have already derived from a more general argument in dealing with unimolecular reactions.

Stationary and Non-Stationary Processes.

The method of calculation given in the last section can easily be generalized to yield an expression of the following form:

$$\text{rate of reaction} = \frac{\text{function of concentrations}}{\left\{\begin{array}{c}\text{factor}\\\text{determining}\\\text{breaking of}\\\text{chains by}\\\text{surface}\end{array}\right\} + \left\{\begin{array}{c}\text{factor deter-}\\\text{mining breaking}\\\text{of chains by}\\\text{collisions in}\\\text{gas phase}\end{array}\right\} + A(1-\alpha)}$$

$$= \frac{F(c)}{f_s + f_c + A(1-\alpha)},$$

where A is a constant or a function of concentration according to circumstances, and α is the number of active particles resulting from one original active particle involved in the propagation of the chain.

With $F(c)$ we are not at the moment much concerned; it depends upon the nature of the chemical act by which the chains are initiated.

f_s and f_c represent the two ways in which chains can be terminated— namely (a) by deactivation at the surface of the containing vessel of one of the molecules which would otherwise have continued the chain, and (b) by deactivation of such a molecule in a collision in the gas phase, without the handing on of the energy.

If α is not greater than unity, the velocity of reaction can only attain a considerable value if f_s and f_c are small, that is, if the chains are not broken very often.

When, however, α is greater than unity, phenomena of a most interesting kind become possible.* This condition that $\alpha > 1$ may be fulfilled in a sufficiently exothermic reaction, and especially one where $X \to 2Y$, or $X_1 + X_2 = 2Y$, each of the Y molecules possessing enough energy to be the potential origin of a new chain. The same thing happens if one atom or radical yields two, as in the reaction

$$O + H_2 = OH + H.$$

It will be evident that under these circumstances the term $A(1-\alpha)$ in the above equation is negative. If the negative value is large enough it may equal $f_s + f_c$; the rate of reaction will then be infinite. The meaning of this is that, on account of the branching of the chains which is now occurring, the number of fresh chains which start in any element of time is greater than the number terminated: thus no

---

* Semenov, Z. Physik, 1927, **46**, 109; ibid., 1928, **48**, 571.

stationary condition is possible. There can be no stable reaction velocity, but only one which increases indefinitely with time. In other words, an explosion occurs.

A distinction, at least in degree, may be drawn between this kind of explosion and a thermal explosion which occurs when the rate of liberation of heat in a system exceeds the rate at which it can be conducted away, so that the temperature rises and the reaction proceeds at an ever increasing rate until ignition results.

Critical Pressure Limits.

The relative magnitudes of the expressions $A(1-\alpha)$ and of f_c+f_s naturally vary with the concentration of the reacting gases and of any foreign gases present. Thus the denominator of the expression for the rate of reaction may be positive for certain concentrations and negative for others. At any concentration where $f_s+f_c+A(1-\alpha)$ just becomes zero there is a critical limit. On one side of the limit a stable velocity is possible, on the other side the number of chains starting is greater than the number terminated, so that the reaction almost instantaneously accelerates to explosion.

The limit may appear to be extraordinarily sharp. The stable velocity on one side of the critical limit may be quite small: at the limit a stationary condition ceases to be possible and the reaction must accelerate; thus, however small the velocity at a point just on one side of the limit, explosion takes place on the other side. The acceleration to the explosive point takes place in a time of the order of that required for chains to develop in the gas; which may be an immeasurably small fraction of a second. Thus we have the remarkable phenomenon of a critical concentration limit, on passing which a very slow reaction suddenly changes into explosion.

The critical limit may be an upper limit or a lower limit. This comes about in the following way. Chains are interrupted either by deactivation at the wall or in the gas phase. The greater the concentration of the gases, the smaller relatively is the influence of the wall factor. When this is the chief means by which the chains are broken there may be a transition from slow reaction to explosion as the pressure increases. When, on the other hand, deactivation in the gas phase is the principal factor in controlling the length of the chains the transition from a stationary to an explosive process may occur as the pressure decreases.

When both factors operate simultaneously there may be both an upper and a lower limit of concentration, above and below which slow reaction occurs but between which lies a region of non-stationary, explosive processes.*

The Lower Explosion Limit.

It had long been known that phosphorus would only glow in oxygen if the pressure of the latter was below a certain limit. But it would hardly have been justified, on the basis of existing observations, to interpret this as a critical pressure in the sense of the last paragraph, in view of Rayleigh's demonstration that the glow of phosphorus is under some conditions a phenomenon depending on heterogeneous catalysis by nuclei of an oxidation product: these nuclei might be poisoned by an excess of oxygen, as well as by the various vapours which are known to inhibit the glow.

Chariton and Walta,† and more conclusively Semenov,‡ found, however, that there is also a lower critical pressure below which the gaseous reaction between phosphorus vapour and oxygen at ordinary temperatures hardly takes place at all, and above which it leads to the production of an explosive ignition. The critical oxygen pressure p_k is quite small, a fraction of a millimetre of mercury, and can be measured by allowing oxygen to enter through a capillary tube into a vessel containing phosphorus vapour and noting the point at which ignition occurs. Measurements on the rate of change of pressure with time, by means of a McLeod gauge, show that the reaction at pressures below the critical is very slow. p_k is decreased if the pressure of the phosphorus vapour, p_{P_4}, is increased, and is also decreased if the size of the vessel is increased. This is because the reaction is a chain reaction and the active particles lose their activity or are destroyed when they collide with the walls of the vessel. This happens relatively less frequently in large vessels: hence the explosive region is reached more easily. The presence of argon lowers the critical pressure, because the foreign gas makes diffusion of the chain carriers to the wall more difficult.

* We have used α to indicate the number of active molecules produced *in the particular act of chemical transformation by which the chain is propagated*. Thus if $X + Y = 2Z$, and the Z molecules are both active, $\alpha = 2$. The two Z's, being exposed to various deactivating influences, do not necessarily survive to complete a cycle of changes. Even though $\alpha = 2$, there may not be explosion: if, for example, only one of the two Z's survives on the average there is no *effective* branching of the chain. Some writers have used α in the sense of this *effective* yield of active molecules: their condition for explosion would be simply $\alpha > 1$, whereas that given above is $A(\alpha - 1) > f_s + f_c$. The difference is only one of definition, but attention is called to it, since otherwise confusion might arise in comparing statements of different writers.

† *Z. Physik*, 1926, **39**, 547.   ‡ Ibid., 1927, **46**, 109.

Similar phenomena are shown by phosphine and oxygen,* the rate of reaction below the limit being immeasurably small.

The simple quantitative treatment of the phenomenon, in terms of the chain theory, is given below. In what follows the example of phosphine and oxygen is used, but the method applies with appropriate modifications to other reactions.

The exact origin of the first centres from which chains are propagated does not affect the following considerations, which deal with the rate of increase of the chains when they are once started.

Let it be supposed that there are a certain number of molecules of activated oxygen, and that these act upon phosphine giving an active product, denoted by the symbol X_P, which reacts with oxygen to give another active product X_O. This in turn reacts with phosphine giving X_P again, and so on until the chain is broken by reaching the wall of the vessel.

In the course of a chain let there be n_1 collisions between X_O and PH_3, n_2 between X_O and O_2, n_3 between X_P and PH_3, and n_4 between X_P and O_2. Let $n_1+n_2+n_3+n_4 = n$. Since X_O only appears when X_P disappears and vice versa, $n_1 = n_4$.

$$n_1/(n_1+n_2) = p_{PH_3}/(p_{PH_3}+p_{O_2}); \quad n_4/(n_3+n_4) = p_{O_2}/(p_{PH_3}+p_{O_2}),$$

whence
$$n_1 = n_4 = \frac{p_{O_2}p_{PH_3}}{(p_{O_2}+p_{PH_3})^2}n.$$

By the Einstein-Smoluchowsky relation, the number of collisions suffered by a particle undergoing a mean displacement d is $1\cdot5d^2/\lambda^2$, where λ is the mean free path.

If we assume that every chain is terminated by the action of the wall of the tube, $n = 1\cdot5d^2/\lambda^2$, d being of the order of magnitude of the diameter of the tube. If some of the chains are 'reflected' from the walls, this is equivalent to an increase in the effective diameter, so that the qualitative nature of the wall may be roughly taken into account by multiplying d by a factor β, which varies from one kind of tube to another. Taking the mean free paths of all the kinds of molecule to be approximately equal, λ is inversely proportional to the total pressure, and thus may be written $\lambda_0(p/_{PH_3}+p_{O_2})$.

Substituting these values we find for n_1 or n_4 the expression

$$p_{O_2}p_{PH_3}\times 1\cdot5\beta^2d^2/\lambda_0^2.$$

Suppose the probability that the chain branches at a given collision to be ν. Then the number of times on the average that the chains

* Dalton and Hinshelwood, *Proc. Roy. Soc.*, A, 1929, **125**, 294.

branch before their existence is ended is $\nu p_{O_2} p_{PH_3} \beta^2 d^2 / \lambda_0^2$. If this average is much less than unity, the branching will not lead to explosion since there is less than an even chance that a new chain so produced will create another before it comes to an end. The condition for explosion is therefore that the above expression is of the order of magnitude unity. Thus at the critical pressure we have the relation

$$p_{O_2} p_{PH_3} \beta^2 d^2 = \text{constant.}$$

To take into account the presence of an inert gas, e.g. nitrogen, the necessary modification of the above calculation is easily made and leads to the relation:

$$p_{O_2} p_{PH_3} \beta^2 d^2 \left(1 + \frac{p_{N_2}}{p_{O_2} + p_{PH_3}}\right) = \text{constant.}$$

The above method of calculation is an approximate one only, since the condition for explosion is not quite rigidly formulated. A more accurate procedure, though one which does not give so clear a picture of the mechanism, is to write down equations for the rate of production and rate of removal of X_O and X_P, and find the condition where a 'stationary state' just ceases to be possible. This leads to an equation reducible with certain approximations to the above simple form.

Thus we have:

$$\frac{d[X_O]}{dt} = k_1 F(c) + k_2[X_P][O_2] - k_3[X_O][PH_3] - K[X_O] = 0, \qquad (1)$$

$$\frac{d[X_P]}{dt} = \alpha k_3[X_O][PH_3] - k_2[X_P][O_2] - K[X_P] = 0. \qquad (2)$$

(1) expresses the fact that X_O is formed both spontaneously, in some way left undetermined, the rate being expressed simply by $k_1 F(c)$, and by collision of X_P with oxygen in the chain; and that X_O is destroyed both by reaction with phosphine and by some process at the wall, the rate of the latter being $K[X_O]$.

(2) expresses similar facts about the production and destruction of X_P. α molecules of X_P are supposed on the average to be formed from one of X_O, thus introducing the condition that the chains can branch. α is greater than unity. No spontaneous production of X_P is allowed for, but it is easily shown that there is no loss in generality on this account. Solving for $[X_O]$ we obtain

$$[X_O] = \frac{k_1 k_2[O_2] F(c) + K k_1 F(c)}{(1-\alpha)k_2 k_3[PH_3][O_2] + k_2 K[O_2] + k_3 K[PH_3] + K^2}.$$

Assuming perfect efficiency for the collisions between X_O and PH_3 and between X_P and O_2, we have $k_2 = k_3$; moreover, K^2/k_2 is probably small, since k_2 is large. Introducing these simplifications, and equating the *denominator* to zero, we find that $[X_O]$ increases indefinitely, i.e. the stationary condition ceases to be possible, when

$$(\alpha-1)k_3[PH_3][O_2] = K([O_2]+[PH_3]).$$

Since K, which determines the rate at which X_O and X_P reach the wall, for unit concentration of either, is for a given tube inversely proportional to the total pressure we have $K = K_0/([O_2]+[PH_3]+[N_2])$.

Thus

$$(\alpha-1)k_3[PH_3][O_2] = K_0([O_2]+[PH_3])/([O_2]+[PH_3]+[N_2]).$$

Since concentrations are proportional to partial pressures, this condition becomes

$$p_{O_2}p_{PH_3}\left(1+\frac{p_{N_2}}{p_{O_2}+p_{PH_3}}\right) = \text{constant}$$

for a given tube, as above.

In general, we have, for any cylindrical tube, and a reaction involving two gases in a symmetrical way,

$$p_1p_2\left(1+\frac{p_{\text{inert gas}}}{p_1+p_2}\right)d^2 = \text{constant}.$$

For a given tube $\dfrac{1}{p_1p_2}$ plotted against $\left(1+\dfrac{p_{\text{inert gas}}}{p_1+p_2}\right)$ should give a straight line.

Melville and Ludlam[*] have improved the above treatment by allowing for the different resistance which different inert gases offer to the diffusion of molecules through them. With this correction it is found that $\dfrac{1}{p_1p_2}$ plotted against $\left(1+\dfrac{p_{\text{inert gas}}}{p_1+p_2}\right)$ gives a straight line, the slope of which is inversely proportional to the diffusion coefficient of the active chain carriers through the inert gas.

It may be said that the general correctness of the picture which these formulae give is quite strikingly demonstrated by experiment. The diameter effect, which reveals the character of the phenomenon perhaps more clearly than any other, has been found, for example, with phosphorus and oxygen,[†] phosphine and oxygen,[‡] hydrogen and oxygen,[§] and with carbon disulphide and oxygen.[||] The inert gas influence, which

[*] *Proc. Roy. Soc.*, A, 1931, **132**, 108.
[†] Semenov, loc. cit; Melville and Ludlam, loc. cit.
[‡] Dalton and Hinshelwood, loc. cit.
[§] Hinshelwood and Moelwyn-Hughes, *Proc. Roy. Soc.*, A, 1932, **138**, 311.
[||] Thompson, *Z. physikal. Chem.*, B, 1930, **10**, 273.

is hardly less significant, has been shown in the following examples among others: phosphorus and oxygen,* phosphine and oxygen,† hydrogen and oxygen,‡ carbon disulphide and oxygen,§ carbon monoxide and oxygen,‖ in all of which systems 'lower limit' phenomena appear under appropriate circumstances. In some of these examples the correlation between the relative effects of different gases and their diffusion coefficients has been very fully established.** Results plotted in the manner indicated above usually give fairly good straight lines. When, however, it comes to an exact quantitative representation of experimental results, the simple theory proves to be only an approximation. This is not in the least surprising, and would indeed be expected: the vessel walls do not necessarily remove the chain carriers with perfect efficiency. Indeed there are indications that this efficiency is quite low—and its actual value depends very much upon the exact state of the vessel wall, in particular upon the nature of the adsorbed gas films. Thus we should expect some tendency to irregular variations from experiment to experiment, and also some systematic distortion of the simple formula. The former are indeed encountered, but can be overcome by the use of a standardized technique. The nature of the latter may be indicated by a few examples.

Semenov's experimental results for phosphorus were best represented by the formula

$$p_{O_2}\sqrt{p_{P_2}}\left(1+\frac{p_{\text{argon}}}{p_{O_2}+p_{P_2}}\right)d^{\frac{3}{2}} = \text{constant.}$$

In the phosphine oxidation, while the relation to the square of the diameter is fairly well satisfied, the product $p_{O_2}p_{PH_3}$ is not quite constant for variations in the relative proportions of the two gases. The same departure from a quite symmetrical relation is found with hydrogen and oxygen. In the latter reaction the diameter influence, although qualitatively that required by the theory, does not conform quantitatively, since the nature and state of the surface as well as the diameter of the tube affect the results. Certain foreign gases are also found, not unnaturally, to exert specific influences not predicted by the theory. These departures from the simple formula are, however, only what would be expected from a critical consideration of its derivation.

* Semenov, loc. cit; Melville and Ludlam, loc. cit.
† Dalton and Hinshelwood, loc. cit.
‡ Hinshelwood and Moelwyn-Hughes, *Proc. Roy. Soc.*, A, 1932, **138**, 311.
§ Ritchie, Brown, and Muir, *Proc. Roy. Soc.*, A, 1932, **137**, 511.
‖ Hadman, Thompson, and Hinshelwood, ibid., A, 1932, **138**, 297.
** Cf. Melville and Ludlam, loc. cit.

Lower critical limits appear in general to be almost independent of temperature. This has been shown experimentally with phosphorus and oxygen, with hydrogen and oxygen, and with carbon monoxide and oxygen, and a few other systems.

The Upper Explosion Limit.

Examples of systems in which upper limits are found are the following: hydrogen and oxygen,* phosphine and oxygen,† sulphur and oxygen,‡ carbon disulphide and oxygen,§ carbon monoxide and oxygen.‖

An idea of the actual pressures is conveyed by the example of a mixture of composition $2H_2 : O_2$ at $550°$ C., where the lower limit is at a pressure of a few millimetres, while the upper limit is at about 100 mm.

In striking contrast to the lower limit, the upper limit is usually, possibly always, nearly independent of the vessel diameter. Moreover, its position does not tend to change much with changes in the state of the vessel wall. In a system such as hydrogen and oxygen a limiting pressure exists for all compositions of the mixture. If the partial pressure of hydrogen is reduced, that of oxygen must be correspondingly raised to prevent explosion. These facts point clearly to the hypothesis that the limit is determined by deactivation in the gas phase. Foreign gases can contribute to the deactivating process. The presence of argon, carbon dioxide, or steam in the hydrogen-oxygen system lowers the partial pressures of the reacting gases themselves at the limit. Thus deactivation by the foreign gases must be occurring to some extent. The actual magnitude of these effects is not in general very great: for example, at $550°$ C., 55 mm. of argon can lower the critical partial pressure of a $2 : 1$ hydrogen-oxygen mixture by 17 mm. (This deactivating effect, although appreciable when the pressure of the inert gas is fairly high, is not, it should be noted, enough to mask the opposing effect of the inert gas at the lower limit, where, for example, 4·4 mm. of argon lowers the partial pressure of hydrogen and oxygen from 4·25 to 2·21 mm.)

The upper limit is usually displaced rapidly in the direction of higher pressures as the temperature rises. The boundaries of an explosion region have therefore the form shown in the figure.

* See page 163.
† Dalton, *Proc. Roy. Soc.*, A, 1930, **128**, 263.
‡ Semenov and Rjabinin, *Z. physikal. Chem.*, B, 1928, **1**, 192.
§ See page 156.   ‖ See page 169.

The lines *ab* and *cd* do not appear to cut quite sharply but bend round as shown. At temperatures below T_0 no explosions occur at all.

This type of behaviour, if not universal, appears at least to be exhibited by a number of systems.

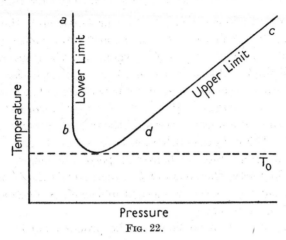

FIG. 22.

With regard to the nature of the deactivation processes occurring in the gas and controlling the position of the upper limit, there are several possibilities. These are as follows: (1) Activated molecules are deprived of their energy by the so-called collisions of the second kind. (2) More often the activated species are free atoms or radicals, and thus molecules of any kind, whether of an inert gas or of the reacting gases, will aid their removal by recombination, e.g. $2H + X = H_2 + X$.

The explosion limit is controlled by the balancing of two processes, the production of fresh active molecules by branching of chains, and the deactivation process. In general, the rate of both these processes will increase with pressure. For there to be an upper limit the second must increase more rapidly than the first. This can most easily come about when the radicals or other active species are produced in binary collisions and removed in ternary collisions.

Many interesting details about the upper limit in the hydrogen-oxygen reaction can be accounted for in this way. The following simple theory* shows some of the results of the assumption.

Let X and Y be two kinds of atom or molecule which collide in the course of a chain and let there be a certain probability that at such

* Grant and Hinshelwood, *Proc. Roy. Soc.*, A, 1933, **141**, 29; Kassel and Storch, *J. Amer. Chem. Soc.*, 1935, **57**, 672. Cf. also Dalton's discussion of the limit in the system phosphine-oxygen: *Proc. Roy. Soc.*, A, 1930, **128**, 263.

a collision the chain branches. If, however, any third molecule arrives while X and Y are associated together, then deactivation occurs. Equating rate of branching to rate of deactivation, we have

$$\nu[X][Y] = Z_1[X][Y][H_2] + Z_2[X][Y][O_2] + Z_3[X][Y][M],$$

M representing an inert gas present. ν is proportional to the probability of branching. The Z factors are proportional to the collision frequencies of the complex XY with hydrogen, oxygen, or the inert gas respectively. From this is follows that at the limit $Z_1[H_2] + Z_2[O_2] + Z_3[M]$ is a constant. Experiment shows, in agreement with this, that at the limit, in the absence of an inert gas, $[H_2] = C - b[O_2]$, and also that on addition of inert gas there is a linear decrease in the partial pressures of hydrogen and oxygen. The influence of helium is considerably greater than that of argon on account of its much greater speed, and consequently greater Z_3 value. Similarly, the constant b, which equals Z_2/Z_1, is much less than unity, since the speed of oxygen molecules is much smaller than that of hydrogen molecules.

The value of Z_M can be shown to be proportional to $\sigma_{XYM}^2/\mu_{XYM}^{\frac{1}{2}}$, where $\mu = \dfrac{m_{XY}\, m_M}{m_{XY} + m_M}$, m_M, etc., being the molecular weights, and σ_{XYM} the sum of the molecular diameters of the complex XY and the colliding molecule M; similarly for Z_{H_2} and Z_{O_2}.

To allow the high speeds of hydrogen and of helium compared with oxygen and argon to have the influence in the calculation which experiment shows them to have in practice, the value of m_{XY} must not be too small. Thus XY must be much heavier than a pair of hydrogen atoms. Given this, the calculation is not very sensitive to the exact mass of XY. This may therefore be taken to be of the order of magnitude of the mass of $H_2 + O_2$. σ_{XY} may also be taken as equal to $\sigma_{H_2} + \sigma_{O_2}$. Using the values for the molecular diameters given in Tolman's *Statistical Mechanics*, one finds that helium should have 1·77 times the effect of argon, while the experimental value is about 1·6. Moreover, the ratio of the Z values for hydrogen and oxygen gives the calculated value of the constant b as 0·39, compared with an experimental value of 0·325. Having regard to uncertainties in the molecular diameters, these agreements are very close, and show that the relative speeds of the different molecules principally determine the variation of the upper limit. Thus the theory of gas phase deactivation of fairly massive complexes in ternary collisions is strongly supported.

Since $\nu = Z_1[H_2] + Z_2[O_2]$ in the absence of an inert gas, it follows that for a given ratio of hydrogen to oxygen, the total explosion pressure will vary with temperature in the same manner as ν (neglecting the relatively small changes in Z_1 and Z_2). ν, being proportional to the probability of branching, will vary according to an Arrhenius equation, which the explosion pressure should also satisfy. This is realized in practice.

If, as here assumed, the probability of branching varies exponentially with temperature, it remains to be seen why the lower limit varies so little. Adapting to the present problem the calculation on pages 155 and 156, and replacing p_{PH_3} by p_{H_2} and X_P by X_H, we find as a condition for the lower limit $\nu p_{O_2} p_{H_2} \beta^2 d^2 / \lambda_0^2 = 1$. For a given vessel and composition, neglecting the small variation of λ_0 with temperature, we have

$$p_{O_2} p_{H_2} = \frac{\text{const.}}{\nu \beta^2}$$

$$p_e = p_{O_2} + p_{H_2} = \frac{\text{const.}}{\beta \nu^{\frac{1}{2}}}.$$

Therefore
$$\frac{d \log p_e}{dT} = -\frac{1}{2} \frac{d \log \nu}{dT} - \frac{d \log \beta}{dT}.$$

Thus, even if β were constant, $\log p_e$ would decrease with temperature only half as fast as $\log P_e$ increases (P_e = upper explosion pressure). β, the reflection factor, will normally decrease as the temperature rises owing to the greater rapidity with which chain carriers are destroyed in surface reactions. This factor still further diminishes the absolute magnitude of the variation of p_e and, being probably quite an important one, may easily reduce the temperature coefficient of the lower explosion pressure to the almost zero value observed.

Some General Characteristics of Chain Reactions.

The criteria by which a chain reaction may be recognized are as follows: (1) in photochemical reactions, an abnormally great quantum yield; (2) in thermal reactions, a retardation of the change by a decrease in the dimensions of the vessel, allowing a smaller path for chains to traverse before reaching the wall; (3) acceleration of the reaction, in some circumstances, by the presence of an inert gas—essentially the inverse of (2); (4) an abnormal influence of the concentrations of the reacting substances on the rate, due to the circumstance that the concentrations affect, not only the number of chains starting in unit time, but also the successfulness of their propagation; (5) a rate of reaction considerably greater than might be expected from a knowledge of the heat of activation and the collision number; (6) sensitiveness of the reaction to inhibitors; (7) in certain examples, the appearance of the remarkable phenomenon of abrupt transitions from negligibly slow reaction to explosion. It must be emphasized that all these characteristics are not necessarily, or even commonly, shown by the same reaction, but examples of all are known.

Which characteristics appear in a given reaction depends upon the length of the chain, and upon the manner of its starting and stopping. We may tabulate matters as follows: chains may start either (a) in the gas phase or (b) at the wall of the vessel. They may be stopped either (α) by a collision in the gas phase with chemical destruction of the chain carrier or (α') by a collision in the gas phase with 'physical' deactivation of an active molecule; (β) by simple collision of an active molecule with the wall of the vessel, or (γ) by a chemical reaction at the wall of the vessel, removing an active particle.

Furthermore, chains may be classified as 'energy' chains or 'material' chains. In the former, the entities responsible for propagating the chain are merely excited molecules of a reactant or product, while in the latter some definite new molecular species, active in virtue of its chemical unsaturation, e.g. a chlorine atom or a hydroxyl radical, is the virtual carrier of the energy. When the deactivation consists in the recombination of atoms or radicals, it is easy to understand the effect of a vessel wall in breaking chains: it acts as a surface catalyst for the recombination process.

In most of the examples studied the intervention of atoms and radicals seems to be definitely proved, and these have been found to intervene in many reactions which at one time were not suspected to involve chains at all. But precisely in the phenomena of explosion limits, where the distinction between a 'thermal' explosion and a 'branching chain' explosion is one of degree rather than of kind, the idea of energy chains is still not quite superfluous.

Discussion of Some Special Reactions.

No attempt can be made within the compass of these pages to give a complete account of all the chain reactions which have now been investigated. In the following pages, however, a few special examples will be discussed, in order to show the principles in a clearer perspective.

The Combination of Hydrogen and Oxygen.*

This was the first gaseous thermal reaction with a stable and measurable velocity where the part played by chains was proved.† In certain regions of concentration explosive chains are also established. The principal facts about this remarkable reaction are as follows:

(1) Below about 520° C. in vessels of porcelain or silica the combination of hydrogen and oxygen occurs mainly on the surface of the vessel, and is approximately of the first order.‡ In silica vessels the rate is almost directly proportional to the hydrogen concentration and nearly independent of the oxygen concentration. It has a low temperature coefficient.

(2) As the temperature is raised from 520° C. to 600° C., and especially as the pressure is raised, a high-order gas reaction comes into prominence. Under some conditions its rate may be nearly proportional to the cube of the hydrogen concentration, and to a power of the oxygen concentration greater than the first. It is accelerated by steam and other chemically indifferent gases, and retarded in an extremely marked degree by reduction of the dimensions of the vessel.§ The accelerating influence of the inert gases is very great, an equal pressure of nitrogen, for example, increasing the rate several times. The order of the accelerating influence for various gases is

$$H_2O > A > N_2 > He.$$

Excess of hydrogen or oxygen exerts an influence analogous to that of an inert gas, and this effect must be estimated and deducted from the total effect before the 'mass action' of the hydrogen and oxygen can be found.

(3) At relatively low pressures an entirely new phenomenon appears; there is an upper and a lower limit of pressure above and below which the reaction is quite slow, and between which explosion occurs.‖

(4) The upper limit is displaced in the direction of higher pressures by increase of temperature; the lower limit is changed only slightly. Argon and certain other gases somewhat lower the partial pressure of

* Hinshelwood and Williamson, *The Reaction between Hydrogen and Oxygen*, Oxford, 1934; Kassel and Storch, *J. Amer. Chem. Soc.*, 1935, **57**, 672.

† Hinshelwood and Thompson, *Proc. Roy. Soc.*, A, 1928, **118**, 170.

‡ Bone and Wheeler, *Phil. Trans.*, A, 1906, **206**, 1; Hinshelwood and Thompson, loc. cit.; Garstang and Hinshelwood, ibid., A, 1931, **130**, 640.

§ Gibson and Hinshelwood, *Proc. Roy. Soc.*, A, 1928, **119**, 591.

‖ Thompson and Hinshelwood, *Proc. Roy. Soc.*, A, 1929, **122**, 610; Kopp, Kovalsky, Sagulin, and Semenov, *Z. physikal. Chem.*, B, 1930, **6**, 307; Hinshelwood and Moelwyn-Hughes, *Proc. Roy. Soc.*, A, 1932, **138**, 311.

hydrogen and oxygen at the upper limit. The lower limit is raised by decreasing the vessel diameter, and lowered by the presence of inert gases. The upper limit is hardly affected by the dimensions and nature of the vessel.

The complete relation between reaction velocity and pressure is shown in the figure.

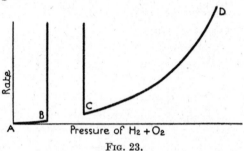

FIG. 23.

It is remarkable that in the neighbourhood just to the right of C we have a state of affairs where the rate of reaction decreases with decreasing pressure, and yet if the pressure be reduced a point will be reached at which the mixture explodes; this illustrates the difference between the explosive chain and the 'thermal' explosion, which at some high enough pressure terminates the curve CD.

(5) H. B. Dixon observed that a trace of nitrogen peroxide lowers the temperature of ignition of hydrogen in oxygen by as much as 200°. Quantitative investigation of the influence of nitrogen peroxide on the rate of combination of hydrogen and oxygen in the region of 400° C., where the normal reaction is quite negligibly slow, revealed the existence of another remarkable 'critical limit' phenomenon.* A sufficiently small trace of nitrogen peroxide produces only a slow catalytic reaction; as the amount is increased, a rather sharply defined limit is reached beyond which almost immediate explosion of the gases occurs when they are admitted to the reaction vessel. With still greater amounts of nitrogen peroxide a second limit is reached, as sharply defined as the first, beyond which explosion no longer occurs, but only a very slow combination.

(6) When crossed streams of hydrogen and oxygen meet in an atmosphere of nitrogen at partial pressures and temperatures such that the low-pressure explosion would occur in a silica or porcelain vessel, no

---

* Gibson and Hinshelwood, *Trans. Faraday Soc.*, 1928, **24**, 559; Thompson and Hinshelwood, *Proc. Roy. Soc.*, A, 1929, **124**, 219; Foord and Norrish, *Proc. Roy. Soc.*, A, 1935, **152**, 196.

flame appears at the region of intersection of the streams. If, however, a quartz or porcelain rod is brought into this region ignition occurs.*

(7) According to Alyea and Haber, the ease of ignition, in the low-pressure region, of mixtures of hydrogen and oxygen streamed through narrow porcelain tubes is much greater when the tube has been 'pre-treated' with oxygen than when it has been 'pre-treated' with hydrogen.

With regard to the interpretation of these facts, (1) requires no further comment.

(2) shows that the gas reaction is a chain reaction in which the chains are broken principally at the wall of the vessel. As far as the influence of the vessel size on the rate of reaction is concerned, they might also start on the wall, since, if they traversed the gas before meeting the wall again, the rate would increase with increasing vessel size in the manner more or less similar to that actually found.

Inert gases act by increasing the length of the path which the chains must traverse before reaching the wall where they are broken. Evidently they do not deactivate the active particles which propagate the chain. This is an indication that the chain carriers are not excited molecules but free atoms or radicals. The conclusion is not, however, an absolutely necessary one since energy exchanges are often very specific.

With regard to (3) the most satisfactory hypothesis seems to be that already outlined, namely, that of branching chains, which either lead to explosion or are prevented from multiplying indefinitely by deactivation at the wall or by deactivation in the gas. All the facts are consistent with the hypothesis that the upper limit is determined by deactivation in the gas phase, and the lower limit by deactivation at the surface.

One of the more striking characteristics of the whole phenomenon is that the mechanism by which chains are propagated in the explosion region at low pressures appears to be largely independent of that by which they are propagated at higher pressures.

(5) will be referred to below.

(6) is evidence that the chains concerned in the low-pressure process start at the wall of the vessel, but gives no reason to doubt that the upper limit is chiefly determined by breaking of branching chains in the gas phase.

Taking all the facts into consideration, it appears most probable that in the low-pressure region chains are propagated through the gas, but

* Alyea and Haber, *Z. physikal. Chem.*, B, 1930, **10**, 193.

are initiated by centres which in the first instance must be formed heterogeneously; at the lower limit surface deactivation plays the important part in stopping the chains, at the upper limit gas deactivation. In the region of higher pressures chains of a somewhat different kind traverse the gas and terminate at the wall.

(7) would apparently result from adsorption hysteresis which influences the heterogeneous production of the centres from which the chains start; it appears, however, that the effect is not a very pronounced one.

With regard to the chemical processes occurring in the chains in the low-pressure region, Thompson and Hinshelwood proposed the branching chain hypothesis, and supposed primary formation of hydrogen peroxide, which reacted with hydrogen to give two excited molecules of steam, and thereby initiated energy chains. Nitrogen peroxide was assumed also to initiate chains at lower concentrations, and, at higher concentrations, to break them.

The free radical hypothesis was introduced by Haber and his collaborators* who regarded the chains as starting by the process $H_2 + O_2 = 2OH$, followed by $OH + H_2 = H_2O + H$. They based this theory upon the existence of the OH bands in the emission spectrum of hydrogen-oxygen flames, and in the absorption spectrum of steam at 1,200° C.; and upon thermochemical data which show the reactions in question to be possible ones.

Frankenburger and his collaborators,† studying the reaction between hydrogen and oxygen under the influence of photochemically produced hydrogen atoms, made a number of important observations consistent with the Haber reaction scheme. In this connexion it should also be mentioned that Haber and others‡ find that hydrogen atoms, photochemically produced from ammonia, can cause the ignition of hydrogen-oxygen mixtures.

The chain-starting action of nitrogen peroxide can be attributed to the free oxygen atom which might be produced by its dissociation. From rather striking analogies between the thermal and the photochemical behaviour of the $H_2 : O_2 : NO_2$ system Norrish§ concluded that the nitrogen peroxide really does act in virtue of the atomic oxygen it liberates, in the thermal as well as in the photochemical reaction. Lewis and von Elbe prefer to regard the active agent as NO_3. Since

* Bonhoeffer and Haber, Z. physikal. Chem., 1928, 137, 263.
† Trans. Faraday Soc., 1931, 27, 431.
‡ Farkas, Haber, and Harteck, Z. Elektrochem., 1930, 36, 711.
§ Griffiths and Norrish, Proc. Roy. Soc., A, 1933, 139, 147.

the latter is an oxygen atom with NO_2 as a 'carrier', only detailed analysis can decide between these views and other similar ones.

Dixon found a remarkable influence of iodine on the ignition temperature of hydrogen in oxygen. This led to an investigation of the effect of halogens on the various chain mechanisms.* Chlorine, bromine, and iodine accelerate the surface reaction occurring at the lower temperatures and pressures, but exert a powerful retarding action on the gaseous reaction occurring at higher temperatures and pressures. They displace the upper critical limit of the explosion region in the direction of lower pressures, and, in greater amounts, prevent the explosion altogether. Iodine is the most effective A fraction of a millimetre of iodine can cause a retardation of many times, and very small traces are enough to exert the maximum possible 'negatively catalytic' influence. The mechanism of the negative catalysis probably depends upon processes such as the following: (a) $OH+HI = H_2O+I$ and (b) $H+I_2 = HI+I$. The iodine can be rapidly regenerated at these temperatures by the reaction $2HI = H_2+I_2$.

The most plausible radical-chain mechanism for the reaction seems at the present time to be the following, which has grown up from the successive suggestions and emendations of a series of investigators:

(0) Initiating reaction : $H_2+M = 2H+M$

(1) $H+O_2 = OH+O$

(2) $OH+H_2 = H_2O+H$

(3) $O+H_2 = OH+H$

(4) $M+H+O_2 = M+HO_2$

(5) HO_2 = inactive products at the wall

(6) $HO_2+H_2 = H_2O+OH$.

(0) is assumed as the most probable starting-point, the heat of dissociation of hydrogen being lower than that of oxygen. (1), (2), and (3) are assumed on grounds of simplicity, energetic admissibility, and because processes giving branching chains are needed. In the region of lowest pressures diffusion to the wall balances branching. Then comes the low-pressure explosion region terminated by an upper limit, at which the ternary collision process (4), occurring in the gas phase, balances the branching. M is any molecule present. (5) and (6) require comment. We must account for the fact that above the upper limit there are still chains and that these are almost certainly broken at the wall. Yet, if possible, we prefer not to assume two kinds of chain of quite

* Hinshelwood and Garstang, *Z. physikal. Chem.*, Bodenstein-Festband, 1931, 656.

independent origin. . Therefore (4) is supposed to stop the *branching* chain, leaving, however, HO_2 which is still capable of giving the *non-branched* chain (6), though only efficiently enough for its contribution to the reaction rate to become considerable at higher pressures, where (6) is favoured in competition with the diffusion of the HO_2 to the wall.

Quantitative working out of these equations gives results in general agreement with experiment, but the comparison is really very complicated since all the gases present not only affect the diffusion of the various chain carriers to the wall, but also modify the adsorbed gas films: these in their turn influence the formation and removal of atoms and radicals which may contribute to the reaction.*

At the higher pressures, where the rate becomes great and thermal explosion becomes imminent, energy chains may play their part also.

In spite of all uncertainties, the foregoing summary will at least have shown that nearly all the characteristic phenomena arising from the existence of chain mechanisms are exemplified by what is, from a purely chemical point of view, one of the most fundamental of all reactions.

The Oxidation of Hydrocarbons.

Much of the early work on the pure chemistry of hydrocarbon combustion is due to Bone,† who discovered the course of the reactions through a series of hydroxylated products. In the oxidation of ethylene, for example, the varied relationships between the possible products can be adequately explained if the following series of changes is assumed:

$$
\begin{array}{ccc}
CH_2 & H.C.OH & H.C.OH \\
\| \;\rightarrow & \| \;\rightarrow & \| \quad \rightarrow HCHO \rightarrow H.COOH \rightarrow H_2CO_3 \\
CH_2 & H.C.H & H.C.OH \\
& & \qquad\quad \downarrow \qquad\qquad \downarrow \qquad\qquad \downarrow \\
& & \qquad CO+H_2 \quad CO+H_2O \quad CO_2+H_2O
\end{array}
$$

The rates of oxidation and decomposition of a given intermediate product vary relatively to one another according to circumstances.

We are here concerned chiefly with the purely kinetic aspect of the problem. A number of investigations have been devoted to the kinetics of the oxidation of hydrocarbons and their simple derivatives, including

---

* For discussion of surface adsorption effects generally see *Trans. Faraday Soc.*, 1932, **28**, 184.

† See Summary, *Proc. Roy. Soc.*, A, 1932, **137**, 243.

ethylene,[*] benzene,[†] acetylene,[‡] methane,[§] methyl alcohol,[§] form-aldehyde,[§||] benzaldehyde,[||] and ethane.[**] Usually the rate is decreased by diminution in the diameter of the containing vessel, though to varying degrees depending upon the relative extents to which the chains are broken in the gas or at the wall. There is often a more or less well-defined 'induction period' during which peroxides or aldehydic substances are produced. But the most remarkable characteristic is perhaps the influence of the various concentrations on the rate of oxidation. In most cases the influence of oxygen is relatively small, and in certain circumstances oxygen may actually retard the oxidation. On the other hand, the rates increase rapidly with the concentration of the combustible gas, sometimes approximately as the cube of its concentration.

This suggests that intermediate oxygenated products (peroxides or aldehydic substances) occur, and that the chains are continued when these collide with fresh molecules of the combustible gas but are broken when they collide with oxygen. The exact chemical constitution of the substances responsible for setting up the chains is at present an open question.

Approximate quantitative theories of the processes have been suggested for special cases.[††]

With hydrocarbons, on the whole it may be said that the various 'explosion limit' phenomena are more of the 'thermal' than of the 'branching chain' type, though doubtless an absolute distinction should not be made.

The Oxidation of Carbon Monoxide.

The earlier investigations of Dixon[‡‡] and others on the propagation of flame and explosion waves in mixtures of carbon monoxide and oxygen showed the important part which water can play in this reaction. The presence of water is not, however, essential for chemical

---

[*] Thompson and Hinshelwood, *Proc. Roy. Soc.*, A, 1929, **125**, 277; Lenher, *J. Amer. Chem. Soc.*, 1931, **53**, 3737.

[†] Fort and Hinshelwood, *Proc. Roy. Soc.*, A, 1930, **127**, 218.

[‡] Kistiakowsky and Lenher, *J. Amer. Chem. Soc.*, 1930, **52**, 3785; Spence, *J. Chem. Soc.*, 1932, 686.

[§] Fort and Hinshelwood, *Proc. Roy. Soc.*, A, 1930, **129**, 284; and, for methane, Norrish and Foord, ibid., A, 1936, **157**, 503; Bone and Gardner, ibid., A, 1936, **154**, 297; Garner and Ham, ibid., A, 1939, **170**, 80.

[||] Askey, *J. Amer. Chem. Soc.*, 1930, **52**, 974.

[**] Bone and Hill, *Proc. Roy. Soc.*, A, 1930, **129**, 434.

[††] Bodenstein, *Z. physikal. Chem.*, B, 1931, **12**, 151; Norrish and Foord, loc. cit.

[‡‡] See Bone and Townend, *Flame and Combustion in Gases*, 1927.

change. The dry gases will combine quite well, but if water is present the indirect oxidation by steam occurs so much more readily than the direct reaction that it naturally accounts for practically all the change. Weston* showed that when dry carbon monoxide and oxygen are sparked at high pressures, explosion occurs and the spectrum emitted differs in certain respects from that of the flame of moist carbon monoxide. Further, Garner† has shown that there is an abrupt change in the nature of the radiation emitted by a carbon monoxide flame when a small amount of hydrogen is added. Both these observations indicate that there are two distinct mechanisms, one for the combustion of the dry gases and one for that of the wet gases.

With regard to the non-explosive oxidation, Bodenstein and Ohlmer found a slow surface reaction in quartz vessels. It has not yet been possible to find conditions suitable for measuring the non-explosive homogeneous reaction of the dry gases, though such measurements should be possible at fairly high temperatures and rather high pressures.

Above about $600°$ C. the dry gases explode between two limiting pressures, the general nature of their behaviour resembling that of hydrogen and oxygen.‡ The lower limit seems to be controlled by the breaking of chains at the vessel wall, the upper limit by gas deactivation. The chains appear to originate from centres on the wall of the vessel. Outside the limits the rate of the reaction is even slower than with hydrogen and oxygen: in particular, there is no sign of the rapid gas reaction which, with the latter gases, becomes prominent at pressures not very far above the upper limit. If the theory of branching chains is accepted in explanation of the explosive reaction, something like the following cycle of changes would be possible:

$$
\begin{aligned}
&(1) &CO+O_2 &= CO_2+O \\
&(2) &O+CO+O_2 &= CO_2+2O \\
&(3) &O+CO+CO &= CO_2+CO \\
&(4) &O+O+\text{inert gas} &= O_2 \\
&(5) &O+CO+\text{inert gas} &= CO_2 \\
&(6) &O+CO &= CO_2.
\end{aligned}
$$

(1) is the primary surface process, (2) provides for the branched chains, (3), (4), and (5) interrupt the chains in the gas, and (6) breaks

* See Bone and Townend, *Flame and Combustion in Gases*, 1927.

† Garner and others, *J. Chem. Soc.*, 1929, 1123; 1930, 2037; 1931, 641.

‡ Kopp, Kovalsky, Sagulin, and Semenov, *Z. physikal. Chem.*, B, 1930, **6**, 307; Topley, *Nature*, 1930, **125**, 560; Hadman, Thompson, and Hinshelwood, *Proc. Roy. Soc.*, A, 1932, **138**, 297; Cosslett and Garner, *Trans. Faraday Soc.*, 1931, **27**, 176; Buckler and Norrish, *Proc. Roy. Soc.*, A, 1938, **167**, 292, 318.

them at the wall. (6) determines the lower limit. The upper limit is probably determined by the removal of oxygen atoms in the gas by recombination or otherwise.

The kinetics of the indirect oxidation in presence of steam are interesting. They are absolutely different from those of the reaction between the dried gases, not merely as regards rate, but in the qualitative relations between rate and concentration.

The 'wet' reaction proceeds by a chain mechanism. The rate* is approximately proportional to the concentrations of water and of carbon monoxide, and, in sharp contrast with the dry reaction, inversely proportional to the concentration of oxygen. That the reaction involves chains, which are broken at the surface of the vessel, is shown by the influence of the vessel diameter. The rate is roughly proportional to the square of the diameter.

The facts can be adequately explained by assuming that there are reaction chains more or less analogous to those occurring in the combination of hydrogen and oxygen, but now including carbon monoxide as a link.

For example,
$$OH + CO = CO_2 + H$$
$$H + O_2 + CO = CO_2 + OH,$$

or something analogous.

The retarding action of oxygen is due to the breaking of the chains by some oxidation process, such as the removal of hydrogen atoms. This can be shown by studying the influence of iodine, which is a very effective chain breaker. In presence of iodine the inhibiting action of oxygen disappears, although the primary process must still be going on. The chain-length has been estimated to be of the order 10^6.

A Further Consideration of Explosion Limits.

The existence of sharp transitions from slow reaction to explosion is a remarkable phenomenon and can be adequately explained by the theory of branching chains. But it is possible that the explanation of these transitions is not the same in every example, and it may be useful to consider here, not only the chain mechanism, but other ways in which discontinuities in the curve connecting reaction velocity and concentration can arise or be simulated.

An explanation which made the surface of the vessel play the all-important part in determining the explosive limits was suggested by

* Proc. Roy. Soc., A, 1932, **137**, 87.

Gibson and Hinshelwood* in connexion with the combination of hydrogen and oxygen in presence of small quantities of nitrogen peroxide. The hypothesis was that there occurred a surface reaction involving the nitrogen peroxide, and that the rate of this reaction first increased and then decreased again as the concentration of the peroxide increased —a well-known type of heterogeneous reaction. If now on certain active points of the surface this hypothetical reaction attains a great enough velocity, it may generate heat rapidly enough to cause inflammation of the gas as a whole. Since the velocity passes through a maximum, there will be a concentration on either side of that corresponding to the maximum where the reaction velocity on the active points has fallen off too much to allow ignition to occur. These concentrations will correspond to the explosion limits. Since the intense local reaction which may cause the ignition is confined to certain active points on the surface, its consumption of the reacting gases need not be large, and if it does not succeed in acting as a sort of detonator to the gas as a whole, it may be almost insignificant. Hence the apparent discontinuity in the reaction rate as the limits are passed.

Later, this explanation of the nitrogen peroxide-hydrogen-oxygen reaction was dropped in favour of the theory of branching chains.

Alyea† called attention to another way in which the existence of an upper explosion limit can be conditioned. He suggested that in mixtures of hydrogen and oxygen above the upper limit a layer of hydrogen covers the wall of the vessel, 'poisoning' it and preventing the departure from it of chains which would branch in the gas phase and give rise to explosion. As the pressure is reduced, a point is reached at which this hydrogen film is discontinuously stripped from the wall (by the attack of the oxygen). From the free wall chains now proceed into the gas and explosion occurs.

This mechanism is a possible one in principle, though there appear to be quite insuperable objections to its application in the particular example. Investigation of the kinetics of the surface reaction itself fails to reveal the presence of the complete hydrogen film; it is very improbable that such a film would be stripped off a silica surface and off a porcelain surface at the same pressure; and, finally, the fact that excess of either hydrogen or oxygen can stop the explosion for any given partial pressure of the other gas proves that the limit is determined by deactivation in the gas phase.

* *Trans. Faraday Soc.*, 1928, **24**, 559.
† Alyea, *J. Amer. Chem. Soc.*, 1931, **53**, 1324.

Another kind of mechanism was tentatively suggested by Hadow and Hinshelwood* to explain a lower limit of explosion in mixtures of oxygen and cyanogen. If there is a finite rate of adsorption of the different gases admitted to the reaction vessel, and if two of the gases compete for possession of the surface, then the relative amounts of the two which are adsorbed immediately after admission to the vessel may be different from the relative amounts adsorbed a fraction of a second later, when equilibrium has been established. This is because the more rapidly adsorbed gas may momentarily take possession of a larger proportion of the surface than corresponds to its share. The rate of reaction between the two gases may at the first moment, therefore, be very different from the rate an instant later: in particular, it may be very much greater. This abnormal initial rate will not in general be perceptible, because it decays very rapidly, and may be succeeded in an immeasurably short time by a quite slow rate corresponding to the true adsorption equilibrium. If, however, this momentary rate becomes rapid enough to inflame the gas as a whole, then obviously there is no question of adjustment to the normal slow value. Thus there will be the appearance of a discontinuous passage from quite slow reaction to explosion, although there was really no discontinuity in the process actually responsible for the ignition. There is evidence that something of this kind may actually occur in the oxidation of cyanogen, but no other example is known in which the mechanism can plausibly be supposed to operate.

The 'Thermal' Interpretation of Explosion Limit Phenomena†

There is clearly enough a distinction in degree between thermal explosions and those due to branching chains. In the former, the reaction velocity is observed to increase steadily as the pressure approaches an ill-defined explosion limit, where the heat produced can no longer be conducted away rapidly enough. In the latter, there is the appearance of a discontinuous change at the point where the chains begin to branch effectively: the reaction velocity passes from almost zero to an explosively great value. The mechanisms discussed in the previous section really depend upon thermal explosions, and the appearance of a discontinuity in the reaction velocity-concentration curve is illusory.‡ It

---

* Hadow and Hinshelwood, *Proc. Roy. Soc.*, A, 1931, **132**, 375.

† Cf. Norrish, ll.cc. *supra*.

‡ Even in the branching chain theory the discontinuity is not really in the velocity-concentration curve: it is determined by the fact that at a certain point dv/dt acquires a positive value.

is caused by the fact that the explosion is conditioned by processes which are independent of the normal slow reaction, and which obtrude themselves at a point not determined by the ordinary reaction velocity in the system as a whole.

This raises the question whether all the explosion phenomena which we have discussed in terms of the chain theory could not just as conveniently be described in terms of a purely thermal theory involving active points on surfaces, local non-isothermal conditions, the thermal conductivity of the various gas mixtures, and so on. Such a theory could probably be constructed but would necessitate the making of many specialized assumptions. For example, in several reactions we should have to endow the active points responsible for the ignition with properties not even qualitatively similar to those of the average surface. The chain theory does not necessitate these arbitrary assumptions to nearly the same extent.

Perhaps the advantage of the chain theory is most clearly seen in the treatment of the influence of inert gases on the lower explosion limit. It could hardly be supposed that the presence of a foreign, non-reacting gas could do other than facilitate the conduction of heat away from active points and assist in the maintenance of isothermal conditions. Yet the presence of the foreign gas does not diminish but increases the ease of explosion. The plain meaning of this seems to be that its action consists, not in aiding the dissipation of heat, but in impeding the diffusion of particles. Once we agree to this last statement, we have virtually adopted the chain theory.

Initiation and Propagation of Reaction Chains. Metastable States.

When an explosion is caused by the branching of reaction chains, the pressure limits between which it is possible are practically independent of the number of original centres. The condition for explosion is that such chains as do start should increase and multiply effectively rather than fizzle out as they traverse the gas. Since, as soon as this condition is satisfied, the rate of growth is very rapid indeed, the number of original centres is unimportant.

Naturally, however, in the extreme case, if no chains start at all, there can be no explosion even though the conditions for branching are favourable.

Now the initiation and the propagation of chains are quite distinct processes. Sometimes, for example, the chains start at the vessel wall and then traverse the gas. If the centres on the wall are 'poisoned' in any way no chains will start. The system will then be in what may be called a metastable state. As soon as a few chains do start, however, the explosion will occur, and the limits between which it is possible will be the normal ones. There is here a rough analogy with the phenomenon of change of state. For the solidification of a liquid two conditions are necessary; first, that there should be nuclei of solid, and secondly, that the temperature and pressure should be such as to allow these nuclei to grow rather than to redissolve. The two sets of conditions are independent. In the same way in a chain reaction, two independent sets of conditions must be fulfilled, centres must be present from which chains can start, and the concentrations must be such that these chains can multiply. For example, the low-pressure explosion of carbon monoxide-oxygen mixtures often fails to occur at all (because the wall from which the chains start becomes poisoned with adsorbed carbon monoxide), but, as long as this complete failure does not occur, the upper limit, at which *propagation* ceases to be possible, is always found at the same pressure for the same temperature and composition.

Completeness of Reaction in Chain Explosions.

As soon as the chains begin to branch to any great extent the concentration of the reaction product rises and this modifies the conditions of propagation. In particular, the effect may be an adverse one, in which case we may have an incipient flame almost immediately quenched. For example, under certain conditions a feeble flame will traverse a carbon monoxide-oxygen mixture and consume only a small proportion of the total gas. It lacks self-propagating power. Similarly, a mixture of phosphine and oxygen may be compressed till explosion occurs: further compression may result in a second flash showing that the first explosion had not been complete. Mixtures of hydrogen sulphide and oxygen will even show a series of explosions occurring spontaneously and separated by short intervals* (during which processes of some kind are taking place making chain branching once more possible).

Induction Periods.

Many reactions, having the characteristics of chain reactions, show 'induction periods', during which the rate of change is apparently almost zero, and at the end of which measurable reaction or explosion sets in.

It is always necessary to ascertain that the induction period is not

* Thompson, *Nature*, 1931, **127**, 629.

merely an apparent one, by which something of the following kind is meant. Suppose we are following the course of a gas reaction by observations of pressure changes: if the first stage of the reaction happened to involve no change in the total number of molecules, while the subsequent stages did, then there would be an apparent induction period, but its significance kinetically would not be great.

Formally, various explanations of a true induction period are possible. Two examples may be mentioned.

If there are heterogeneous centres from which branching chains can proceed, but these centres are initially poisoned, and if by the chemical action of one of the substances introduced they are slowly 'cleaned', there will come a point when they can begin to function, and explosion may then ensue.

But the classical explanation of induction periods, dating from van 't Hoff, connects them with autocatalysis, whether by the final product of reaction or by some intermediate product. First, to take a rather artificial example, suppose nitrogen peroxide were slowly generated in a system containing hydrogen and oxygen: nothing much would be observed till the critical lower concentration of nitrogen peroxide was reached, and then an explosion would occur. An effect of this kind does actually take place when phosphine and oxygen are exposed to ultra-violet light, the catalytic substance in this case being formed from the phosphine itself.

According to Semenov* the induction period may be due to the actual time required for branching chains to develop. Ordinarily, since the chain carriers are very reactive, the complete cycle of the chain is over very rapidly indeed, and the complete development from the initiation of the chains to explosion occupies an immeasurably short time. Sometimes, however, one of the links may involve a comparatively stable product, capable nevertheless of continuing the chain. Thus a slow development occurs. Semenov also argues that the slow development of branching chains may explain the induction period even in cases where no explosion finally results: the reaction velocity grows considerably, but before it becomes high enough to pass into true explosion, the influence of the reaction products prevents further branching. He thinks that reactions like the oxidation of hydrocarbons may be of this type, which he calls a 'degenerate explosion'. In view of the known chemical complexity of the various stages of some of these reactions, however, it seems difficult to deny that simple autocatalysis,

* Z. physikal. Chem., B, 1931, **11**, 464.

without the supplementary hypothesis of Semenov, may be a sufficient explanation.

The conception of some slow reactions as 'degenerate explosions' may, however, be a very useful one. For example, Gibson and Hinshelwood found two explosion limits for nitrogen peroxide-hydrogen-oxygen mixtures. Later, Norrish found, with a different experimental technique, two limits in the identical positions, outside which little happened, and inside which there occurred, not explosion, but 'rapid reaction'. Norrish's 'rapid reaction' would correspond to the 'degenerate explosion' of Semenov, or the 'slow flame' of Hadman, Thompson, and Hinshelwood.*

* *Proc. Roy. Soc.*, A, 1932, **138**, 297.

NOTE ADDED JULY 1945

The hydrogen-oxygen reaction†

According to the reaction scheme given on page 167 the continuation of the chains above the second limit by process (6) should lead to a third explosion limit at still higher pressures. Normally this is masked by the thermal explosion, but in reaction vessels coated with alkali chlorides the third explosion limit of the branching chain system is observable and susceptible to fairly precise measurement. The dependence of the limit upon hydrogen-oxygen ratio and upon the presence of inert gases is in good agreement with the reaction scheme given.

Combination of measurements on the third explosion limit with determinations of the rate of reaction below this limit provide further good evidence for the general correctness of the theory outlined, and permit the drawing of conclusions about the nature of the initiating process, which are probably more closely related to experiment than those reached by any other method.

† Lewis and von Elbe, *J. Chem. Phys.*, 1939, **7**, 710; 1942, **10**, 366; Willbourn and Hinshelwood, *Proc. Roy. Soc.*, A, 1945 (in press).

VIII

THE KINETICS OF HETEROGENEOUS REACTIONS

The Adsorption Theory.

THE molecules of a gas are not, except perhaps in very special instances, brought into a chemically active condition by mere mechanical impact with the solid surface. The highly specific action of different surfaces, illustrated, for example, by the hundreds of examples quoted in Sabatier's work *La Catalyse en Chimie Organique,** at once rules out so simple an hypothesis.

Intermediate compound formation between the molecules of the gas and those of the catalysing surface is not always a very helpful hypothesis.

All the advantages of the intermediate compound theory without most of the disadvantages are, however, possessed by what may be called the chemical adsorption theory.

Faraday went to the root of the matter and stated at the outset that the films of gas known to be adsorbed by surfaces were the seat of the chemical changes. This idea has long been used in the interpretation of catalytic phenomena, and, without further specific assumptions about the nature of the films, has been accepted for many years.

The simplest supposition to make is that the increased concentration in the condensed film brings about increased velocity of reaction in virtue of a purely mass action effect. This theory, however, has been shown in many ways to be untenable. The clearest proof of its inadequacy is afforded by the study of those reactions in which the same substance can undergo transformation in alternative ways. Thus alcohol vapour can suffer decomposition into ethylene and water or into aldehyde and hydrogen according to the equations†

$$C_2H_5OH \begin{cases} \nearrow C_2H_4 + H_2O & \text{(i)} \\ \searrow CH_3CHO + H_2. & \text{(ii)} \end{cases}$$

Different surfaces accelerate the alternative reactions to quite different degrees. For example, copper at 300° C. causes the decomposition of alcohol into aldehyde and hydrogen, while alumina at the same temperature favours the rival reaction almost entirely.

Although different increases in the concentration of the alcohol vapour are doubtless produced at the different surfaces, these increases,

---

* Second edition. (Paris and Liége, 1920.) † Sabatier, loc. cit.

in so far as they have a simple mass action effect, should operate to exactly the same extent in respect of the alternative reactions, because the rate of each is directly proportional to the concentration of alcohol. Different catalysts would be expected to produce different changes in the total rate of transformation of the reactant, but to be without effect on the relative amounts of the products.

Additional examples of such alternative reactions where the relative rates are influenced by the nature of the surface are the following:

$$H.COOH \begin{cases} H_2O+CO \\ H_2+CO_2* \end{cases}$$

and
$$2CH_3COOC_2H_5 \begin{cases} (CH_3)_2CO+2C_2H_4+CO_2+H_2O \\ (CH_3)_2CO+C_2H_4+C_2H_5OH+CO_2 \cdot \dagger \end{cases}$$

Surfaces must therefore be supposed to have some specific influence on the stability of molecules adsorbed upon them. That these specific influences, of the kind usually called 'chemical', play an all-important part has long been recognized, and has often been expressed by the assumption of 'complex' formation.‡

Langmuir§ put forward an extremely definite form of this idea. The adsorbed molecules are supposed to be held to the surface by ordinary 'valency forces'. Thus the kind of union between tungsten and oxygen adsorbed on its surface, to take one of Langmuir's examples, differs in no essential way from that which exists in tungsten oxide. The only difference between adsorption and oxide formation is that in adsorption the atoms of the metal, though attached to oxygen, remain also firmly held to their neighbours, whilst in oxide formation these linkages between the tungsten atoms themselves are completely dissolved.

The 'nickel-hydrogen complexes' responsible for catalytic hydrogenation differ only from nickel hydrides in that the affinity of the hydrogen for the nickel is not sufficient to overcome the forces holding the nickel atoms in the space lattice of the solid. Carbon monoxide being able, on the other hand, to detach the nickel atoms from their places, a definite carbonyl results. With platinum neither hydrogen nor carbon monoxide can loosen the atoms from their lattice, but the films which are formed are nevertheless held by the linkages charac-

---

* Sabatier and Mailhe, *Compt. Rend.*, 1911, **152**, 1212.
† Sabatier, loc. cit., *supra*.
‡ Compare Armstrong and Hilditch, *Proc. Roy. Soc.*, A, 1922, **100**, 240.
§ *J. Amer. Chem. Soc.*, 1916, **38**, 2221.

teristic of hydrides and carbonyls respectively. When other examples are reviewed, such as the adsorption of ammonia by silica, or carbon monoxide by the silicates in glass, less conviction may be felt about the correctness of this point of view, but the vast literature relating to coordination compounds shows how varied the possible types of linkage are.

If adsorption really takes place in this way, the surface should become saturated as soon as it is covered with a single layer of molecules of the adsorbed gas; only in exceptional instances will the formation of a second layer be possible.

The unimolecular nature of the adsorbed layer was emphasized by Langmuir, and has been regarded as an essential part of the theory. The alternative view is that the adsorption film is 'atmospheric' in character with a high density of gas in immediate contact with the surface, thinning continuously with increasing distance until the normal density of the gas phase is reached.

The whole trend of modern researches into the chemistry of interfaces has been in the direction of showing that molecules at the boundary of two phases have a definite orientation. Thin layers of the higher fatty acids upon water, for example, turn their carboxyl groups into the water and stand erect with methyl groups directed outwards. The orientation and properties of such boundary layers are largely governed by the presence of 'polar' groups, or groups which are the seat of a certain chemical unsaturation. Groups such as the hydroxyl or carbonyl radical are typical polar groups.

Molecules in adsorbed layers have also a definite orientation. If a complete layer is formed over a surface, with those groups possessing the greatest attraction for the surface turned inward, we have virtually a new surface with properties determined by the nature of the groups which are directed outwards. There seems to be no very good reason why this, in certain cases, should not adsorb a second layer of molecules. Indeed, the assumption that this double-layer adsorption occurs has occasionally been found helpful. But there is a large difference between this extension of the single-layer theory and the 'atmospheric' theory.

The theory of the unimolecular layer has two supports. First, it is a natural consequence of the view that definite chemical linkages unite adsorbed molecules to surfaces, for then saturation is obviously reached when the single layer is complete. Secondly, a good deal of direct experimental evidence has been brought forward in its favour. The general theoretical argument must be acknowledged to be strong, and the result not only to be free from the vagueness of the alternative suppositions but also to be an excellent compromise between the intermediate compound theory and the theory of a purely 'physical' adsorption.

Langmuir* made measurements on the amounts of gas adsorbed at very low pressures by means of direct readings with a McLeod gauge, and came to the conclusion that saturation was reached with the completion of a unimolecular layer.

Carver† measured the amount of toluene vapour adsorbed by glass and arrived at the same conclusion.

For more recent work on adsorption at low pressures the detailed studies of J. K. Roberts‡ should be consulted.

Measurements are sometimes difficult to interpret with certainty, since the true area of the adsorbing surface, which determines the number of molecules of the adsorbent actually exposed to the gas, is represented at best roughly by the apparent area, and often bears no relation to it. This is especially marked in the case of non-crystalline materials such as glass.

Perhaps the most convincing series of measurements are those of Paneth and Vorwerk,§ made, however, with solutions. The true molecular surface of a specimen of lead sulphate powder was determined by the radioactive indicator method, and this powder was then used as an adsorbent for dye-stuffs. The amount of dye removed from solution by the powder was determined colorimetrically. The results obtained by this method supported the theory of the single layer very well.

Although this theory must contain a great deal of truth, it is probably to be regarded as an ideal limiting case. The possibility of the following complications must always be borne in mind.

(i) Actual penetration of the gas into the solid may sometimes occur.

This process may be a slow one compared with the simple surface adsorption,‖ but, even where solution equilibrium takes years to reach, there is always the possibility that penetration to the depth of a few molecular layers of the solid takes place within quite a short time. Palladium, platinum, iron, and silica all become definitely permeable to hydrogen at high temperatures.

* *J. Amer. Chem. Soc.*, 1918, **40**, 1361.   † Ibid., 1923, **45**, 63.
‡ *Inter alia, Proc. Roy. Soc.*, A, 1935, **152**, 445.
§ *Z. physikal. Chem.*, 1922, **101**, 445, 480.
‖ Cf. Bangham and Burt, *Proc. Roy. Soc.*, A, 1924, **105**, 481.

(ii) The adsorbing surface may not be homogeneous.

In non-crystalline substances like glass or vitreous silica the greatest variety of surface configuration is possible, including sponge-like structures with pores of different magnitudes. But even with metals and other crystalline solids the surface may be very far from possessing the uniform 'chequer-board'-like structure, to use Langmuir's phrase, of the ideal solid. The researches of Beilby, described in his book, *The Aggregation and Flow of Solids*,* showed that the greatest complexities of surface structure may arise in metals. Surface films of a granular nature are often formed, and this irregularity may well descend to units of molecular magnitude.

H. S. Taylor† has laid great stress on this inhomogeneity of catalytic surfaces. He suggests that the atoms constituting a metallic surface can exist in different degrees of saturation, varying from that which would be characteristic of a perfect plane crystal face down to that of a single atom attached at one point only. This would lead one to suppose that adsorption occurs not uniformly over the surface but predominantly on certain 'active points' of the surface. We shall have evidence in favour of this view in a later section.

(iii) Different kinds of adsorption have sometimes been distinguished.‡

The distinction is not very sharp, but is made on the following grounds. Adsorption of gases by inert materials, such as charcoal, seems to be roughly proportional to the ease with which the gas can be liquefied. This suggests a condensation of a physical kind on the adsorbent, possibly by liquefaction in its pores. On the other hand, the adsorption of gases by metals, such as platinum, nickel, and iron, is highly specific. Not even approximate parallelism with condensability is to be observed. If this distinction between the two kinds of adsorption is justified, which seems a little doubtful, it is the second kind—the so-called primary adsorption—which is evidently responsible for catalytic phenomena.§

Our immediate object, however, is to discuss the kinetics of catalytic reactions, and for this purpose an exact knowledge of the mechanism of adsorption is not absolutely essential. All that is required is a know-

---

* Macmillan, 1921.   † *Proc. Roy. Soc.*, A, 1925, **108**, 105.

‡ Cf. Benton, *J. Amer. Chem. Soc.*, 1923, **45**, 887

§ For a discussion of the forces involved in adsorption see *Faraday Society*, 'Adsorption of Gases by Solids', 1932 (*passim*). For 'activated adsorption' see page 209. For an interesting study of discontinuities in adsorption isotherms see a series of papers by Allmand and Chaplin and Allmand and Burrage in *Proc. Roy. Soc.*, 1930–2.

ledge of the relation between the amount of gas adsorbed on the solid and the pressure of the gas in the homogeneous phase. To obtain the equation expressing this relationship it is not necessary to make hypotheses concerning the nature of the forces acting, nor is it essential to have pronounced definitely upon the question of unimolecular or multimolecular layers, nor, for many purposes, to have decided whether the surface of the catalyst displays a homogeneous array of atoms or the highly complex structure with active points which Taylor believes to be probable.

It is, on the other hand, necessary to adopt one or other of the really fundamental alternatives, namely, whether there is a definite saturation limit to adsorption, or whether the adsorption goes on increasing indefinitely with increasing concentration in the gaseous phase. The simplest form of the first alternative is the unimolecular layer theory, the simplest form of the second the atmospheric theory. It might be thought that an experimental decision between these two possibilities could be made quite easily. The matter is, however, not quite simple, since slow solution effects and other complications are often superposed on the true adsorption when the concentrations in the gas phase are high, and these make it very difficult to decide quite certainly whether or not a true saturation limit exists. On the whole, however, it seems to be quite clear that, apart from complicating factors, there is a real and definite limit, as the unimolecular layer theory would lead one to expect.

The theoretical treatment of the 'atmospheric' theory is very difficult, and an empirical equation has to be used for the relation between the amount of gas adsorbed and the pressure.

If x be the amount of gas adsorbed on the surface of the solid when the pressure is p, then

$$x = ap^n,$$

where n is a fraction always less than unity and a is a constant.

This is the well-known Freundlich 'adsorption-isotherm'.[*] Both a and n are functions of temperature.

The value of n is frequently sufficiently small to make the curve bend round sharply from linearity. Both a and n must be found empirically from the experimental observations.

Fig. 24 shows the sort of curve which represents the usual adsorption isotherm.

Curve 1 is represented by $x = ap^n$, where n is less than 1. There

* See Freundlich, *Kapillarchemie*; Adam, *Physics and Chemistry of Surfaces*, 1938.

is no definite limit to the value of x, but the curve may be made
to bend round as sharply as desired by taking sufficiently small values
of n.

Curve 2 reaches a definite saturation limit. A simple equation representing this type of curve is derived in the next section.

If the range of experimental observation is confined to the region to
the left of the line AB, almost any set of values, to whichever type of

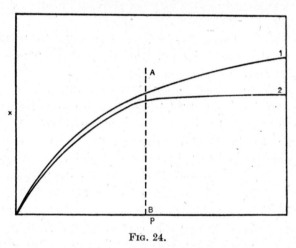

Fig. 24.

curve they really belong, can be expressed by the Freundlich equation,
when an appropriate choice of the constants is made, and, even in the
region to the right of AB, the complications to which reference has
already been made make a choice between the two types of curve rather
difficult. If the surface is not strictly uniform but possesses regions
with varying adsorptive capacity—as may often be found when material
of a granular nature is used—the determination of whether or not a
definite saturation limit exists becomes specially difficult. The superposition of two curves, such as (a) and (b) below, each of which may
tend to a definite limit, gives rise to (c) which apparently does not
(Fig. 25).

Until it leads to definite inconsistency with facts, which does not
seem likely, we shall therefore do well to adopt the theory of the definite
saturation limit. We may also accept, with reservations, the view that
it represents a unimolecular layer covering the active points of the
catalyst. This theory has the following advantages: it is inherently
probable, it leads to a simple relation between the amount adsorbed
and the pressure, and the equation expressing this relationship hardly

differs in the numerical results it gives from the empirical equation of the alternative theory. We will now proceed to find this relation.

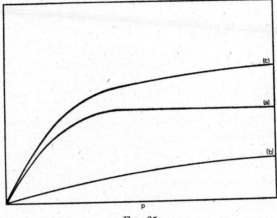

Fig. 25.

The Equilibrium between the Gas Phase and the Adsorbed Layer according to the Theory of the Definite Saturation Limit.

The theory of this was worked out in a simple manner by Langmuir.[*]

Let gas at pressure p be in equilibrium with unit area of the surface of a solid.

Let σ be the fraction of the surface covered with adsorbed gas. Then $(1-\sigma)$ is the fraction left uncovered. In view of the possibility that the surface is not homogeneous and that adsorption only occurs on active centres, 'fraction of surface covered' must be understood to mean the fraction of the available surface which is actually covered. Thus, from the point of view of adsorption, the surface might be 'covered' when certain patches only were completely occupied by adsorbed molecules, and the rest of the surface might be incapable of taking up gas at any pressure.

Equilibrium is established when the rate of condensation of gas on to the surface is equal to the rate of evaporation from the surface.

At constant temperature we have

$$\text{rate of condensation} = k_1 p(1-\sigma),$$

where k_1 is a constant, since the absolute rate of condensation is proportional to the number of impacts per second on the uncovered part of the available surface, and this number is proportional to the pressure of the gas and to $(1-\sigma)$.

* J. Amer. Chem. Soc., 1916, **38**, 2221.

For the opposing process we have

$$\text{rate of evaporation} = k_2 \sigma,$$

where k_2 is constant, since the rate of evaporation depends only on the amount of gas on the surface.

For equilibrium, therefore,

$$k_1 p(1-\sigma) = k_2 \sigma,$$

$$\sigma = \frac{k_1 p}{k_2 + k_1 p}.$$

This expression involves a constant, k_2/k_1, which must be determined from experimental data.

Two Important Special Cases.

In two limiting cases, which occur frequently in practice, this equation reduces to a simple form which is theoretically rather important.

(1) *Surface only sparsely covered with adsorbed molecules.*

When the adsorption is slight, the equation

$$k_1 p(1-\sigma) = k_2 \sigma$$

reduces to
$$k_1 p = k_2 \sigma,$$

since, when σ is very small, $(1-\sigma)$ is approximately equal to 1.

Thus
$$\sigma = \frac{k_1}{k_2} p.$$

When, therefore, the adsorption is small the amount of gas adsorbed is directly proportional to the pressure.

(2) *Surface nearly saturated.*

The equation $$k_1 p(1-\sigma) = k_2 \sigma$$

now reduces to $$k_1 p(1-\sigma) = k_2,$$

since, when σ is nearly equal to unity, the variations in σ itself are negligible compared with the corresponding variations in $(1-\sigma)$.

Thus
$$(1-\sigma) = \frac{k_2}{k_1} \times \frac{1}{p}.$$

When, therefore, the adsorption is large and the surface is nearly saturated we have the important result that the amount of free surface remaining is inversely proportional to the pressure of the gas.

These two propositions will find frequent application when we come to the discussion of the kinetics of catalytic reactions.

The simple formulae we have just derived, although sufficiently accurate for most practical purposes, sometimes fail to represent the facts completely. Examples are known where the adsorption isotherm is linear over a considerable range of concentration in the continuous phase and then bends sharply round at the saturation value. In general, however, the simple formulae are very fair approximations.

KINETICS OF HETEROGENEOUS REACTIONS

A. One Reacting Gas: the Reaction is unretarded by the Products.

In the sections immediately following we assume that adsorption equilibrium is established rapidly compared with the actual rate of the chemical changes undergone by the adsorbed molecules. This condition is usually fulfilled. The case where it is not fulfilled is discussed later.

It has to be realized that the seat of the reaction is the adsorbed layer and that, except in so far as it acts as a reservoir which regulates the concentration of the molecules in this layer, the gas phase is completely outside the reaction.

The law of mass action holds in its ordinary form for heterogeneous reactions, but the 'active mass' is no longer the simple concentration of the gas in the homogeneous phase. The amount of gas adsorbed, and therefore in a position to react, is the real active mass.

Kinetically the reaction equations assume the simplest form in the extreme cases of very small adsorption on the one hand and almost complete saturation on the other.

When the adsorption is small the amount of gas adsorbed is directly proportional to the pressure. If the change taking place in contact with the surface involves one molecule only of the gas, that is, if it is a truly unimolecular change, we have simply that the rate of change is directly proportional to the number of adsorbed molecules and, therefore, directly proportional to the pressure of the reacting gas. If, then, p is the pressure at time t of the gas undergoing chemical transformation, the reaction proceeds in accordance with the equation

$$-dp/dt = kp.$$

The ordinary first-order law is thus obeyed.

Many examples of this type of reaction are known; the decomposition of arsine;[*] the decomposition of phosphine on surfaces of glass,[†] porcelain,[‡] silica;[§] the decomposition of formic acid vapour on a variety

[*] van't Hoff, *Études de dynamique chimique*, p. 83.
[†] van't Hoff and Kooij, *Z. physikal. Chem.*, 1893, **12**, 155.
[‡] Trautz and Bhandarkar, *Z. anorg. Chem.*, 1919, **106**, 95.
[§] Hinshelwood and Topley, *J. Chem. Soc.*, 1924, **125**, 393.

of different surfaces—glass, platinum, rhodium, titanium oxide, and others;* the decomposition of nitrous oxide on the surface of gold;† the decomposition of sulphuryl chloride on the surface of glass;‡ the decomposition of hydrogen iodide on the surface of platinum;§ the decomposition of hydrogen selenide on the surface of selenium.‖ A general discussion of reactions of this type is given by Bodenstein and Fink.** All those which have just been enumerated proceed in accordance with the first-order law.

As an example we may quote some figures relating to the decomposition of nitrous oxide on gold at 900° C.

Time in minutes	Per cent. decomposed	$\dfrac{1}{t}\log\dfrac{100}{(100-x)}$
t	x	(t in seconds)
15	16·5	0·000201
30	32	0·000215
53	50	0·000218
65	57	0·000217
80	65	0·000219
100	73	0·000218
120	78	0·000210

In the experiment from which these figures are taken the time required for the decomposition of half the nitrous oxide was 53 minutes, the initial pressure being 200 mm. When the initial pressure was 400 mm. the time of half-change at the same temperature was found to be 52 minutes, showing in another and more conclusive way the first-order character of the reaction equation.

If the adsorption is small, and the reaction depends upon an essentially bimolecular process among the adsorbed molecules, for example $2A \to A_2$ or $2A \to B+C$, then, since the chance that two molecules occupy adjacent positions on the surface depends upon the square of the surface concentration, the rate of reaction is proportional to the square of the gas pressure, and the reaction is kinetically of the second order.

Examples of this particular case are uncommon. As we have already seen, the decomposition of nitrous oxide, which is of the second order in the homogeneous phase, becomes of the first order on the surface of gold—and also of platinum. Langmuir,†† however, finds that the

* *J. Chem. Soc.*, 1923, **123**, 1014.
† Hinshelwood and Prichard, *Proc. Roy. Soc.*, A, 1925, **108**, 211.
‡ Id., *J. Chem. Soc.*, 1923, **123**, 2725.
§ Hinshelwood and Burk, *J. Chem. Soc.*, 1925, **127**, 2896.
‖ Bodenstein, *Z. physikal. Chem.*, 1899, **29**, 429.
** *Z. physikal. Chem.*, 1907, **60**, 46.   †† *J. Amer. Chem. Soc.*, 1916, **38**, 1145.

combination of hydrogen atoms to the molecular form is probably a bimolecular reaction at the surface of tungsten. The decomposition of nitric oxide at the surface of platinum* and that of acetaldehyde† at various metal surfaces probably involve two molecules of the reacting

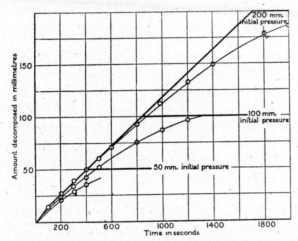

FIG. 26.—Rate of decomposition of ammonia on a tungsten wire at 856°, showing approach to theoretical behaviour of a reaction of zero order. The lines on which no experimental points are marked represent the ideal zero-order change. The 'half-life' periods at 50, 100, and 200 mm. initial pressure are in the ratio 1 : 1·92 : 3·52. In the ideal case this would be 1 : 2·0 : 4·0. In a first-order change all would be equal.

gases; but kinetically the reactions are not simple changes of the second order.

When the adsorption is great, and the surface is saturated or nearly saturated, considerable amounts of gas may be removed by chemical change without the amount in the adsorbed layer suffering appreciable diminution, since that which reacts and leaves the surface is at once replaced from the gas phase. Thus there is a constant rate of reaction in spite of diminishing concentration in the gas phase, and the reaction appears to be of 'zero order'. When the pressure is sufficiently reduced, however, a point must come when the surface is no longer saturated, and the zero-order reaction passes into one of the unimolecular type.

In solutions this type of reaction is common with enzymes; it is also frequently found in the catalytic hydrogenation of liquids. An example of a nearly zero-order gas reaction is to be found in the catalytic decom-

* Bachmann and G. B. Taylor, *J. Physical Chem.*, 1929, **33**, 447.
† *Proc. Roy. Soc.*, A, 1928, **121**, 141.

position of ammonia on the surface of tungsten,* and also on the surface of molybdenum and osmium.† Thus at 856° C., with 200 mm. of ammonia in contact with a heated tungsten wire, 59 mm. were decomposed in 500 seconds, while in 1,000 seconds 112 mm. were decomposed. The falling off from linearity is but slight. This is illustrated by Fig. 26 where the thicker lines represent the theoretical curves for a reaction of zero order.

Another example of a reaction nearly independent of pressure in this way is the catalytic decomposition of hydrogen iodide on the surface of a heated gold wire.‡ The initial pressure of the gas can be varied from 100 mm. to 400 mm. with a resulting change in the absolute rate of reaction which amounts to about 45% only instead of 400%.

Intermediate cases are found where the main part of the reaction takes place while the adsorption varies along the portion XY of the adsorption isotherm (Fig. 27).

Two arbitrary constants are now needed. The rate of reaction varies in proportion to the fraction of surface covered, and therefore to $k_1 p/(k_2+k_1 p)$. We have, therefore, $-dp/dt = kp/(1+bp)$. According to this the rate increases less rapidly than in direct proportion to the pressure, and therefore it is possible to use as an approximation the equation

$$-\frac{dp}{dt} = kp^n,$$

n being an appropriately chosen fractional number. Each of the equations has two disposable constants, and therefore they may be almost indistinguishable within the limits of experimental error.

The second is the form of equation which Stock and Bodenstein§ found to express the rate of decomposition of antimony hydride at 25° C. The value used for n was 0·6. The reaction took place on an extended surface of metallic antimony.

The hydrides of phosphorus, arsenic, and antimony thus form an interesting transition series. On similar sorts of surface antimony hydride is the least stable, decomposing with measurable speed at ordinary temperatures, and phosphine is the most stable, not decomposing at an appreciable rate below a red heat. Arsine occupies an intermediate position. At low temperatures the adsorption is con-

* Hinshelwood and Burk, *J. Chem. Soc.*, 1925, **127**, 1116.

† Burk, *Proc. Nat. Acad. Sci.*, 1927, **13**, 67; Kunsman, *J. Amer. Chem. Soc.*, 1928, **50**, 2100; Arnold and Burk, *J. Amer. Chem. Soc.*, 1932, **54**, 23 (for the quite different picture shown by 'active' tungsten at low temperatures see Frankenburger and Hodler, *Trans. Faraday Soc.*, 1932, **28**, 229).

‡ *J. Chem. Soc.*, 1925, **127**, 1552.   § *Ber.*, 1907, **40**, 570.

siderable, and, as a result, the stibine decomposition requires the p^n equation, while the more stable hydrides, which only decompose rapidly at higher temperatures where the adsorption is smaller, obey the first-order law. It is interesting, moreover, that with stibine itself the exponent n increases towards unity as the temperature at which the reaction takes place is raised.

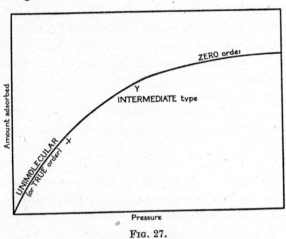

FIG. 27.

When the surface is almost completely covered there is no distinction kinetically between processes which involve one molecule only of the reacting gas and those which involve two. Thus the changes $A \to B+C$ and $2A \to B+C$ would both be of zero order and indistinguishable.

Retardation of the Reaction by its Products.

If any of the products of the reaction are themselves adsorbed strongly enough to occupy an appreciable fraction of the surface, less space becomes available for the reacting molecules, and the rate of transformation is proportionately diminished. There is now a competition, for places on the surface of the solid, between the molecules of the reactant and those of the product. In the general case this leads to a rather complicated equation for the progress of the reaction.

Let σ be the fraction of the active surface which is covered with molecules of the reactant when the pressure of this is p, and let σ' be the fraction covered with molecules of the adsorbed product when the pressure of this is p'.

Then, for the fraction of surface left free from adsorbed molecules we have $(1-\sigma-\sigma')$, and, equating for each gas the rate of condensation

on the uncovered surface and the rate of evaporation from that part
of the surface which it occupies, we have for the adsorption equilibria

$$k_1 p(1-\sigma-\sigma') = k_2\sigma \quad \text{and} \quad k_1'p'(1-\sigma-\sigma') = k_2'\sigma'.$$

The rate of reaction is proportional to the number of molecules of
reactant on the surface and therefore to σ, but to express σ in terms
of the pressures two arbitrary constants are needed.

We shall therefore consider in detail the simpler case where the
adsorption of the reacting gas itself is small, that is to say, when it has
very little influence on the adsorption of the product, and its molecules
only occupy a small fraction even of such space as the molecules of the
product leave for it.

Under these conditions

$$\sigma' = \frac{k_1'p'}{k_2'+k_1'p'}$$

and therefore

$$1-\sigma' = \frac{k_2'}{k_2'+k_1'p'}.$$

The rate of reaction is then given by the product of this free surface
and the specific reaction rate per unit free surface, which is proportional
to the pressure of the reactant.

Thus

$$-\frac{dp}{dt} = k(1-\sigma')p.$$

Therefore

$$-\frac{dp}{dt} = \frac{kk_2'p}{k_2'+k_1'p'}.$$

If a is the original amount of the reactant and x the amount transformed at time t, then p is proportional to $(a-x)$ and p' is proportional
to x.

The equation for the rate of reaction then becomes

$$\frac{dx}{dt} = \frac{k(a-x)}{1+bx},$$

where k and b are new constants.

An example of a change satisfying this equation very closely is to
be found in the catalytic decomposition of nitrous oxide on the surface
of platinum.* This reaction is retarded by the oxygen† produced in
the change itself, and its rate is expressed by the equation

$$-\frac{d[N_2O]}{dt} = \frac{k[N_2O]}{1+b[O_2]},$$

where $[N_2O] = a-x, \qquad [O_2] = x.$

* *J. Chem. Soc.*, 1925, **127**, 327.

† At *low pressures* the principal retardation appears to be due to *atomic* oxygen
(H. Cassel and E. Glückauf, *Z. physikal. Chem.*, B, 1932, **17**, 380).

The integrated form of this is

$$k = \frac{1+ab}{t} \log \frac{a}{a-x} - \frac{bx}{t}.$$

The applicability of this expression may be tested as follows. If we write $\frac{1}{t}\log\frac{a}{a-x} = k_m$ and $x/t = v$, then it will be seen that k_m should be a linear function of v, and the linearity of this relation is a characteristic test of the form of the equation not influenced by the choice of the actual values of the constants, which only determines the slope of the line and its intercepts on the axes. Since

$$v = (a+1/b)k_m - k/b,$$

the slope of the line will be $a+1/b$ and the intercept on the v-axis will be $-k/b$. The following experiment is an illustration of the use of the method:

Temperature 741° C. $a = 95$

x	t	v	k_m	$v+0.0135$	$(v+0.0135)/k_m$ $= a+1/b$
10	315	0.0318	0.000353	0.0453	129.8
20	750	0.0267	0.000315	0.0402	127.8
30	1400	0.0214	0.000271	0.0349	128.6
40	2250	0.0178	0.000243	0.0313	128.8
50	3450	0.0145	0.000216	0.0280	129.5
60	5150	0.0116	0.000194	0.0251	128.9

0.0135 is the intercept on the line $k_m = 0$.

The linearity of the relation between k_m and v is shown by the constancy of the slope as recorded in the last column.

When the adsorption of the retarding gas is so strong that the limiting law holds, namely the free space is inversely proportional to the pressure, the reaction velocity equation assumes a still simpler form. The rate of change is now directly proportional to the pressure of the reactant and inversely proportional to that of the product.

Thus
$$\frac{dx}{dt} = \frac{k(a-x)}{x}.$$

This limiting case is almost realized in the decomposition of ammonia on the surface of a heated platinum wire,[*] in the region of 1,000° C. In the first few instants the reaction velocity appears to be extremely high, but falls off as soon as the smallest traces of hydrogen make their appearance; the surface seems to become almost saturated with hydrogen at quite low pressures. Thereafter the reaction proceeds at a

[*] J. Chem. Soc., 1925, 127, 1114.

rate which is inversely proportional to the pressure of hydrogen. The following figures taken from the results of experiments, in which varying amounts of hydrogen were added initially to the ammonia, illustrate this inverse relationship.

Temperature, 1,138° C. Initial pressure of ammonia, 100 mm. of mercury

Amount of ammonia decomposed in 120 seconds	Pressure of hydrogen added initially
33	50
27	75
16	100
10	150

The equation expressing the retarding action of the products is not always of such a simple form. While the decomposition of ammonia on platinum is well enough represented by the simple equation

$$-\frac{d[NH_3]}{dt} = \frac{k[NH_3]}{[H_2]},$$

Bodenstein and Kranendieck* found that the decomposition on the surface of quartz glass was retarded by hydrogen according to a much more complicated law.

In the equation $$\frac{dx}{dt} = \frac{k(a-x)}{1+bx}$$

the factor $1/(1+bx)$, which represents the retarding effect, reduces as we have seen to $1/bx$ for large values of b and becomes equal to unity naturally when b vanishes. For intermediate conditions it may be represented approximately by an inverse fractional power of x. This is the origin of the relation sometimes found empirically that the retarding effect of a gas on a reaction is proportional to the square root of its pressure. No significance is to be attached to the square root. It means simply a fractional power in the neighbourhood of 0·5.

The complexity of the catalytic surface sometimes reveals itself in experiments on the retarding action of gases. Burk,† for example, finds that the rate of decomposition of ammonia on molybdenum, although strongly retarded by nitrogen, does not approach zero as the surface becomes saturated with nitrogen. This shows that there must be certain parts of the active surface which the nitrogen cannot poison, or else that the nitrogen film itself has a certain catalytic activity. Schwab‡ finds the rate of decomposition of ammonia on platinum, at lower pressures, to be retarded by nitrogen as well as by hydrogen, while, at

* Nernst-Festschrift, 1912, p. 99.   † Proc. Nat. Acad. Sci., 1927, 13, 67.
‡ Z. physikal. Chem., 1927, 128, 161.

higher pressures, Hinshelwood and Burk found no retardation. It is evidently unwise, therefore, to extrapolate measurements much beyond the range of pressure in which the observations are made. At low pressures the most active centres of the surface may be those principally concerned; at higher pressures quite other centres may be the most important, the more active ones being already poisoned, while the less active ones have resisted poisoning.

The 'Order' of Heterogeneous Reactions.

A gaseous reaction of zero order is one in which the absolute rate of change is independent of the pressure of the reacting gas. A reaction of the first order is one in which the rate is proportional to the pressure, or in which the *fraction* of the total which is transformed in a given time is independent of the concentration.

The time required for the transformation of half the total amount of substance is one of the most useful criteria. In reactions of zero order it is directly proportional to the initial pressure, in reactions of the first order independent of the initial pressure, and in reactions of the nth order inversely proportional to the $(n-1)$th power of it.

We adopt this kinetic definition of reaction order without reference to the actual number of molecules involved in each act of chemical transformation. It will be convenient to call the order inferred from the effect of pressure on the time of half-change the *apparent order*, and to refer to the number of molecules involved as the *true order* of the reaction. We have now to consider the relation of the true and the apparent order in various cases.

First, when the reaction is unretarded by the products there are two extreme cases. If the adsorption is small the true and apparent orders are equal. We consider still the case of one reacting gas.

The chance that n molecules shall occupy positions on the surface sufficiently close to render interaction possible depends on the nth power of the surface concentration, and this in its turn depends on the nth power of the pressure.

If, on the other hand, the surface is completely covered, the apparent order is zero, whatever the true order may be, since the number of groups of n molecules cannot change with pressure so long as the surface remains covered.

In intermediate cases the apparent order is between zero and the true order, but this value itself varies with the pressure. Moreover, it should change considerably with temperature. If, therefore, a value for the reaction order is found which does not decrease towards zero as the pressure increases, and which, moreover, does not vary with temperature, it may be taken as the true order.

Secondly, with retarded reactions further complications arise. We will consider the case where the products of reaction are so strongly adsorbed that the free surface is inversely proportional to their pressure.

Let the true order of the reaction be the first. Then the velocity equation assumes the form

$$\frac{dx}{dt} = \frac{k(a-x)}{x}.$$

Integrating, $kt = a \log a - a \log(a-x) - x.$

If τ is the time of half-change, we find by putting $x = \frac{1}{2}a$

$$\tau = \frac{1}{k}(a \log 2 - \tfrac{1}{2}a).$$

This shows that the half-life increases in direct proportion to the initial pressure. This would indicate an apparent reaction order of zero. Expressed loosely, the reaction appears to be faster at low pressures than at high pressures. This is illustrated by the curves in Fig. 28.

Again, if the true order of reaction is the second,

$$\frac{dx}{dt} = \frac{k(a-x)^2}{x},$$

whence it is easily found that

$$\tau = \frac{1}{k}(1 - \log 2).$$

Thus the half-life is independent of the initial pressure. The apparent order is thus the first.

In general, then, the effect of a strong retarding action by the products of reaction is to reduce the apparent order of the reaction to one below the true order.

From the foregoing discussion it will be seen that some circumspection is necessary in inferring the true order of a heterogeneous reaction from the influence of pressure, but that when all the circumstances are taken into account this order can usually be found. There is no evidence that reaction products can ever exert a retarding action proportional to a higher power of their pressure than the first, nor is there any theoretical ground why they should possibly be able to do so. Hence, when we find a reaction, such as the decomposition of nitrous oxide, proceeding relatively faster at lower pressures, it is quite certain that the true order cannot be higher than the first.

The decomposition of nitric oxide at the surface of a hot platinum wire* is apparently of the first order, as judged from experiments on variation of the initial pressure. Retardation by oxygen was observed, but was not at first considered marked enough to have reduced the

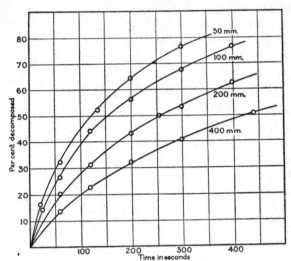

Fig. 28.—Influence of initial pressure on catalytic decomposition of nitrous oxide.

order from two to one. Further investigation by Bachmann and Taylor† showed that the oxygen retardation was very considerable; and that therefore we have here an example of the reduction of the true order two to an apparent order of one.

B. Two Reacting Gases.

Reactions which are unretarded by the products will first be considered. When the adsorption of all the reacting gases is small, the numbers of molecules of each which are present on the surface of the catalyst at any moment are proportional to the respective pressures. The reaction occurring on the surface will therefore follow the same kinetic equation as that which would be followed if the identical reaction took place homogeneously.

As an example of this we may take a heterogeneous reaction between two molecules of A and one of B. The surface being but sparsely

* *J. Chem. Soc.*, 1926, 1709.   † *J. Physical Chem.*, 1929, **33**, 447.

covered with A and B the chance that two molecules of A and one of B occupy positions sufficiently near together for them to be able to interact depends upon the square of the number of A molecules and upon the number of B molecules. Since these in turn depend upon the pressures we have

$$\frac{dx}{dt} = k[A]^2[B].$$

Similarly, the catalytic combination of ethylene and hydrogen in the presence of metallic copper is approximately of the second order between 150° and 250° C.*

As soon, however, as one or other of the reacting gases is rather strongly adsorbed, the reaction kinetics become much more complicated. In the combination of ethylene and hydrogen on copper Pease† found that at 0° and 20° C. the simple course is no longer followed. The velocity still increases more or less in proportion to the hydrogen concentration, but actually decreases with increase in the concentration of ethylene. This means that the ethylene, at these lower temperatures, nearly saturates the surface, so that further increase in its pressure cannot appreciably augment the number of molecules adsorbed, but may, and does, lead to an actual displacement of the less strongly adsorbed hydrogen.

Langmuir's investigation of the interaction of hydrogen and oxygen on the surface of heated platinum wires‡ may be taken as a further example. Over a certain range of temperature the velocity of reaction on the platinum surface is proportional to the pressure of oxygen but inversely proportional to the pressure of hydrogen. This proves that the hydrogen is preferentially adsorbed, and may displace the oxygen.

These principles will now be exemplified by the discussion of some typical reactions.

(a) The Interaction of Carbon Monoxide and Oxygen.

The progress of this reaction on the surface of quartz was studied by Bodenstein and Ohlmer.§ The velocity was found to vary in direct proportion to the pressure of oxygen, and in inverse proportion to the pressure of the carbon monoxide itself.

The interpretation of this result seems to be as follows. Carbon

---

* Grassi, *Nuovo Cimento*, [6], 1916, **11**, 147; Pease, *J. Amer. Chem. Soc.*, 1923, **45**, 2235.
† Pease, *J. Amer. Chem. Soc.*, 1923, **45**, 1196.
‡ *Trans. Faraday Soc.*, 1922, **17**, 621.
§ *Z. physikal. Chem.*, 1905, **53**, 166.

monoxide is strongly adsorbed. Therefore the amount of space left uncovered on the catalyst is inversely proportional to its pressure.

Oxygen is but slightly adsorbed. Therefore the rate of reaction is proportional to the pressure of oxygen. It is further evident that for interaction to occur it is not sufficient for an oxygen molecule merely to strike an adsorbed molecule of the monoxide, for this would simply make the rate of reaction independent of the carbon monoxide concentration, but it must itself become adsorbed on that part of the surface which is free. This assumption makes the rate proportional to the extent of the free surface as well as to the oxygen pressure. The supply of carbon monoxide molecules on the surface is so large that nearly all the oxygen molecules which take up their abode on the catalyst find a molecule of carbon monoxide adjacent to them. The only effect of the pressure of the monoxide is therefore in determining the free space. The rate of reaction is thus proportional to $[O_2]/[CO]$.

These inverse proportionality relationships, which are quite common, are very important in showing that, in some instances at least, adsorption of both reacting substances on the surface of the catalyst itself is necessary. A must not merely strike adsorbed B, but must be adsorbed adjacent to it. Otherwise excess of B could not actually retard the combination.

With a different quartz glass Benton and Williams* found a different law, namely, that the rate varies as $[O_2][CO]^{\frac{1}{2}}$. This illustrates the varying adsorptive properties of various kinds of quartz.

Langmuir† made experiments at low pressures on the combination of carbon monoxide and oxygen on the surface of platinum. Up to 700° abs. the rate of reaction was found to be directly proportional to the pressure of oxygen and inversely proportional to that of the carbon monoxide.

At temperatures between 750° and 1,050° abs., however, the adsorption of carbon monoxide being evidently much less, a simpler reaction took place. This proceeded with a velocity proportional to the pressure of oxygen when the carbon monoxide was in excess, and to the pressure of the carbon monoxide when the oxygen was in excess. At these temperatures the two gases appear to compete for the surface of the platinum on more or less equal terms.

In the low-temperature region interesting curves are obtained when the pressure of the reacting gases is plotted against time, the rate of

* *J. Physical Chem.*, 1926, **30**, 1487.   † Loc. cit.

diminution of pressure, of course, measuring the rate of reaction. They have the form shown in Fig. 29.

When oxygen is in excess the curve has a form indicating that the rate of reaction increases as the carbon monoxide is used up. The film of carbon monoxide remains practically complete until nearly all the

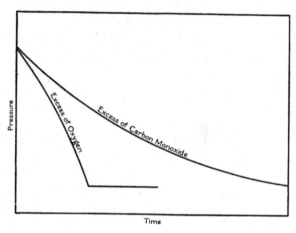

FIG. 29.

supply in the gas phase is exhausted, and then the reaction comes to an abrupt end.

When carbon monoxide is in excess the film is never completely burnt off the platinum, and the rate of reaction falls off gradually as the oxygen is used up.

When more or less equivalent proportions are used the increase in rate due to the increasing number of gaps in the carbon monoxide film is almost exactly counterbalanced by the falling off in rate due to the diminishing pressure of oxygen, and nearly straight lines are found.

(b) The Interaction of Hydrogen and Oxygen.

Langmuir,* investigating the interaction on the surface of platinum, found once more that the character of the reaction changed with temperature. Both in the low-temperature region and in the high-temperature region the results were analogous to those which he had found with carbon monoxide and oxygen. The hydrogen now plays a role analogous to that of the monoxide in the other reaction.

In contact with silver Benton and Elgin† find the rate to be proportional to the pressure of the hydrogen, and independent of that of

* Loc. cit.   † J. Amer. Chem. Soc., 1926, **48**, 3027.

the oxygen: it is reduced by the presence of steam. In contact with gold* the rate is directly proportional to the square of the hydrogen pressure and the first power of the oxygen pressure, and inversely proportional to the pressure of water vapour.

(c) The Interaction of Nitrous Oxide and Hydrogen.

On a platinum surface the hydrogen forms apparently an almost complete film, in the gaps of which the nitrous oxide reacts.† The reaction, $N_2O + H_2 = N_2 + H_2O$, follows a course almost exactly analogous to that of the oxidation of carbon monoxide at low temperatures. Curves almost exactly similar to those already described in connexion with that reaction are obtained, the change coming to an abrupt end when the nitrous oxide is in excess, and reaching its end asymptotically when the hydrogen is in excess.

(d) The Combination of Ethylene and Hydrogen.

Besides the investigations of Grassi and of Pease,‡ with which we have already dealt, there are available some observations of Rideal,§ who employed nickel as a catalyst. He found the rate of the reaction

$$C_2H_4 + H_2 = C_2H_6$$

to vary in direct proportion to the pressure of hydrogen when ethylene was in excess, and in direct proportion to the pressure of ethylene when the hydrogen was in excess. Ethane had no influence on the rate of combination.

(e) The Interaction of Hydrogen and Carbon Dioxide.

The progress of the reaction

$$CO_2 + H_2 = CO + H_2O$$

on the surface of a heated platinum wire was studied by Hinshelwood and Prichard.‖ The measurements were made in the region of 1,000° C. The reaction was made irreversible by the continuous removal of the water formed. The rate of reaction was proportional to the pressure of hydrogen at least up to 300 mm. of mercury. It was proportional to the pressure of carbon dioxide for small pressures, and more or less inversely proportional to the pressure of the carbon dioxide at high pressures of this gas. This relationship is shown in Fig. 30.

---

* Ibid., 1927, **49**, 2426.
† Hinshelwood, *Proc. Roy. Soc.*, A, 1924, **106**, 292.
‡ Loc. cit.   § *J. Chem. Soc.*, 1922, **121**, 309.
‖ *J. Chem. Soc.*, 1925, **127**, 806.

The low-pressure part, AB, of the carbon dioxide curve corresponds to Rideal's observation of the influence of ethylene pressure on the rate of interaction of ethylene and hydrogen in presence of nickel, while the high-pressure part, CD, corresponds to the results of Pease for the influence of the ethylene pressure on the combination in presence of copper. We have the initial increase due simply to the increasing

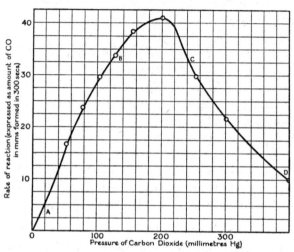

FIG. 30.—Influence of carbon dioxide pressure on the rate of the reaction $CO_2 + H_2 \rightarrow CO + H_2O$ at 1,000° C. Pressure of hydrogen, 100 mm.

number of molecules of carbon dioxide on the surface, followed by the passage through a maximum and subsequent decrease as the carbon dioxide displaces the hydrogen more and more.

The examples we have quoted illustrate nearly all the possible kinds of behaviour.

Reference may here be made to the combination of ethylene and bromine on ordinary glass surfaces, where the rate of reaction was found by Stewart and Edlund* to be proportional to the concentration of the bromine vapour and of the ethylene. This would mean small adsorption of each gas. But further investigation of the reaction reveals more complex and varied behaviour.†

It is hardly necessary to point out that all these various kinds of behaviour would be shown successively in the same reaction if the pressure of each of the reacting gases were varied from the highest to the lowest value. Every experimental study made under conditions circumscribed by the limitations of practical technique reveals only

---

* J. Amer. Chem. Soc., 1923, **45**, 1014.   † Williams, J. Chem. Soc., 1932, 1747.

a fragment of the complete set of relations. Differently prepared catalysts frequently show quite different behaviour. It should be noted that the purpose of the present chapter is accordingly to illustrate *types of reaction*, rather than to be a description of the properties of specific catalytic substances.*

Retarded Reactions. The Interaction of Sulphur Dioxide and Oxygen.

As an example of a retarded reaction we may take the classical investigation of Bodenstein and Fink† on the reaction

$$2SO_2 + O_2 = 2SO_3.$$

When it takes place in contact with platinum this reaction is retarded by the sulphur trioxide which is formed.

The rate of reaction is proportional to the quantity

(amount of SO_2 adsorbed) $\times$ (amount of O_2 adsorbed).

The exact equation expressing this as a function of the various concentrations is very complicated, since the sulphur trioxide displaces both of the other gases to a greater or smaller extent.

In practice the rate of reaction is found to be sufficiently well represented by the equations

$$\frac{d[SO_3]}{dt} = \frac{k[O_2]}{[SO_3]^{\frac{1}{2}}}$$

when sulphur dioxide is in excess, and

$$\frac{d[SO_3]}{dt} = \frac{k[SO_2]}{[SO_3]^{\frac{1}{2}}}$$

when oxygen is in excess.

The term $\dfrac{1}{[SO_3]^{\frac{1}{2}}}$ is an empirical expression proportional to the amount of surface left free when the concentration of the sulphur trioxide in the gas phase is $[SO_3]$.

The Diffusion Theory of Heterogeneous Reactions.

One of the most striking features about heterogeneous reactions is the frequency with which the change is retarded either by the products of the reaction or by one of the reacting substances when it is present in excess. Before the development of the current method of regarding

---

* This is a very necessary reservation, as is shown especially by the work of Roberts (see *Ann. Rep. Chem. Soc.*, 1938, 52) who has found that surfaces previously considered clean may have had complete gas films adsorbed on them.

† *Z. physikal. Chem.*, 1907, **60**, 1.

these phenomena, an interpretation of a rather different kind was placed upon them.

It was supposed that the actual rate of reaction at the surface of the catalyst was great compared with the rate at which the reacting substances could diffuse through a continuous layer of the retarding gas.

This theory was a development of Nernst's diffusion theory of reactions taking place between substances in different phases, but it is by no means inseparably connected with this. It was employed and developed by Bodenstein, and can usually be made to account more or less satisfactorily for the influence of the various concentrations on the rate of reaction.

One illustration will suffice. The equation

$$\frac{d[SO_3]}{dt} = \frac{k[SO_2]}{[SO_3]^{\frac{1}{2}}},$$

representing the reaction between sulphur dioxide and excess of oxygen on the surface of platinum, can be derived by assuming the platinum to be covered with a continuous layer of sulphur trioxide, the thickness being proportional to the square root of the pressure. Through this layer the molecules of sulphur dioxide and of oxygen must thread their way up to the surface of the catalyst. When oxygen is in excess in the gas phase, there will always be a plentiful supply of it in contact with the platinum, and every molecule of sulphur dioxide which arrives there will be able to react at once. The observed rate of reaction is therefore determined simply by the rate at which molecules of sulphur dioxide diffuse through the sulphur trioxide film. In accordance with the well-known law of diffusion, this rate is proportional to the concentration gradient in the film, which is expressed by

$$\frac{\text{concentration in the gas phase} - \text{concentration at the surface}}{\text{thickness of film}}.$$

Since the reaction at the surface is assumed to be very rapid, the concentration here is maintained at zero. The rate of combination is thus proportional to

$$\frac{k[SO_2]}{[SO_3]^{\frac{1}{2}}}.$$

In those reactions where the rate is inversely proportional to some function of the pressure of one of the reacting substances it becomes necessary to assume that a film of this substance covers the surface, and that the other reactants have to diffuse through it. The interaction must be supposed only to accomplish itself at the actual surface of the catalyst.

Explanations may be devised with the aid of this theory almost as well as with the aid of the rival theory. Simple unretarded reactions demand, it is true, rather forced hypotheses about diffusion into the catalyst, or about the existence of permanent skins of foreign gas on the surface, but the real evidence against the diffusion theory is of a more general character.

One of the most important of the arguments against it is a quantitative one.* To account for the extreme slowness of some reactions it would be necessary to suppose the existence of retarding layers of such thickness that they would be of visible dimensions.

Between the highest and the lowest temperatures at which measurement is practicable the variation of reaction rate is many thousandfold. If the diffusion theory is applicable at all, the layer through which the reacting molecules have to pass cannot very well be less than a single molecule in thickness, even at the highest temperature, for a very simple calculation shows that the rate at which molecules of the reactant could come into contact with the bare surface is many times greater in most instances than the fastest measurable rate of reaction. At the lowest temperatures, then, the diffusion layer would have to be many thousands of molecules in thickness. This is easily shown to be a quite inadmissible supposition. No such difficulty is encountered when the variation in the observed reaction rate is attributed to the specific effect of temperature on the actual chemical transformation at the surface of the catalyst, to the uncovered portions of which the molecules of reactant are supposed to have free access.

Rate of diffusion varies as the square root of the absolute temperature. Heterogeneous reactions have the high temperature coefficients characteristic of all chemical changes. If, therefore, the simple diffusion theory is adopted, there is no alternative but to suppose that the thickness of the retarding layer changes rapidly with temperature. The objections to such a supposition have been indicated. To meet these it might be suggested that only those molecules can reach the surface of the catalyst and react, the kinetic energy of which is sufficient to enable them to penetrate a permanent adsorbed layer of some kind, this process being rather different from ordinary diffusion, where all the molecules thread their way through the obstacle. This hypothesis, even if there were anything to be said for it on general grounds, which is open to question, would be ruled out by observations on the temperature coefficients of those reactions where a single molecule under-

* Cf. Langmuir, loc. cit., *supra*.

goes alternative transformations. According to the hypothesis the total reaction velocity should vary with temperature in accordance with the Arrhenius equation, whereas experiment shows that the velocities of the separate transformations vary independently, and each according to an equation of the Arrhenius form. The temperature coefficient of the total reaction velocity is thus a composite one. This is inconsistent with the assumption that the variation in rate is governed by a process common to both of the alternative reactions, namely the penetration of an impeding film by the molecule of the reactant.

It should perhaps be pointed out that if the diffusion theory were true, our previous conclusions about the relation between the true and apparent order of the reaction would have to be modified. In general, the reaction rate would depend upon the first power of the concentration of that reactant which happened to be in defect, or to have the lowest diffusion coefficient.

Mobility of Adsorbed Molecules on Surfaces and a Modified Diffusion Theory.*

The mobility of adsorbed molecules on the surfaces of solid bodies is a question of some general importance. Experiments† on the growth of mercury crystals from the vapour seemed to indicate that adsorbed molecules of mercury could occupy the crystal surface without forming part of its structure, and that they possessed mobility. It also appeared that molecules of benzophenone could move over the surface of glass. In the light of these observations, catalytic reactions on a solid surface present a slightly different picture from that of Langmuir's original theory, though the essential kinetic relationships are not profoundly modified. For example, suppose we have small adsorption and proportionality between gas pressure and adsorbed amount for each of two reacting substances A and B. If the molecules of A and B are rigidly held, reaction depends upon their alighting from the gas phase to adjacent positions on the surface: the probability of which is proportional to the product of the two pressures. If A and B are freely mobile they may, on the other hand, seek each other out in the adsorption layer: but, although the mechanism is somewhat different, the probability of an encounter is still proportional to the product of the pressures. In fact, it seems clear that the relation between the probability of reaction and the gaseous concentrations ought to be the

---

* See Lennard-Jones, *Proc. Phys. Soc.*, 1937, **49**, 140.

† Volmer and Adhikari, *Z. Physik*, 1925, **35**, 170; *Z. physikal. Chem.*, 1926, **119**, 46.

same whether the movement of the molecules is realized by translation over the surface or by passage through the gas. Surface mobility is formally equivalent to a shorter time of sojourn on the surface in Langmuir's sense.

It is by no means certain, however, that the powerful adsorption forces acting between surfaces and reacting gases such as oxygen, hydrogen, or carbon monoxide will allow mobility in any degree comparable with that found in Volmer's experiments. Polanyi and Welke show that different parts of a charcoal surface are associated with very different adsorption energies, and that the density and mobility of the adsorbed molecules must vary over a correspondingly wide range.* Quite probably, the most important cases catalytically are those where very strong binding produces great internal changes in the molecules and at the same time greatly reduces or inhibits mobility.

The case where there is some, but not perfectly free, mobility is an interesting one. Molecules may remain anchored to one point on the surface most of the time, but be capable of migrating from point to point by a discontinuous series of motions executed when they acquire enough energy. This process† has been called 'activated diffusion'. The molecular or atomic structure of any surface naturally ensures that there are arrays of points at which an adsorbed molecule is more strongly held than at any immediately adjacent points. To pass from one of these stable positions to another the molecule needs energy, but this energy may be less than that which would allow it to evaporate from the surface completely. Under these conditions there could be a slow migration of adsorbed molecules of different kinds towards one another; or a slow migration of an adsorbed molecule across a surface to some active centre, or towards a crystal edge or corner. The importance of such edges and corners and of phase boundaries in general has been emphasized by Schwab and Pietsch,‡ who have considered the kinetics of heterogeneous reactions from this point of view.

Kinetics of Surface Reactions where one of the Gases is adsorbed Slowly.

We must now consider how the kinetics of a heterogeneous reaction are modified when one of the reacting gases reaches adsorption equilibrium very slowly.

(1) The simplest kind of reaction will be when there is slow adsorption of gas A followed by a relatively rapid chemical reaction between

---

* *Z. physikal. Chem.*, 1928, **132**, 371.
† Cf. *Faraday Society Discussion* ref., p. 308.
‡ *Inter alia, Z. Elektrochem.*, 1929, **35**, 573.

the adsorbed A and the second gas B. The speed of the reaction will be determined simply by the rate of adsorption. Since A will be removed from the surface as quickly as it is taken up, the rate of adsorption will be proportional to the pressure of A in the gas phase, the whole surface remaining practically uncovered, except in so far as the products of reaction remain adsorbed. Leaving this latter factor out of account, the total rate of reaction will be proportional to the pressure of A and independent of the pressure of B.

(2) A more general relation is as follows: the amount of A on the surface increases by adsorption and decreases by reaction, a stationary condition being established when the two rates are equal. Let the fraction of the surface covered under these conditions be σ.

Then rate of adsorption of $A = k_1[A](1-\sigma)$ and the rate of removal by reaction $= k_2\sigma[B]$.

By equating these σ is found to be $\dfrac{k_1[A]}{k_1[A]+k_2[B]}$ and the rate of reaction will be $k_2\sigma[B] = \dfrac{k_1k_2[A][B]}{k_1[A]+k_2[B]}$.

This reduces to a simpler form in two extreme cases: when k_1 is large in comparison with k_2 the rate becomes proportional to $[B]$, while when k_2 is large in comparison with k_1 the rate is proportional to $[A]$.

This means simply that when the rate of adsorption is relatively great the surface becomes completely covered, so that the reaction is independent of $[A]$, while when the rate of reaction is much greater than the rate of adsorption, the surface is, as it were, kept clean, and the A molecules are used up at the rate at which they get adsorbed.

The above discussion neglects the re-evaporation of the adsorbed A molecules, and also postulates that reaction occurs when B strikes adsorbed A. The first simplification would probably be justified in examples of practical importance: it becomes quite valid, of course, when the reaction is fast compared with the adsorption.

The equations for a more complete treatment allowing for the adsorption and re-evaporation of both gases are easily written down. In general, the relations between rate of reaction and concentration will be complicated.

When the slow interaction between the solid and the gas affects more than the surface layer of atoms of the solid, and there is the possibility of actual compound formation, as, for example, with oxygen and certain metals, the relations will be more complex still. Surface compound formation might, for example, proceed to a certain point and then bring about a change of space lattice. According to whether this had occurred or not, the reaction between the surface compound and the second gas might be slow or rapid. Reaction between the second gas and the surface compound might be governed by the formation and growth of nuclei. The number of possibilities is indefinitely great, and the variety of phenomena correspondingly complicated. Examples of complex and remarkable surface behaviour are to be found in the work of Chapman and others on the catalytic action of silver on the union of hydrogen and oxygen.

Activated Adsorption.

Slow establishment of adsorption equilibrium is probably not an important factor in catalytic phenomena at high enough temperatures, for example, in experiments where the catalyst is an incandescent metal wire. But an important class of examples has been discovered by H. S. Taylor and others, where the rate of adsorption is slow and has a considerable temperature coefficient. Taylor calls the adsorption occurring under these conditions 'activated adsorption'.* The forces called into play in adsorption being often of the same nature as those by which chemical compounds are formed, the adsorption may take place with a characteristic velocity determined by the same kind of factors as those which govern the rate of chemical changes. In particular, a definite energy of activation may be necessary for the formation of the adsorbed system. For example, Taylor and Williamson,† studying the adsorption of hydrogen by manganous oxide, or by mixtures of manganous oxide and chromium oxide, found that the process was slow and that its rate had a well-defined positive temperature coefficient. With manganous oxide the process is slow at 100° C. Between 184° and 305° the rate at which hydrogen is taken up increases tenfold. By applying the Arrhenius equation a 'heat of activation' for the formation of the 'surface hydride' of about 10,000 calories is found.

In general, heats of activation found in this way vary both with temperature and with the amount of gas taken up. This can be interpreted in terms of a varying activity of different parts of the surface, or by supposing that two types of adsorption are occurring simultaneously (one depending on the 'chemical' forces and the other on forces of the van der Waals type). In some examples, especially where gases are taken up by metals, it is maintained by some that the slow adsorption which increases in rate with temperature is to a considerable

* J. Amer. Chem. Soc., 1931, 53, 578.   † Ibid., 1931, 53, 813, 2168.

extent at least a process of solution or of penetration of the gas into the interior of the solid. When this factor is of serious consequence the heat of activation calculated from the Arrhenius equation will not have a direct significance. In the ideal case, however, it will be almost exactly analogous to the heat of activation of an ordinary chemical reaction.

The Adsorption of Mixtures of Gases.*

If we assume a uniform homogeneous adsorbing surface, then, by writing down the equations for the rate of condensation and rate of evaporation of two gases which are simultaneously adsorbed, it may be shown that the relative amounts of each taken up by the adsorbent should be independent of the absolute pressure of the gases, and dependent only on the relative pressures of the two. Indications that this condition is not always fulfilled have been interpreted by assuming:

(1) that multimolecular layers are formed, in which a unimolecular film of one gas may itself hold molecules of a second gas;†

(2) that the surface of the adsorbent is not homogeneous. Further reference to this assumption will be necessary in the next chapter.

(3) that the adsorbed molecules of the two kinds exert forces on one another. This must be true *in general*, though there will be many cases where the assumption of approximately 'perfect' behaviour will be reasonable.

Reference should be made here to the work of Palmer,‡ who used the method of measuring the 'cohering' voltage between metallic filaments for investigating the nature of the gas films adsorbed by metals. The interpretation of the results depends upon certain assumptions, the validity of which is a little difficult to estimate, but the phenomena observed are of much interest. In particular, it is found that when a mixture of gases is admitted to the metal the initially formed film appears to differ somewhat in composition from that existing when equilibrium is established. The explanation is probably as follows: the gases first condense on the surface in proportion to the numbers of molecules of each striking it, i.e. in direct proportion to the partial pressures and the molecular velocities. The final equilibrium depends also on the rates of evaporation. If the gases are both strongly adsorbed, so that their rates of evaporation are small, the equilibrium may take a measurable time to be established.

---

* Cf. Hückel, *Adsorption*, p. 217.
† Cf. Hurst and Rideal, *J. Chem. Soc.*, 1924, **125**, 694.
‡ *Proc. Roy. Soc.*, A, 1924, **106**, 55; A, 1926, **110**, 133; A, 1929, **122**, 487.

It may be a similar phenomenon which is encountered when a gaseous reaction product formed *in situ* on a surface retards the reaction, while the same gas added from without has no retarding influence.

The Influence of Heterogeneous Catalysts on the Equilibrium Point in Reversible Reactions.

In heterogeneous reactions we frequently find relations between rate of reaction and concentration quite different from those which the law of mass action would indicate to be valid for a homogeneous system. It is a little difficult, at first sight, to see how, by equating the rates of the forward and reverse reactions, we are still to arrive at the correct equilibrium relations. The general problem is very complex, but one simple example may be given to illustrate the manner in which conflict with the second law of thermodynamics is avoided.

Let the reaction $AB \rightleftharpoons A + B$ take place in contact with a heterogeneous catalyst.

Suppose AB is only slightly adsorbed, B very strongly adsorbed, and A slightly adsorbed.

Then we might have for the rate of the direct reaction

$$\frac{-d[AB]}{dt} = \frac{k_1[AB]}{[B]}.$$

But just because B is strongly adsorbed, the rate of the reverse reaction might become independent of B and we should have

$$\frac{d[AB]}{dt} = k_2[A].$$

By equating these rates we arrive at the normal expression for the equilibrium constant

$$\frac{[AB]}{[A][B]}.$$

ACTIVATION IN HETEROGENEOUS REACTIONS

In order to take part in a heterogeneous reaction molecules must be adsorbed by a catalyst. But attachment to the surface is not by itself sufficient to cause their transformation. They require activation just as in homogeneous reactions.

There is a general correlation between adsorptive capacity and catalytic effect to the extent that all the metals show some capacity for adsorbing those gases the interaction of which they are able to promote. Beyond this the correlation does not extend in the simple kind of reaction. In cases where activated adsorption occurs, there are interesting connexions between this and the catalytic activity.

There is ordinarily no quantitative proportionality between degree of adsorption and rate of reaction. Nor is any such close relation to be expected. Indeed, at temperatures where reaction attains a measurable speed adsorption is often quite small. Thus, although the adsorption of ethylene by certain kinds of copper catalyst can be demonstrated at lower temperatures, the velocity of interaction of ethylene and hydrogen only attains an appreciable speed at temperatures where the adsorption becomes almost too small to measure.

It is clear, therefore, that thermal activation plays a part in surface reactions as important as that which we have seen it to play in homogeneous changes.

Heterogeneous reaction velocities nearly always satisfy the Arrhenius equation $d \log k / dT = E / RT^2$, and the values of the constant E are not of a different order of magnitude from those belonging to purely gaseous reactions. In many instances the value of E is in the neighbourhood of 30,000 calories.

Until more definite information is forthcoming about its real meaning we may call E the *apparent heat of activation.*

As we have seen, there is abundant evidence that the heat of activation in homogeneous reactions represents the thermal energy with which the molecules must be supplied, by collision or otherwise, before they can enter into reaction. There is every reason to believe that, in heterogeneous reactions, adsorbed molecules must be supplied with energy in an analogous way.

This is evident when the mechanism of a heterogeneous reaction is considered in more detail. Molecules from the gas phase strike the surface. They may rebound or they may become attached to the surface and sojourn there for a period.

One of two things may then happen. After a time they may re-evaporate. This depends upon their acquiring sufficient kinetic energy to carry them beyond the range of attraction of the surface forces. Escape may be rendered easier at certain times if the attractive force passes periodically through a minimum value as a result of internal changes both in the adsorbed molecules and in the molecules of the surface.*

On the other hand, during their sojourn on the surface the adsorbed

* For the quantum-mechanical discussion of these processes see Lennard-Jones and others in a series of papers in *Proc. Roy. Soc.*, A, 1935–8: e.g. Lennard-Jones and Strachan, ibid., 1935, **150**, 442; Lennard-Jones and Devonshire, ibid., 1936, **156**, 6, 29, 37; 1937, **158**, 242, 253, 269; Lennard-Jones and Goodwin, ibid., **163**, 101.

molecules may undergo chemical change, consisting either in simple rearrangement or decomposition, or in interaction with adjacent molecules.

In whichever of these ways the chemical transformation comes about, all the information about the nature of chemical change which has been derived from the study of reactions in the gaseous phase justifies the conclusion that the molecules must be activated by the acquisition of thermal energy considerably above the mean. This energy we may call the *true heat of activation*.

The actual processes of molecular transformation in surface reactions cannot be fundamentally different from those in homogeneous reactions. Gas molecules come almost at once into thermal equilibrium with the surface on which they are adsorbed. Among them there is a distribution of internal energy, determined by the temperature of the surface. Although their internal configuration, and consequently their stability, is modified profoundly by the forces acting between them and the molecules constituting the surface, the adsorbed molecules form a system possessing a certain uniformity within its own bounds. A heterogeneous reaction may indeed be regarded as a homogeneous reaction in two dimensions instead of three.

Serious confusion arises unless one thing is taken carefully into account. Only those molecules which are actually adsorbed are in a position to participate in the reaction. Velocity constants, however, are always calculated in terms of the total amount of gas in the reaction vessel. If we have to deal with a unimolecular reaction in a single phase, the velocity constant is equal to the fraction of the total number of molecules which reacts in unit time. Since all the molecules have an equal chance of being in the activated state, direct correlation between the velocity constant and the heat of activation may reasonably be sought. In a heterogeneous reaction all the molecules have not an equal chance of being in the activated state. Only those which are adsorbed have this chance.

Thus the only correlation which may reasonably be sought is one between the heat of activation and the velocity constant expressed, not as a fraction of the total number of molecules, but as a fraction of the number actually adsorbed at any moment. If k_{obs} is the observed velocity constant, calculated in terms of the total gas, and α is the fraction of the total gas which is actually adsorbed, then the 'true' velocity constant would be k_{obs} divided by α. This we may represent by the letter χ.

We are now in a position to see the difference between the true and apparent heats of activation. The true heat of activation, Q, is given by

$$\frac{d \log \chi}{dT} = \frac{Q}{RT^2},$$

while the apparent heat of activation is given by

$$\frac{d \log k_{\text{obs}}}{dT} = \frac{E}{RT^2}.$$

Since the adsorption varies with temperature, α is not independent of T. E and Q are therefore not necessarily equal.

Relation between the True and Apparent Heats of Activation.

For simplicity we will assume that only one gas takes part in the chemical change. Unretarded reactions, and reactions retarded by the presence of their products, must be considered separately, because there are important differences between the results for these two classes.

In dealing with the unretarded reactions it will be best to restrict ourselves to those in which the adsorption of the reacting gas is small, so that the amount adsorbed is proportional to the pressure. Further, in dealing with retarded reactions we shall assume that the adsorption of the retarding gas is sufficiently great for the free surface to be inversely proportional to its pressure. Such loss of generality as this method involves is not very serious, because, in the first place, very many reactions are found in practice to conform to the conditions we are supposing, and, in the second place, a more complete investigation of the most general case leads to results which are too complicated to apply to actual experimental data.

We further assume that the rate of establishment of adsorption equilibrium at a given temperature is considerably greater than the rate at which the adsorbed molecules undergo the actual chemical change.

1. Unretarded Reactions.

Let σ be the fraction of the active surface which is covered with adsorbed molecules of the reactant when the pressure in the gas phase is unity.

The establishment of the adsorption equilibrium is rapid in comparison with any disturbance of it due to the removal of the molecules in chemical change. Equating, therefore, the rate of evaporation and the rate of condensation we find an expression for σ.

Rate of condensation on to the surface $= a(1-\sigma)$, where a is constant at constant temperature, but varies slightly with temperature.

Rate of evaporation from surface $= x\sigma$, where x is the rate of evaporation, at temperature T, for unit area of covered surface.

Since evaporation can only take place when the adsorbed molecules acquire a definite amount of kinetic energy, directed away from the surface, we may express the variation of x with temperature in the form

$$x = be^{-\lambda/RT},$$

where b is constant, and λ may formally be called the 'energy of desorption'.

Thus for equilibrium we have

$$a(1-\sigma) = be^{-\lambda/RT}\sigma.$$

Since σ is small compared with unity, $(1-\sigma)$ is nearly equal to 1; hence $\sigma = Ce^{\lambda/RT}$, where C is a new constant equal to a/b.

If χ is the true velocity constant of the reaction, per unit area of the catalyst actually covered, then the observed velocity constant, k_{obs}, is proportional to $\chi\sigma$.

Therefore $\qquad k_{obs} = \text{const.}\,\chi\sigma = \text{const.}\,\chi Ce^{+\lambda/RT},$

but $\qquad\qquad\qquad\qquad \chi = \text{const.}\,e^{-Q/RT},$

where Q is the true heat of activation.

Therefore $\qquad k_{obs} = \text{const.}\,e^{-(Q-\lambda)/RT}.$

The constant varies but slightly with temperature—approximately as the square root of the absolute temperature.

Thus $\qquad\qquad\qquad \dfrac{d\log k_{obs}}{dT} = \dfrac{Q-\lambda}{RT^2}.$

The apparent heat of activation is given by

$$\frac{d\log k_{obs}}{dT} = \frac{E}{RT^2}.$$

Therefore $\qquad\qquad E = Q-\lambda.$

2. *Retarded Reactions.*

Let σ' be the fraction of the active surface covered with the retarding gas at unit pressure. Then the fraction left free is $(1-\sigma')$, and of this let a fraction σ be occupied by the reactant when its concentration in the gas phase is unity.

The adsorption equilibrium of the retarding gas is expressed as follows: $\qquad$ rate of condensation $= a'(1-\sigma'),$

σ being small compared with unity;

$$\text{rate of evaporation} = x'\sigma',$$

where x' is the rate of evaporation at temperature T for unit area covered.

By the same argument as before

$$x' = b'e^{-\lambda'/RT},$$

where λ' is the 'energy of desorption' of the gas.

Equating the two rates we obtain

$$a'(1-\sigma') = b'\sigma'e^{-\lambda'/RT},$$

but now σ' is nearly equal to unity; therefore

$$(1-\sigma') = \text{const. } e^{-\lambda'/RT}.$$

Further, for the reactant we have as before

$$\sigma = \text{const. } e^{+\lambda/RT}.$$

Now the observed velocity constant k_{obs} is proportional to the true velocity constant multiplied by $\sigma(1-\sigma')$, since $(1-\sigma')$ is the fraction of the total active surface which is available for molecules of the reactant, and σ is the fraction of this fraction which is actually occupied.

Thus

$$k_{\text{obs}} = \text{const. } \chi e^{-\lambda'/RT}e^{+\lambda/RT}$$

$$= \text{const. } e^{-Q/RT}e^{-\lambda'/RT}e^{+\lambda/RT}$$

$$= \text{const. } e^{-(Q+\lambda'-\lambda)/RT}.$$

Therefore

$$\frac{d\log k_{\text{obs}}}{dT} = \frac{Q+\lambda'-\lambda}{RT^2}.$$

Comparing this with the equation

$$\frac{d\log k_{\text{obs}}}{dT} = \frac{E}{RT^2},$$

it follows that

$$E = Q+\lambda'-\lambda.$$

General Discussion of Temperature Coefficients of Heterogeneous Reactions.

When the products of reaction exert no retarding influence, the apparent heat of activation is less than the true value by an amount λ, which determines the variation with temperature of the adsorption.

The existence of a marked retarding influence of the products has, on the other hand, the effect of increasing the apparent heat of activation.

There is one important special case in which the apparent heat of activation becomes equal to the true value. This is when the surface is completely covered with the reactant over the whole range of temperature, and there is no retardation due to the presence of the products of reaction. σ has the constant value unity, and the variation of the observed reaction velocity is due entirely to the changing rate of the actual chemical transformation.

In general, since the adsorption is often too small to be measured directly, it is rather difficult to estimate the magnitude of the correction which should be applied to the apparent heat of activation. It may sometimes be very great. When the adsorption is quite small, for example when there is a simple first-order decomposition, it is possible that the energy changes accompanying adsorption are also small. The temperature coefficient of the number of molecules adsorbed would then be small compared with that of the actual chemical change.

Direct measurement of heats of adsorption, however, reveals relationships of some complexity.* The integral heat of adsorption of gases like hydrogen on metals such as nickel may amount to 10,000 or 20,000 calories. Moreover, the differential heat of adsorption varies in a complicated manner. Since hydrogen itself is probably adsorbed, partly at least, in the atomic form, and the resolution is highly endothermic while the adsorption of the atoms is exothermic, and since different parts of the catalytic surface have different activity, the complexity of the thermal phenomena is understandable.

In the absence of more detailed information about the actual magnitude of the adsorption in specific instances, it is at least worth while to see what regularities, if any, reveal themselves when the apparent value of E is used as an approximation for the true value.

The natural line of inquiry is to study the progress of a given reaction on various catalytic surfaces, to determine the relative numbers of molecules adsorbed on each surface, and to seek a correlation between the heat of activation, using provisionally the apparent value as a sufficiently good approximation to the true value, and the velocity of change referred to equal numbers of adsorbed molecules. Unfortunately, almost all examples reveal unexpected complexities. For one thing the existence of centres of varying activity further complicates the interpretation even of direct measurements of adsorption.

There is not, in general, any observable correlation between the

---

* Beebe and Taylor, *J. Amer. Chem. Soc.*, 1924, **46**, 43; Fryling, *J. Physical Chem.*, 1926, **30**, 818; Kistiakowsky, Flosdorf, and Taylor, *J. Amer. Chem. Soc.*, 1927, **49**, 2200; Burk, *J. Physical Chem.*, 1928, **32**, 1601.

apparent E and the reaction velocity, as is shown by the following example, which refers to the reaction $HCOOH = H_2 + CO_2$.

Surface	E_{CO_2}	Relative velocity
Glass	24,500	0·05
Gold	23,500	2
Silver	31,000	2
Platinum	22,000	100
Rhodium	25,000	500

Thus glass and rhodium give approximately the same value for the heat of activation, yet the reaction proceeds 10,000 times as rapidly on the rhodium surface. The lack of correlation is sufficiently evident.

But it is not at all difficult to admit that the number of molecules adsorbed on parts of the glass surface possessing catalytic virtue may be ten thousand times smaller than the number which rhodium can accommodate.

If sufficient confidence is felt, on general grounds, in the existence of an exact correlation of the kind we have been seeking, then these results could be used in a converse manner to calculate the relative numbers of formic acid molecules accommodated by various surfaces.

A similar lack of correlation between the observed rate of reaction and the value of E was found by Kunsman* for the decomposition of ammonia on various catalysts.

A second possibility of revealing a correlation presents itself in the study of alternative reactions.

Formic acid decomposes in the two ways:

$$H.COOH \begin{cases} H_2 + CO_2 & (1) \\ H_2O + CO & (2) \end{cases}$$

Both of these reactions take place simultaneously on the surface of glass.

If molecules of formic acid can be adsorbed in two distinct ways on the surface of glass, and if reaction (1) and reaction (2) are respectively characteristic of the two modes of adsorption, then we are virtually dealing with two different catalysts, and the situation is not very different from the one which we have already discussed. But if, as we might perhaps have expected, there were only one mode of adsorption, and decomposition of the formic acid molecules in one or other of the alternative ways were governed purely by some internal probability,

* J. Amer. Chem. Soc., 1928, **50**, 2100.

then we should be justified in looking for some connexion between the heat of activation associated with a given mode of decomposition and the relative probability of its occurrence.

On the surface of glass, in the neighbourhood of 280° C., the two alternative reactions take place with nearly equal speeds, yet the heats of activation are very different.* E_{CO}, the heat of activation associated with the decomposition into carbon monoxide and water, is about 16,000 calories, while E_{CO_2} is about 28,000 calories. If the numbers of molecules which are activated for the two possible reactions are proportional respectively to $e^{-E_{CO}/RT}$ and $e^{-E_{CO_2}/RT}$, and if, moreover, there is any connexion between the chance of the molecules becoming activated and the occurrence of a given transformation, then the reaction yielding carbon monoxide should predominate over the competing reaction to an overwhelming extent. The ratio of the rates of the two reactions should be $e^{-28,000/RT}$ divided by $e^{-16,000/RT}$, so that about e^{10} molecules should split up into carbon monoxide and water for every one splitting up into carbon dioxide and hydrogen. But the numbers of molecules decomposing in the two ways are roughly equal.

This result shows that the values of the energies of activation are not by themselves sufficient to determine the course of the chemical transformation.

Thus the assumption that there is only one way in which the molecules of formic acid can be attached to the surface of the catalyst is probably not admissible. There is, indeed, evidence against the assumption. Constable† found that the two simultaneous reactions undergone by allyl alcohol when passed over heated copper were differently influenced by the physical state of the catalyst. This points to the conclusion that there are two independent centres of activity on the catalyst surface with two different modes of adsorption, or, at any rate, centres where the energy of adsorption is so different that different reactions are facilitated. Hoover and Rideal‡ find that the two alternative decompositions of ethyl alcohol by thoria show a different behaviour towards poisons, which points to the same conclusion.

The heterogeneous decomposition of nitrous oxide in contact with a heated gold wire is interesting, though undoubtedly rather excep-

* Hinshelwood, Hartley, and Topley, *Proc. Roy. Soc.*, A, 1922, **100**, 575.
† *Proc. Roy. Soc.*, A, 1926, **113**, 254.
‡ *J. Amer. Chem. Soc.*, 1927, **49**, 104.

tional. The reaction is unimolecular with respect to nitrous oxide. The heat of activation, obtained from the temperature coefficient of the reaction velocity, is 29,000 calories.

If we assume the very simple decomposition mechanism that nearly all the molecules of nitrous oxide which strike the wire and acquire from it energy greater than E can decompose, then we have

$$\frac{\text{number of molecules reacting in unit time}}{\text{number of molecules striking the wire in unit time}} = e^{-E/RT}.$$

From this equation a value of E equal to 30,000 calories is found. This is in rather striking agreement with the value found from the temperature coefficient. It would appear that the course of the reaction could be explained by the supposition that every molecule striking the wire in an appropriate manner reacts forthwith. But this is only a possible explanation. It is by no means necessarily the correct one, and it is certain that so simple a mechanism could not be made to explain all, or even many, other heterogeneous reactions. It seems clear that, in general, actual sojourn of the molecules on the surface is necessary, and this applies *a fortiori* when reaction depends upon the interaction of two or more species of molecules. Schwab and Pietsch* find that the thermal decomposition of methane at the surface of a hot wire is very much more rapid than could be accounted for by the number of methane molecules striking the wire with the appropriate kinetic energy of translation. This supports the conclusion that the methane molecules actually sojourn on the wire and derive energy from the atoms constituting the surface.

In a zero-order reaction the true and apparent energies of activation are equal. If we assume that the number of molecules, n, on each square centimetre of the surface is equal to that for a close-packed layer, then for the number reacting per square cm. per sec. we shall have $fne^{-E/RT}$, where n is known.

It has been pointed out by Topley† that when the adsorbed molecules are simple, such as ammonia or nitrous oxide, then it may be reasonable to assume that every molecule decomposes within an interval $1/f$ of receiving the activation energy from the underlying solid, f being simply the atomic vibration frequency of the solid. Taking f as 10^{12}, he finds that the calculated rate agrees with the observed rate quite well for a number of zero-order reactions taking place on metallic wires.

---

* *Z. physikal. Chem.*, 1926, **121**, 189. † *Nature*, 1931, **128**, 115.

Reaction	Number of molecules reacting	
	obs.	calc.
NH_3 on W	4×10^{17}	4×10^{17}
	2×10^{19}	13×10^{19}
NH_3 on Mo	$5-20 \times 10^{18}$	2×10^{18}
Dissociation of Pt(CO) complex	4×10^{16}	2×10^{16}

These results show that there is a deep-seated analogy in statistical character between the simplest type of heterogeneous reaction and the simplest type of homogeneous reaction.

Topley also shows that the calculation can be extended to first-order reactions if we are prepared to calculate the number of adsorbed molecules from the heat of adsorption, using the Boltzmann principle (page 40). The only energy entering into the final formula is then the *apparent* heat of activation, so that the difficulty referred to above may be circumvented. In one or two examples, such as the decomposition of hydrogen iodide on platinum, this procedure gives the correct order of magnitude for the absolute rate of reaction.

These results are important in that they show that in some examples the absolute reaction rate at least approximates to that which would follow from mechanisms of ideal simplicity.

As explained at the outset, all the foregoing discussion applies in the first instance to those reactions in which the rate of establishment of adsorption equilibrium is great compared with the rate of the actual chemical change of the adsorbed molecules. When we have to deal with examples where 'activated adsorption' occurs the matter must be approached in a somewhat different way.

Let us consider the ideal case of a reaction

$$X_2 + Y_2 = 2XY,$$

catalysed by a surface consisting of an array of M atoms. It would be possible for the adsorption of X_2 to be the rate-determining process. The molecule X_2, on being taken up by the surface, might be resolved into X atoms, with the formation of $M-X$ linkages instead of $X-X$ linkages. For this to occur a considerable contribution of activation energy might have to be supplied by the X_2 molecule, the adjacent M atoms, or all jointly. The reaction between the $M-X$ systems and the Y_2 molecules might now occur with great readiness. The temperature coefficient of the whole reaction would be governed by the heat of activation of the adsorption process.

In the more general case where the rates of adsorption of two substances are of the same order of magnitude, and where the rate of interaction of the adsorbed substances is comparable with the rate of adsorption, extremely complex relationships will be found. If to these complications are added those due to the retarding action of the products of the change, and the varying activity of different parts of the surface, the difficulties of analysis become almost insuperable.

What would be interesting would be to collect a number of examples where the rate of the total chemical change could be shown equal to the rate of adsorption of one of the reacting gases, and then to seek a correlation between the 'heats of activation of adsorption' and the rates.

Comparison of Homogeneous and Catalysed Reactions.* Influence of the Catalyst on the Heat of Activation.

A heterogeneous catalyst may influence a reaction in two ways. It may modify the mechanism of the reaction by allowing it to proceed along a path which would not be possible for the homogeneous change, and it may also facilitate the change by lowering the energy of activation. This second influence will only be detectable under such conditions that the true and apparent heats of activation are nearly equal. Reactions which are markedly retarded by their products are thus ruled out of consideration.

We will discuss the problem by reference to the three reactions:

$$2N_2O = 2N_2 + O_2,$$

$$2HI = H_2 + I_2,$$

$$2NH_3 = N_2 + 3H_2.$$

The first two reactions have been proved experimentally to depend upon collisions in the gaseous phase. The homogeneous decomposition of ammonia has not been measured, but it seems very probable that it would resemble the others in this one respect at least.

The modification of the reaction path is obvious when we consider that the thermal decomposition of nitrous oxide or of hydrogen iodide on the surface of platinum or of gold takes place in a manner independent of collisions. The metal surfaces seem to act in virtue of their affinity for free atoms. The nitrous oxide decomposition appears, for example, to occur in the stages $N_2O = N_2 + O$; and $O + O = O_2$. The

---

* Hinshelwood and Prichard, *J. Chem. Soc.*, 1925, **127**, 327, 1552; *Proc. Roy. Soc.*, A, 1924, **106**, 284; Hinshelwood and Burk, *J. Chem. Soc.*, 1925, **127**, 1105, 2896.

metal surface acts as a temporary abode for oxygen atoms until they encounter others of their kind and evaporate. It is quite possible even that a permanent film of atomic oxygen exists on the metal, unless the latter has been heated in a vacuum to a high temperature. This film would be a very effective agent in removing the oxygen atoms from the N_2O molecules, and giving rise to oxygen molecules in the process.

The homogeneous decomposition of nitrous oxide depends upon collision and has an activation energy of about 58,000 calories. The heats of activation associated with the transformations on the surface of platinum and of gold are 32,500 calories and 29,000 calories respectively Thus the homogeneous reaction demands activation to a total extent of about 58,000 calories, while the heterogeneous transformations demand activation to the extent of about half this amount only. The catalysts may therefore be said to reduce the energy of activation, but of course they do this in the rather indirect way of changing the whole reaction mechanism.

The values 32,500 and 29,000 for the heats of activation are uncorrected for the change with temperature of the number of molecules adsorbed, and this obviously detracts from the conclusiveness of the results. In the other two instances which we proposed to discuss this uncertainty can, fortunately, be eliminated, or at least considerably reduced.

As we found in an earlier section, there is one type of catalytic reaction in which the observed heat of activation does not require correction for the changing adsorption of the reactant, namely, reactions of zero order. In these the surface of the catalyst is completely covered with adsorbed molecules, and, so long as increase of temperature does not cause the reaction order to change from zero, the number of molecules participating in the reaction may be regarded as constant. So long as this condition is fulfilled there seems no good reason for doubting that the observed heat of activation is a measure of the energy required to enable the adsorbed molecules to enter into reaction. It is a real measure of the molecular stability.

The decomposition of hydrogen iodide on the surface of gold, and the decomposition of ammonia on the surface of tungsten, nearly conform to the condition.

For the hydrogen iodide decomposition the heat of activation is 25,000 calories. This is very considerably lower than the value 44,000 calories associated with the homogeneous reaction.

It is instructive to compare with this the heat of activation which the hypothetical *unimolecular* homogeneous reaction would possess. From the known thermochemical data we have

$$2HI = H_2 + I_2 - 3,000 \text{ cals.,}$$
$$H_2 = 2H - 103,000 \text{ cals.,}$$
$$I_2 = 2I - 36,000 \text{ cals.,}$$

whence $\qquad HI = H + I - 71,000$ cals.

Thus the *minimum* activation would be 71,000 calories.

It is probable that the actual mechanism of the surface decomposition is unimolecular, but, the observed order of the reaction being zero, we cannot tell whether the molecules decompose singly or by interaction with their neighbours. The catalytic decomposition of hydrogen iodide on the surface of platinum can actually be shown to be unimolecular. The heat of activation in this instance is even lower (14,000 cals.), but is again subject to the same uncertainty as the values for the unimolecular reactions of nitrous oxide.

The homogeneous decomposition of ammonia, being immeasurably slow even at temperatures in the region of 1,000° C., must have a heat of activation greater than 70,000 or 80,000 calories. The heterogeneous decomposition on the surface of tungsten has a heat of activation of 39,000 calories.

We may conveniently summarize these various relationships in the form of a table.

Reaction. Thermal decomposition of	Total activation required for the homogeneous change	Total activation required for the heterogeneous change
Hydrogen iodide	44,000	25,000 (gold)
Nitrous oxide	58,500	29,000 (gold)*
		32,500 (platinum)*
Ammonia	probably > 80,000	39,000 (tungsten)

* Plus correction.

The function of the surfaces in these examples seems thus to be to replace the collisional activation process by a process with an energy of activation only about half as great.†

Reactions in which the Retarding Effect of the Products is marked.

The relation between the true and apparent heats of activation is given by the equation

$$E_{app} = E_{true} + \lambda' - \lambda.$$

† The extent to which the metal catalysts are active in virtue of atomic films or even oxide layers does not affect the truth of these energy considerations.

In considering the interaction of carbon monoxide and oxygen on the surface of platinum, a reaction which takes place at a rate inversely proportional to the pressure of the carbon monoxide, Langmuir* assumed that the change with temperature of the reaction velocity was entirely due to the variation in the rate of evaporation of carbon monoxide molecules from the retarding film. This assumption was equivalent to equating E_{app} and λ'. He speaks, therefore, of the observed heat of activation, 31,800 calories, as the 'heat of evaporation of the adsorbed carbon monoxide'. This cannot be absolutely correct in principle, although in special instances λ' may be large compared with the other terms. In the example which Langmuir was studying the assumption is to some extent justified by the circumstance that at higher temperatures, when the platinum surface becomes almost denuded of adsorbed molecules of the monoxide, the rate of reaction is very great and practically determined by the rate at which the molecules can come into contact with the surface. Under these conditions, moreover, the rate of reaction becomes almost independent of temperature. This shows, probably, that E_{true} is small compared with λ'. In general, however, both terms will be of considerable importance. This means that retarded reactions will tend to have rather high temperature coefficients, the analysis of which will be difficult.

The decomposition of ammonia on the surface of platinum takes place at a speed which is inversely proportional to the pressure of the hydrogen present. The combined influence of the two terms E and λ' produces an apparent heat of activation of more than 100,000 calories. This is in striking contrast with the value of E_{true}, 39,000 calories for the unretarded reaction on the surface of tungsten. The decomposition of ammonia on molybdenum is of zero order, but retarded by nitrogen; the value of E according to Burk is 53,200 calories. Kunsman finds 32,000 calories only. Here the effect of the retardation by nitrogen seems to be quite marked, and, moreover, variable.

The Nature of Catalytic Surfaces.

We have hitherto given most of our attention to the adsorbed molecules of the reactant. We must now consider more closely the part played in catalytic phenomena by the nature of the surface itself. The question to be solved is, in its simplest terms, what the catalyst does to the adsorbed molecules to influence their stability.

The first step in the elucidation of this difficult problem is to ascertain

* *Trans. Faraday Soc.*, 1922, **17**, 621.

whether the whole surface of the catalyst is uniformly active. We have already referred to the view expressed by Taylor* that only a small fraction of the total surface is necessarily active in catalysing a given reaction, and, moreover, that this fraction is a function, not merely of the surface itself but of the reaction catalysed. The centres which are active in respect of one reaction may be quite inactive in respect of another, although the surface, regarded as a whole, catalyses both equally well.

This theory is based upon evidence of several different kinds. First, the ease with which catalytic activity can sometimes be destroyed by heating is considered by Taylor himself to indicate that a very active surface is still far from possessing the completely regular arrangement of atoms which is characteristic of the true space lattice of the solid. He supposes that there exist, at the surface of the solid, groups of atoms in varying degrees of saturation. Some groups are part of the completed lattice, while others consist of small numbers of atoms rising in the form of peaks from the surface. In extreme cases there may be isolated atoms attached to the main groups by a single valency only. On these isolated peaks several molecules of a gas might be adsorbed, instead of the single molecule which could be held by an atom in a normal space lattice. The effect of heat on a catalyst with this surface structure would be to bring about a more regular arrangement of the atoms and thereby destroy the active peaks.

Whether or not this picture of the surface is a legitimate one, it must be remarked that the destruction of catalytic activity by heat is only observed in the case of finely divided solids, and here it can be equally well explained by supposing that heating brings about a diminution of the total surface.

Other and more conclusive evidence about the existence of active centres, whatever their nature may be, is, however, available. Catalytic poisons sometimes destroy the activity of a surface towards a particular reaction without reducing the total adsorption of the reacting substances to anything like a proportionate extent. Taylor quotes some experiments of Pease, in which quantities of carbon monoxide quite insufficient to displace all the hydrogen or ethylene from a copper catalyst completely inhibited the reaction between these two gases.

An even more remarkable fact is that catalysts may be 'poisoned' with respect to one reaction while retaining their activity with respect to other reactions. Vavon and Huson† found that the hydrogenation

* Proc. Roy. Soc., A, 1925, **108**, 105.   † Compt. Rend., 1922, **175**, 277.

of propyl ketone in presence of colloidal platinum was inhibited by amounts of carbon disulphide insufficient to prevent the hydrogenation of piperonal and nitrobenzene. Further amounts of carbon disulphide stopped the hydrogenation of piperonal but not that of nitrobenzene.

Another instance of the same curious phenomenon can be cited. Hydrogen has a most pronounced inhibiting effect on the thermal decomposition of ammonia at the surface of a heated platinum wire. On the other hand, it is found to be almost without influence on the decomposition of hydrogen iodide on the surface of the same wire, and actually at a lower temperature. This cannot be explained by the assumption that the hydrogen iodide displaces the hydrogen while the ammonia is unable to do so, for the decomposition of hydrogen iodide is of the first order under these circumstances, and this indicates that its adsorption is but small. Similarly, carbon dioxide has practically no effect on the rate of decomposition of nitrous oxide in contact with platinum, but can exert a very pronounced inhibiting action on the water-gas reaction.

The observation of Burk has already been mentioned, namely, that the rate of decomposition of ammonia on molybdenum, although reduced by the presence of nitrogen, does not approach zero as the surface becomes saturated with nitrogen. This is easily interpreted in terms of the theory of centres of different activity; but there is also the possibility that the nitrogen film itself has some catalytic activity. The possibility that unimolecular gas films on surfaces may themselves be the catalysts in certain reactions should not be ignored, and in many examples would provide an alternative to the hypothesis of non-uniformity of the surface. But the cumulative evidence for this latter assumption is strong.

Maxted and Lewis,* however, find no evidence from a quantitative study of the poisoning of platinum by mercury ions that its catalytic surface is other than uniform in the decomposition of hydrogen peroxide. In particular, the activation energy is independent of the amount of poison over a considerable range: this would not be expected if centres of varying activity were progressively poisoned.

A further detailed study of the energetic homogeneity of various surfaces for various reactions was also made by Maxted and others, the results indicating a greater degree of uniformity than might have been expected.†

* J. Chem. Soc., 1933, 502.
† Maxted and Stone, ibid., 1934, 26, 672; Maxted and Moon, ibid., 1935, 393, 1190; 1936, 635.

Turning now to evidence from a different field of observation, the heat of adsorption of oxygen by charcoal was found by Garner and Blench* to be as much as 220,000 calories for the first amounts of oxygen taken up, and less for subsequent amounts. The initial value is very much greater than the heat of combustion of solid carbon. Since solid carbon has a very great latent heat of vaporization, the heat of combustion of gaseous carbon is very great. Thus those carbon atoms which adsorb the first traces of oxygen are apparently in a state half-way between that of solid carbon and that of vaporized carbon. This seems to agree with Taylor's picture of a surface with atoms in varying degrees of saturation.

In some reactions the relative degrees of adsorption of different gases which have to be postulated for the purpose of interpreting the kinetics of the reactions seem to bear no relation to the measured degrees of adsorption on the surface as a whole.

These various observations, revealing the potential complexity of at least some catalytic surfaces, do not render necessary any appreciable modification of what we have said about the actual kinetics of hetero-geneous reactions. There is, moreover, no reason why sometimes the whole surface may not be uniformly active. In the general case, how-ever, we must be prepared to recognize that, even in respect of one given reaction, a surface may present centres of various degrees of activeness. The kinetics of a reaction taking place on such a surface would be almost the same as on a surface of uniform structure, except that the quantitative relations between reaction rate and pressure would not be so clear-cut. Since, however, the simple formulae derived from theory seldom apply with complete numerical exactness, this does not really introduce anything new.

The actual spacing of the atoms in the solid catalyst has a very pronounced influence on the catalytic activity.† The evidence for this is of two kinds.

Adkins and Nissen,‡ for example, found that alumina prepared in different ways exhibited very varying catalytic activity towards the decomposition of formic acid. This could hardly be due simply to the different surface areas of the several preparations, since the variation was not confined to the total speed of reaction but affected also the relative speeds of the two alternative decompositions which formic acid

* J. Chem. Soc., 1924, 125, 1288.

† Langmuir, Trans. Faraday Soc., 1922, 17, 607; W. C. McC. Lewis, ibid., 661; Bunn, Proc. Roy. Soc., A, 1933, 141, 567.

‡ J. Amer. Chem. Soc., 1923, 45, 809.

undergoes. Moreover, the apparent heats of activation varied from one kind of alumina to another.

They found analogous results for the catalytic reactions of various alcohols and esters on surfaces of material prepared in different ways.*

Palmer and Constable† found that the catalytic activity of copper towards the dehydrogenation of alcohols depended upon the temperature at which the copper had been reduced from its oxide in preparation, and that the heat of activation likewise depended on the method of reduction of the copper.

The activity of many catalysts increases with the number of times that they have been used to bring about a given reaction. There is no absolutely conclusive proof that this is not due to an actual increase in the total surface, but in certain instances it is so pronounced and happens so quickly that it seems more easily attributable to a change in the configuration of the surface.

Rather closely connected with this question of surface configuration is that of the so-called 'promoter action'.‡ The essential fact about this phenomenon is that a composite surface may possess catalytic properties of which the constituents are quite devoid. If a metal M forms a solid solution with another metal N, then at the interface M/N the forces exerted on an adsorbed molecule will be quite different from those which are exerted on a molecule adsorbed on either M or N separately.

Thus far attention has been given to the nature and spacing of the points on the surface to which the molecules of the adsorbed substance attach themselves. We will now regard the matter in the light of a principle of great importance, namely, the orientation of molecules in surface layers.

The effect of orientation is illustrated in an interesting manner by some experiments of Palmer and Constable§ on the rate of dehydrogenation of alcohols in presence of metallic copper. Primary alcohols appear to be adsorbed with the —CH_2OH group attached to the catalyst. The hydrogen is lost from this group in the chemical change, so that it appears reasonable to suppose that this is the portion of the molecule which must be activated. The hydrocarbon chain, therefore, would not be expected to have much influence on the process, and it was indeed found by experiment that the rates of reaction of five

* J. Amer. Chem. Soc., 1924, **46**, 130.   † Proc. Roy. Soc., A, 1924, **106**, 250.

‡ Compare Taylor, J. Physical Chem., 1924, **28**, 915 (other references there); Hurst and Rideal, J. Chem. Soc., 1924, **125**, 685; Griffith, Contact Catalysis, Oxford, 1936.

§ Proc. Roy. Soc., A, 1925, **107**, 255.

primary alcohols are equal. Moreover, the temperature coefficients of the reaction velocity are also equal.

Burk* has laid much stress on the possibility that a molecule might be attached to a surface at more than one point, whereby a distortion, or partial separation of its atoms, is produced. Ammonia, for example, might be held to the surface of a metal by a hydrogen atom and a nitrogen atom simultaneously. Such a distortion is thought of as lowering the heat of activation and facilitating decomposition. This idea has been developed by Balandin into a theory of 'multiplet' adsorption.†

The orientation of molecules at interfaces is closely connected with the phenomenon of boundary potential differences. To quote from Hardy,‡ the interfacial region 'has a configuration or structure which is intrinsically unstable at the given temperature and pressure, and acquires stability only by the intervention of the forces at the interface. Moreover, the (boundary) phase is the seat of an electric field of prodigious intensity'. This is a principle which cannot be ignored in relation to chemical transformations at catalytically active surfaces.

It is connected, on the one hand, with the view that adsorption is governed to a great extent by the 'dipole' character of the adsorbed substance, and, on the other hand, with the theory that there is a close relationship between chemical change and ionization. With regard to the first, the balance of evidence seems to show that dipole forces are not of primary importance in determining adsorption.§ Finch and Stimson,‖ following up some earlier work of H. Hartley,** have shown that gases such as oxygen, hydrogen, carbon monoxide, carbon dioxide, and steam impart electrical charges to hot metal surfaces. But whether or not the charged molecules adsorbed on the surface have any connexion with chemically active molecules, or whether the thermionic phenomena are quite independent, is hard to say. The answer given to this question would probably depend upon the attitude adopted to the more general question of the relation between ionization and chemical reaction. On the whole it is probable that the connexion is not an essential one.

It must not be forgotten that a purely 'chemical' view of surface action has its advantages. If we regard molecules of hydrogen, adsorbed on the surface of an active nickel catalyst, as held by single valency

---

* Burk and Gillespie, *Proc. Nat. Acad. Sci.*, 1928, **14**, 470.

† For references to this work and a summary see J. C. W. Frazer, 'Eighth Report of the Committee on Contact Catalysis', *J. Physical Chem.*, 1930, **34**, 2129.

‡ 'Chemistry at Interfaces', *J. Chem. Soc.*, 1925, **127**, 1207.

§ Cf. Polanyi, *Trans. Faraday Soc.*, 1932, **28**, 316 (Adsorption Discussion).

‖ *Proc. Roy. Soc.*, A, 1927, **116**, 379.   ** Ibid., A, 1914, **90**, 61.

bonds to the atoms of nickel we are already taking a very definitely chemical view of the matter. The system we are considering differs from a hydride of nickel only in that the nickel remains attached to the surface instead of being carried away into the gas phase. Under these circumstances we can only expect catalytic phenomena to be of an extremely specific nature.

At this stage the question of 'activated adsorption' comes to the fore. In this one of the energetically most important steps in the whole chemical reaction is the initial association of one of the reacting substances with the adsorbent. Here, very definitely, we have an approximation to the formation of a sort of two-dimensional intermediate compound.

Langmuir pointed out that the adsorption of such gases as oxygen and hydrogen by metals is probably accompanied by the resolution of the molecules into atoms. This production of atoms naturally has the effect of enhancing the reactiveness of the gases. It also renders possible the occurrence of such reactions as $N_2O = N_2 + O$ (ads.) or $N_2O + O$ (ads.) $= N_2 + O_2$, which provide mechanisms with lower activation energy than the homogeneous collision reactions. It should be mentioned that the experiments of Gauger,[*] Wolfenden,[†] and Kistiakowsky[‡] on the critical potentials of adsorbed hydrogen and nitrogen seem to provide direct evidence that these gases are taken up by metal surfaces in the atomic form.

In the exploration of the question of the part played by dissociation mechanisms in heterogeneous reactions—and analogy with homogeneous reactions, where atomic and radical mechanisms have proved to be common, would lead one to expect this part to be an important one—the use of para-hydrogen and of deuterium has been of great help.[§] By measurement of the relative ease of para-hydrogen conversion and of hydrogenation of a substrate, or by the observation of the relative ease of para conversion and of deuterium-hydrogen exchange, evidence can often be obtained about the rate determining steps in catalytic processes. For the catalytic exchange between deuterium and ammonia the following two schemes have been suggested:

$D_2 = D + D$	$D_2 = D + D$
$D + NH_3 = NH_2D + H$	$NH_3 = NH_2 + H$
$H + D = HD$	$D + NH_2 = NH_2D$
	$H + D = HD$

* J. Amer. Chem. Soc., 1924, **46**, 674.   † Proc. Roy. Soc., A, 1926, **110**, 464.
‡ J. Physical Chem., 1926, **30**, 1356.
§ See Melville, Ann. Rep. Chem. Soc., 1938, 70.

The rate of the ortho-deuterium conversion being much greater than that of the exchange reaction, it follows that there will always be D atoms available and that the D_2 dissociation is not the rate-determining step. Farkas has given evidence that the process goes by way of the ammonia dissociation.

In spite of the specific nature of catalytic phenomena it is difficult not to form the impression—although this *may* be illusory—that homogeneous reactions in general take place much less readily than surface reactions, and the question always obtrudes itself whether the operation of some general cause is not superimposed on the various specific influences.

When two or more molecules must interact, their encounter is obviously facilitated by a more or less prolonged sojourn of one of them on a surface. It is not difficult to believe that adsorption in adjacent positions on a surface comes about more often than an appropriate encounter of the molecules moving at random in the free state. Born and Weisskopf* developed this view of the matter still further in a quantum-mechanical theory of surface catalysis. The idea underlying their theory can be illustrated by an analogy. In a homogeneous collision reaction two molecules must meet possessing the energy of activation; quantum-mechanically there is a finite probability of transformation whether they possess this energy or not. But during the short time of a collision the probability is vanishingly small unless the energy is practically equal to or greater than the activation energy. When adsorbed on a surface the sojourn of molecules in proximity to one another is long enough for the probability of transformation to attain a finite value. The theory is thus a combination of the old chemical idea that the surface keeps in proximity molecules which otherwise would have little opportunity to react, and the principle underlying the Gamow theory of radioactive change with its extensions to the spontaneous chemical changes in molecules. Born and Weisskopf took an idealized picture of a molecular rearrangement, namely, two mass points acting on each other with forces and capable of existing in two positions of stable equilibrium at different separations. Thus there will be two sets of states corresponding to various energy levels of the initial and final products of the quasi-chemical rearrangement. If there were no interaction between the two sets of states the Schrödinger equations for them would be independent, but a perturbation term is introduced on account of the mutual potential energy of the

* *Z. physikal. Chem.*, B, 1931, **12**, 206.

atoms and the crystal surface on which they are assumed to be adsorbed. When there are two energy levels, one in the initial set and one in the final set, which correspond, transition by quantum-mechanical resonance occurs. The exact correspondence of energy would be extremely unlikely without the crystal surface, which may act in one of two ways. It either takes up itself the difference between the two energies, or it makes the transition possible in virtue of the strong and variable mutual potential energy between atoms and surface. A rather elaborate calculation leads to the result that the probability of transition depends very markedly on the displacement which the atoms have to suffer in the process. If this is of the order of 0.5 Å. it appears that the transformation can occur in a few seconds. Born and Weisskopf remark that this picture of adsorption catalysis is not the only possible one: 'lowering of the energy threshold, resolution of chemical linkages under the influence of the adsorption forces, intermediate reactions with the atoms of the surface, etc., may be essential factors.' The experimental evidence does indeed seem to show that all these factors, and especially the first, are in fact of great importance. How much room this leaves for the operation of the quantum-mechanical leakage phenomenon is a difficult question. Up to date specifically quantum-mechanical theories have not proved of great help.

This brings us back once again to the possibility that the appearance of a general reduction in molecular stability accompanying adsorption on surfaces is illusory, and that the stability of molecules is increased as often as it is diminished. When the stability happens to be increased or the reactivity diminished, naturally no effect is observed. That some heterogeneous catalyst can be found for almost any reaction is perhaps only in accordance with probability. From the nature of the case it is only those examples where positive specific influences exist which are noted and which contribute to the impression of a general influence. If the specific influences alone are operative, further progress depends upon the solution of the wider problem of the general relation between mode of chemical union and properties. In the meantime, by empirical means, a special inorganic and organic chemistry of interfaces is being built up.

IX

SOME GENERAL ASPECTS OF CHEMICAL KINETICS

In this chapter we shall deal with some very general aspects of chemical kinetics: attention will no longer be confined to the gaseous state. Indeed part of the discussion will bear upon the relation of gas reactions to reactions in the condensed phase. In many respects the differences between them are not fundamental. This being so, certain general matters are now conveniently illustrated by examples taken from among the greater abundance of material relating to reactions in solution.

The first matter to be considered is the light which the statistical mechanical theory of equilibrium can throw on problems of reaction velocity.

The Transition State Method of expressing Reaction Rates.

In a chemical reaction there must be a stage at which the identity of the initial substances is just merging into that of the products. This is called the transition state. To define it fully we, naturally, must specify the energy of the system and the configuration of all the atoms constituting it. Geometrically and dynamically there are two equivalent ways of doing this. First, we may bring the reacting molecules up to a defined distance from one another, orientate them correctly, and stretch or compress any linkages as required; we also specify the total energy and any conditions about its distribution. This is equivalent to specifying the need for the appropriate encounters, the activation energy, and the other geometrical and energetic conditions which must be fulfilled. If these factors are all known we can calculate the reaction rate from an equation of the form $PZe^{-E/RT}$.

Secondly, instead of specifying what we do to the reacting molecules to bring them into the transition state, we may suppose the transition state to be attained already and specify its properties as though it were a molecule with an independent existence. Unless, of course, the result of the two specifications is the same, a mistake must have been made in one or the other, because there is no difference except in the order in which the descriptions have been made.

Regarding the transition complex as a molecule, we may use the general statistical mechanical result (page 34) to write down the equilibrium constant

$$K = \frac{\text{concentration of transition complexes}}{\text{product of concentrations of reactants}}.$$

It is given by

$$K = \frac{\text{product of partition functions for active complex}}{\text{product of partition functions for reactants}} \times e^{-E/RT},$$

where E is the activation energy, which here corresponds to the energy of formation of the transition complex.

The rate of reaction must be proportional to this K, and the study of its form may be very illuminating from the kinetic point of view.

To find the multiplying factor which gives the absolute rate of reaction the following argument is used.* The transition complex is regarded as a molecule which is normal except in respect of one co-ordinate along which it suffers disruption into the products. This degree of freedom may be regarded as a weak vibration, the partition function for which is nearly enough given by $kT/h\nu$. This term is first factorized out of the expression for K given above. If we assume that the complex breaks up at the end of each vibration giving products, then the rate of formation of products is ν times the concentration of transition complexes.

Thus we have:

reaction rate constant

$$= \frac{\text{product of partition functions for active complex, omitting one}}{\text{product of partition functions for reactants}} \times \frac{kT}{h\nu} \times \nu e^{-E/RT},$$

$$k = \frac{\prod (f_A)}{\prod (f_{\text{reactants}})} \times \frac{kT}{h} \times e^{-E/RT}$$

This assumes that all the transition complexes pass into products. For generality the above expression can be multiplied by what Eyring calls a transmission coefficient, which he takes as unity, and which Evans and Polanyi take as $\frac{1}{2}$. This assumption about the transmission coefficient is not really quite self-evident, and may not in general be true. One may, however, accept it tentatively.

If, now, we are in a position to write down the partition functions for the activated state, then, in principle, we can calculate the reaction velocity in absolute measure, just, of course, as we can if we are able to write down the collision number and multiply it by the chance of the appropriate orientations and internal conditions. Unfortunately we are seldom in a position to do either of these things. Nevertheless consideration of the above expression for the reaction rate is extremely illuminating, and especially so if it is taken in comparison with the collision formula. The ultimate identity of the two methods is shown

* Adapted from Eyring, *J. Chem. Physics*, 1935, **3**, 107; and Evans and Polanyi, *Trans. Faraday Soc.*, 1935, **31**, 875.

by the calculation already given on page 35, where a method practically the same as the transition state method is used to calculate the collision number itself. But when two angles of approach to a problem are available, certain aspects are usually more clearly visible from the one than from the other, so that both are valuable.

Comparison of Two Methods of expressing Reaction Rate.

It is instructive to compare the calculation of a reaction velocity by the two methods in the simplest possible kind of bimolecular reaction, and then to see in what manner the difficulties increase as we pass from the simplest to more complex cases.

From the point of view of the kinetic theory, the simplest assumption that we can make is that the activation energy resides in two square terms, and that all the collisions with enough energy lead to reaction. This gives for the rate at unit concentration

$$\left\{8\pi kT\left(\frac{1}{m_A}+\frac{1}{m_B}\right)\right\}^{\frac{1}{2}}\sigma^2 e^{-E/RT}.$$

If we wish to make the calculation for more complex cases we must make assumptions about the number of degrees of freedom in which the activation energy resides, and about the orientations, and about the internal phases of the molecular motions, and so on. In general, we do not know what to assume about these, and all that we can do is to investigate whether they appear to change in the right direction when we pass from one example to another.

Turning now to the transition state method, we must write down K. For the transition complex we shall have a product of three translational partition functions, one rotational (three-dimensional) partition function, and a whole series of vibrational partition functions; for the reactants, we have a product of three translational partition functions for each molecule concerned, a rotational function for each, and a whole series of vibrational ones. In the simplest case, say the union of two atoms to form a molecule, the expression for the K reduces to the form $T_a^3 R_a/T^6$, where T_a^3 means a product of three translational partition functions for the activated state.

Putting in the values for the different kinds of partition function, and multiplying by kT/h and by $e^{-E/RT}$, we obtain for the rate

$$\frac{\dfrac{\{2\pi(m_A+m_B)kT\}^{\frac{3}{2}}}{h^3}\dfrac{8\pi^2 IkT}{h^2}\dfrac{kT}{h}}{\dfrac{(2\pi m_A kT)^{\frac{3}{2}}}{h^3}\dfrac{(2\pi m_B kT)^{\frac{3}{2}}}{h^3}}e^{-E/RT}.$$

We must now put in the value for the moment of inertia. If this is written as $\mu\sigma^2$, where σ is the sum of the normal radii of the reactants, then we have made an assumption not very different from that of the simple kinetic theory. If we wish to assume a very different value, then we are doing something which must be equivalent to making the assumption of an abnormal target area in the kinetic theory. In one method, as in the other, it is difficult to know what value we should take, if for any reason we believe the normal one to be inadmissible. There will be, of course, small differences according to whether we take σ to be the diameter of the product or that of the unchanged pair of reactants, but it is no exaggeration to say that the difference is well within the limits of the other uncertainties. Taking σ as the normal value, we obtain for the rate the expression

$$(8\pi kT)^{\frac{1}{2}}\left(\frac{m_A+m_B}{m_A m_B}\right)^{\frac{3}{2}} I e^{-E/RT}.$$

Since $I = \dfrac{m_A m_B}{m_A+m_B}\sigma^2$, this becomes

$$\left\{8\pi kT\left(\frac{1}{m_A}+\frac{1}{m_B}\right)\right\}^{\frac{1}{2}}\sigma^2 e^{-E/RT},$$

which, of course, agrees with that obtained the other way.

In more complicated cases the partition products do not reduce to the simple form. We obtain products involving a number of vibrational and rotational partition functions for the activated state divided by a similar product for the reactants. The closer study of these products reveals several interesting things. If we are dealing with an association reaction* there will be a number of vibrational partition functions for the activated state divided by rotational functions for the reactants. It will be convenient to compare K for a reaction involving the union of two complex molecules, with the value K_a for the union of two atoms to form a diatomic molecule.* K will contain three translational partition functions, a three-dimensional rotational, and n vibrational partition functions for the active transition complex of the two reactants, divided by six translational, two three-dimensional rotational, and l vibrational partition functions for the two separate reactants. We may represent this symbolically by $T^3 R^3 V^n/T^6 R^6 V^l$. Since the total number of degrees of freedom before and after union of the reactant molecules to the complex must be the same, $l = n-6$. K_a, on the other hand, will contain T^3 and R^2 and V for the diatomic molecule,

* Bawn, *Trans. Faraday Soc.*, 1935, **31**, 1536.

divided merely by T^6 for the two atoms, giving T^3R^2V/T^6. (We are not formulating one of the vibrations here as a translation along a coordinate in which decomposition occurs: this is unnecessary, since the corresponding terms will cancel in the ratio K/K_a.) If the energies of activation are equal for the two kinds of reaction under consideration, K/K_a becomes of the form V^5/R^5, i.e. a product of five one-dimensional vibration functions divided by a three-dimensional and a two-dimensional rotation function. The vibrational functions are those of the new vibrational degrees of freedom which come into being when half the translations and rotations of the reacting molecules lose their individuality in the complex. If $h\nu$ is fairly small, V reduces to the form $kT/h\nu$; R, apart from a small numerical factor, is $\sqrt{(2\pi IkT)}/h$. Bawn (loc. cit.), taking $kT/h\nu$ as equal to unity for each of the V terms, and all the moments of inertia to be 10^{-39}, shows that V^5/R^5 may be very small. Thus, if P were unity for the atomic reaction, it would be very small for the reaction of the complex molecules.

The kinetic interpretation of this is clearly that in an association reaction rotational degrees of freedom disappear and new linkages appear with associated vibrations, and that this process can only take place when the mutual orientations of the reactants are suitable, and when the relative motions of various atoms are also suitable for the creation of the new bonds. As regards the possibility of making quantitative calculations, from the kinetic point of view it is evident at once that to specify the orientations and phases correctly is a very difficult task. To write down the appropriate partition functions may sound formally a matter capable of treatment with greater precision. But this can hardly be true in actual practice. The vibrational partition function depends upon the frequency of the vibration in question, and can easily vary by one or two powers of 10. A product of several can thus vary by many powers of 10. The value of the frequency depends upon the strength of the binding, and precisely in an activated complex, where some bonds are being broken and others formed, we are likely to be very much in the dark as to the appropriate values to take. It is probably not unfair to say that our chances of writing down the correct values of the partition functions are about the same as those of specifying the orientations and phases correctly. On the other hand, the 'resistance' to reaction, which the disappearance of the rotations offers, is very clearly and elegantly emphasized in the statistical formulae.

Eyring has calculated the rate of the reaction $2NO + O_2 = 2NO_2$, but, interesting as the calculation is, it would seem that the assumptions made about the properties of the transition complex are somewhat *ad hoc* and would be difficult to justify except in relation to the final result. It must be remembered that there is much latitude in specifying the degrees of freedom and partition functions of the transition complex and that there is an elasticity of many powers of 10 in the results obtainable. Therefore it would perhaps be best to regard the method as one for exploring by trial and error the properties of the transition state itself. For this the method is obviously invaluable, and it will be interesting to build up an extensive empirical knowledge of such properties. But the absolute prediction of rates, except in the simplest examples, is usually too detailed a task for present knowledge.

The transition state method further possesses the merit of focusing attention on the relation between velocity problems and equilibrium problems, which is often helpful. An example will appear in the course of the present chapter.

Entropy and Free Energy of Activation.

The activation energy E may be regarded as the energy increase accompanying the process of conversion from the normal to the transition state, and if we envisage an equilibrium between the two states, then it plays the part of the quantity ΔU of the conventional thermodynamic formulae.

We may write, therefore, $E = \Delta U_a$, so that

$$k = A e^{-\Delta U_a/RT} = e^B e^{-\Delta U_a/RT}$$

In thermodynamics we have the well-known relation

$$\Delta F = \Delta U - T \Delta S,$$

where ΔF is the change of free energy and ΔS that of entropy.

Putting $e^B = e^{\Delta S_a/R}$,

$$k = e^{-(\Delta U_a - T \Delta S_a)/RT} = e^{-\Delta F_a/RT}.$$

Thus $$\Delta F_a = -RT \ln k.$$

These equations relate formally the logarithm of the velocity constant to a *free energy of activation*, and the logarithm of the temperature-independent factor of the Arrhenius equation to an *entropy of activation*. The latter term calls attention once more to the connexion between entropy and probability. A reaction in which A ($= PZ$) is small can be said to involve improbable processes, or, alternatively, it can be said that activation is attended by a large decrease in entropy. It is a matter of taste which mode of expression is employed.

Confusion may arise from the idea that the constant A of the Arrhenius equation is temperature-independent, while entropy, like other thermodynamic quantities, is in general a function of temperature. The fact is that A and E both vary slowly with temperature: and that the Arrhenius equation is an approximation. In this same approximation, which in practice is rather a good one (pages 43, 44, 55), the entropy is also constant.

Chemical Reactions in the Different States of Matter.

In gases the molecules move freely about space, and except during collisions are practically free from external influences. The part played by collisions in chemical changes has been abundantly illustrated in earlier chapters: molecules may react in the collision itself, or they may emerge from the collision in such a condition that they are transformed after an internal evolution of some kind. When they are adsorbed on solid surfaces they suffer profound modifications of reactivity. It remains to inquire what happens when they themselves become part of liquid or solid phases.

As a preliminary to this it will be well to consider what catalytic influences are exerted by foreign molecules in gas reactions themselves. On the whole it may be said that these influences fall under two headings: those depending upon the direct communication of activation energy to the reacting molecules, and those, much more marked, but also rarer, where a profound specific interaction of some kind leads to a complete change of reaction mechanism.

Homogeneous Catalysis of Gaseous Reactions.*

(a) Introduction.

Ostwald compared the action of a catalyst to that of a lubricant. In employing this simile he was emphasizing the fact that a catalyst present in small quantity does not change the position of thermodynamic equilibrium, or modify the total heat of reaction. The essential fact was that the catalyst acted in some other way than by contributing energy. But the metaphor proved unfortunate, because it suggested that catalytic reactions have the same inner mechanism as the corresponding uncatalysed reactions, and that all that the catalyst does is in some way to multiply the velocity constant by a greater or smaller factor, leaving the other kinetic relationships unchanged. The decomposition of acetaldehyde, under appropriate conditions, occurs at a rate

* Cf. *J. Chem. Soc.*, 1939, 1203.

determined by activating collisions among the aldehyde molecules themselves. The reaction is strongly catalysed by a little iodine. The lubrication metaphor suggests that the fundamental mechanism will be unchanged, but that the velocity constant will be much greater. In fact, however, the catalysed reaction follows a quite different kinetic equation and depends upon an entirely different mechanism.

We might indeed define catalysis as the operation of any mechanism which provides an alternative reaction path by which the same products can be produced more rapidly.

The whole evidence of chemical kinetics shows that the most important single factor determining the rate of a chemical reaction is usually the magnitude of the energy of activation. If the alternative mechanism which becomes possible in the presence of the catalyst is associated with a smaller energy of activation, then an acceleration of the chemical change will be observed. While it is by no means the only one, the lowering of the energy of activation by the catalyst proves to be perhaps the most important factor in catalysis. From the kinetic point of view, the lubrication metaphor would be better replaced by one in which the catalyst is likened to a by-pass road with easier gradients.

(b) *Influence of Homogeneous Catalysts on the Heat of Activation and on the Position of Equilibrium.*

Thermodynamically the heats of activation of the direct and inverse reactions in a balanced change must be related to the heat of reaction by the equation $$E_1 - E_2 = Q.$$

The separate values bear, however, no general relation to Q.

Unless a catalyst actually combines with an appreciable amount of one of the substances present it can have no influence on the position of equilibrium in a reversible reaction. When the change $AB \rightleftharpoons A + B$ has reached equilibrium the product

$$\frac{[AB]}{[A][B]}$$

is constant at a given temperature and entirely independent of the mechanism by which equilibrium is established. Otherwise it would be possible to circumvent the second law of thermodynamics.

Certain supposed shifts of equilibrium are all attributable to an actual finite alteration in the concentration of one or more of the substances, owing to combination with the catalyst. If this alteration is

R

not taken into account, incorrect values of the concentrations are used in the expression for K, which then appears to be changed.

So many different catalytic mechanisms are possible that the kinetic interpretation of this simple thermodynamical result is rather complex, but the general principle is easily illustrated. Suppose the reaction $AB \to A+B$ is accelerated by a homogeneous catalyst, which forms a complex with the molecule AB. The reaction would be accelerated if the molecular compound $AB.C$ had a much lower energy of activation for the change $AB.C \to A+B+C$ than the molecule AB had for the simple decomposition.

Let the energy of activation of the simple reaction be E_1 and that of the catalysed reaction be (E_1-e_1). Now at equal concentrations the complexes will decompose more rapidly than the molecules of AB in the ratio

$$e^{-(E_1-e_1)/RT} / e^{-E_1/RT}$$

which equals $e^{e_1/RT}$.

Now, it is important to remember that the activated state of AB is identical with the activated state of $(A+B)$ in collision, the reactant and the products being probably indistinguishable in the condition corresponding to activation. Hence if activated AB molecules are capable of being attached to C molecules, the colliding complex of $A+B$ is also capable of being so held. Moreover, the activated systems have equal chances of meeting molecules of C, whether they are formed from AB molecules or by the collision of A and B.

Further, if E_2 be the energy of activation of the uncatalysed reaction $A+B \to AB$, and that of the catalysed reaction be (E_2-e_2), then, since $E_1-E_2 = Q$ and $(E_1-e_1)-(E_2-e_2) = Q$ also, it follows that e_1 is equal to e_2.

Thus, for equal concentrations the catalysed reaction is accelerated in the same ratio $e^{e_1/RT}$ as the direct reaction. The equilibrium position is thus unaltered. Other more complex mechanisms may be analysed in the same way.

When the 'catalyst' is present in the form of a complete atmosphere of solvent true shifts of equilibrium can occur, since the reacting molecules are the whole time under the influence of the catalyst molecules, and have virtually become new species.

(c) Some Examples of Catalysed Reactions.

That a foreign gas should exert a catalytic influence is on the whole the exception rather than the rule. For example, oxygen and nitrogen do not seriously influence the rate of decomposition of chlorine monoxide. The same general lack of marked influence is revealed by the failure of most gases to be of much assistance in communicating the activation energy to molecules in unimolecular reactions of complex molecules: the specific effect of hydrogen in these examples is not quite unique, being exerted also by ethane and occasionally other gases in appropriate circumstances, but such effects are exceptional.

Helium, nitrogen, carbon dioxide, and other gases accelerate the decomposition of nitrous oxide, but rather large amounts are necessary to produce a marked effect: their action appears simply to consist in the communication of the activation energy to the molecules of nitrous oxide. A similar influence of foreign gases is found in the decomposition of the fluorine oxides, F_2O_2* and F_2O.† The decomposition of acetaldehyde is hardly influenced by nitrogen, carbon dioxide, or ethylene, but is accelerated by hydrogen.

Some remarkable catalytic influences are exerted by iodine. It accelerates the decomposition of acetaldehyde many hundred times.

The type of decomposition which occurs here is a rather general one.‡ It was first discovered in connexion with the catalytic decomposition of isopropyl ether under the influence of iodine. The chemical change involved is of the type:

$$\begin{array}{c}CH_3 \\ \diagdown \\ CH_3 \diagup \end{array}CH \cdot O \cdot CH \begin{array}{c} CH_3 \\ \diagdown \\ \diagup CH_3 \end{array} \longrightarrow \begin{array}{c}CH_3 \\ \diagdown \\ CH_3 \diagup \end{array}CO + \begin{array}{c}CH_3 \\ \diagdown \\ \diagup CH_3 \end{array}CH_2.$$

It is interesting to note that all these reactions depend upon the transfer of a hydrogen atom, and the mechanism seems to be that the hydrogen is bodily removed from the molecule by the iodine, a cycle of changes occurring of which the following is typical:

$$CH_3CHO + I_2 = CH_3I + HI + CO,$$
$$CH_3I + HI = CH_4 + I_2,$$

i.e.
$$CH_3CHO + I_2 = CH_4 + CO + I_2.$$

The concentration of iodine has been shown to fall during the reaction and then rise again to its original value.§

Iodine also exerts a remarkable catalytic influence on the decomposition of nitrous oxide. Chlorine and bromine exert similar influences.‖

---

* Frisch and Schumacher, *Z. physikal. Chem.*, B, 1937, **37**, 18.

† Koblitz and Schumacher, ibid., B, 1934, **25**, 283.

‡ Hinshelwood, Clusius, and Hadman, *Proc. Roy. Soc.*, A, 1930, **128**, 88; Glass and Hinshelwood, *J. Chem. Soc.*, 1929, 1815; Clusius and Hinshelwood, *Proc. Roy. Soc.*, A, 1930, **128**, 82; Clusius, *J. Chem. Soc.*, 1930, 2607.

§ Faull and Rollefson, *J. Amer. Chem. Soc.*, 1936, **58**, 1755.

‖ Musgrave and Hinshelwood, *Proc. Roy. Soc.*, A, 1932, **137**. 25.

These reactions differ considerably from the catalytic decompositions of the aldehydes and ethers. There is evidence that the halogen atom rather than the molecule is the effective catalyst. For equal total concentrations iodine is very much more effective than chlorine or bromine, but if allowance is made for the different degrees of dissociation the divergences between the three halogens largely disappear.

The oxygen atom of the nitrous oxide is probably removed as a halogen oxide, which, of course, does not need to be stable enough to survive any collisions beyond the one in which it is formed.

Nitric oxide catalyses the decomposition of nitrous oxide:* over a fair range the rate of the reaction is proportional to $[N_2O][NO]$. The catalytic collisions, however, are only about eight times as effective as normal collisions between nitrous oxide molecules. It is not impossible that we have here an example of intermediate reactions thus:

$$N_2O+NO = N_2+NO_2 \quad \text{followed by} \quad 2NO_2 = 2NO+O_2.$$

Other catalytic actions of nitric oxide are known, e.g. on the decomposition of chloral.

If a catalytic agent makes possible a reaction possessing an energy of activation ΔE smaller than that of the uncatalysed change, then, other things being equal, the new reaction is faster in the ratio $e^{\Delta E/RT}$. It may be of interest to collect together a few examples of direct experimental evidence that modification of the heat of activation is one very important factor in catalytic phenomena.

The mechanism of the catalytic reaction being usually different from that of the uncatalysed reaction, only qualitative comparisons are possible in general. Nevertheless the marked reduction in E is evident in the following examples of iodine-catalysed decompositions:

Decomposition of	$C_3H_7 \cdot O \cdot C_3H_7$	$C_2H_5 \cdot O \cdot C_2H_5$	CH_3CHO	$CH_3 \cdot O \cdot C_2H_5$
$E_{uncatalysed}$	60,500	53,500	45,500	47,000
$E_{catalysed}$	28,500	34,300	32,500	38,000

In the catalytic decomposition of nitrous oxide by halogens the heats of activation vary round about 49,000 calories, a value considerably lower than that for the uncatalysed reaction, and here again the catalysis is undoubtedly accompanied by a profound change of mechanism. The decomposition of chloral is catalysed by nitric oxide, the activation energy being reduced from 49,000 to 37,000 calories.† Whether this is a case of activating collisions between CCl_3CHO and NO or whether the nitric oxide acts by extracting the H atom bodily from the chloral is not definitely known.

---

* Ibid., A, 1932, **135**, 23.   † Verhoek, *Trans. Faraday Soc.*, 1935, **31**, 1521.

(d) The Influence of Moisture on Chemical Change.

Examples have not infrequently been found of reactions which involve the intervention of some impurity in the system, not at first imagined to be playing any part in the chemical change. For example, the rate of decomposition of hydrogen peroxide in aqueous solution is very variable, and Rice and Kilpatrick* traced the cause of this behaviour to the fact that the decomposition is mainly determined by the catalytic action of dust particles. As a result, the view has sometimes been held that pure substances are in general very unreactive, and that velocity measurements have no absolute significance, because the reaction mechanism is quite different from what it appears to be and involves the participation of accidental impurities. Among such impurities water occupies the most prominent position.

The phenomena attending the complete desiccation of chemical systems, interesting and important as they may be, can, however, be regarded in a quite exaggerated perspective. The objections to the view that moisture, or indeed 'impurities', are necessary to chemical change in general, or that the rate of chemical reactions is determined by the rate at which molecules can come into association with such catalysts, can be summarized as follows.

Where the rate of reaction depends upon the presence of an accidental catalyst, measurements are characterized by great lack of reproducibility. Most homogeneous reactions, on the other hand, have quite definite and reproducible rates.

The general coherence of the whole picture of chemical reactions which can be constructed without the aid of such an hypothesis makes it superfluous.

Finally, the insufficiency of any positive evidence for the hypothesis has to be admitted. Most of the reactions where, for example, inhibition by drying has been described are kinetically of a fundamentally different type from the homogeneous reactions we have been considering. No specific claim has ever been made to have retarded by drying more than a negligible proportion of the reactions described in this book. Of the examples where inhibition by drying has been reported the great majority are interactions between substances in two different phases, where the great influence of an adsorbed film in poisoning or promoting the activity of a boundary surface, or of nuclei, can be understood. Some others, which might at first sight appear to be homogeneous reactions, are really heterogeneous, as, for example, the

* J. Physical Chem., 1927, **31**, 1507.

union of ethylene and bromine, where the 'polar' nature of the surface is known to be of great influence. Retardation of such reactions by drying is an interesting and important fact, but not one upon which generalizations about homogeneous reactions should be based. Apart from the photochemical reaction between hydrogen and chlorine, the only reaction on which normal velocity measurements have been made, and which is said to have been retarded by drying, is the union of nitric oxide and oxygen.* But this is equally definitely stated to proceed just as well in the absence of water.†

Many phenomena which look like the operation of homogeneous catalysis are really nothing of the kind. The characteristic reactions of atomic hydrogen only appear in the presence of water vapour, which might seem to show that water catalysed the formation. Wood, however, has definitely shown that the action of the water is to 'poison' the walls of the discharge tube, which otherwise cause an immediate catalytic recombination of the atoms. Similar imitation of catalytic effects is found with active nitrogen, where the presence of electro-negative impurities appears to catalyse the formation, but in reality stabilizes the active product in a quite indirect way.

It is perhaps desirable to consider briefly what bearing, if any, the experiments on 'dry liquids' have on the matter. The fundamental experimental fact, stated without prejudging any theoretical issue, is that a liquid which has been sealed up with phosphorus pentoxide for a considerable time frequently will not give a rapid continuous stream of vapour unless it is heated to a considerably higher temperature than would have been necessary before the drying process. This means either that some inner equilibrium in the liquid has been displaced, or that the rate of evaporation from the liquid surface has been considerably lowered, rendering the liquid very liable to what is virtually super-heating.‡ On general theoretical grounds the latter alternative appears much more probable, since it is easy to understand that during the storage with phosphorus pentoxide either something (such as water or colloidal dust particles) is removed which would have facilitated evaporation, or that something (such as phosphorus pentoxide itself) is introduced which by concentrating itself in the surface layer impedes the free passage of molecules into the vapour phase. The former alternative would be very surprising from the thermodynamic standpoint,

* Baker, *J. Chem. Soc.*, 1894, 611.
† Briner, *J. Chim. Physique*, 1926, **23**, 848.
‡ Compare *inter alia* E. Cohen and W. A. T. Cohen de Meester, *Proc. K. Akad. Wetensch. Amsterdam*, 1930, **33**, 1003; S. Lenher, *J. Physical Chem.*, 1929, **33**, 1579.

since it would mean that a small quantity of a foreign substance produced a change in free energy of the system out of all proportion to
that produced by further additions. This would be extremely remarkable since thermodynamic functions in general are linear in the concentration for small additions. From a kinetic point of view it would
also be remarkable, since if a very small addition of water produced
a finite shift in equilibrium through the bulk of a liquid phase it would
mean that each water molecule exerted an influence far beyond the
range of ordinary molecular forces. J. W. Smith* studied the distillation of ethyl bromide from one evacuated bulb to another across a
constant temperature gradient, and found that the rate decreases considerably as the 'drying' of the liquid proceeds. The vapour pressure,
however, remained unaltered, and there was no evidence of any frac-
tionation of the dried liquid during distillation, such as would be
expected if a shift in an inner equilibrium had occurred. This observation is parallel to that of Rodebush and Michalek, who observed that
the rates of evaporation and of condensation of ammonium chloride
were diminished by a process of drying. The earlier observation of
Smith and Menzies that dry calomel had zero vapour pressure also
means that the rate of evaporation was zero under the conditions of
the experiment rather than that the equilibrium value had been reduced
to nought. There are two analogies, differing in principle, in terms of
which these various results may be explained. One is the apparent
zero value of the vapour pressure which would be found for slightly
contaminated mercury at ordinary temperatures, the other is the complete non-efflorescence of a perfect salt hydrate crystal in the absence
of nuclei. In any case it seems clear that the phenomena have no direct
connexion with those of homogeneous reaction kinetics.

It will be interesting to consider a few typical reactions where
inhibition by drying has actually been found.

The explosion of carbon monoxide and oxygen takes place much
more readily in the presence of moisture than in its absence.† Dixon
explained this by showing that the series of reactions

$$CO + H_2O = CO_2 + H_2$$
$$2H_2 + O_2 = 2H_2O$$

takes place more readily than the direct oxidation. It is now known
that the direct oxidation as well as the indirect oxidation of carbon
monoxide is possible, and actually predominates at high pressures.

* *J. Chem. Soc.*, 1931, 2573.   † Dixon, *Phil. Trans. Roy. Soc.*, 1884, **175**, 617.

The mechanism of the slow oxidation is rather complex and depends upon a chain reaction (page 169). In the presence of water additional chain processes become possible.

The union of hydrogen and chlorine under the influence of visible light has been said to be inhibited if the partial pressure of water vapour is reduced below 10^{-7} mm., while at all higher partial pressures of water vapour it proceeds normally. If this effect is real there are several possible explanations: either the water might form a catalytically active film over a surface, saturation of this film being complete at a very low partial pressure of the vapour; or the water might combine with some reactant, such as a chlorine atom in the hydrogen-chlorine combination, present in such small amount, and having such a long life, that all of it would be certain to meet with water molecules before being destroyed in any other way. This being so, the concentration of the water would only have an influence up to a certain point. If the chlorine atoms had to associate themselves with water in this way, their life, according to Chapman, would have to be about $\frac{1}{50}$ second.

Another way in which water might exert remarkable influence is by being concerned in the initiation of a chain reaction, which, once started, proceeds without further intervention of the water.

The union of hydrogen chloride and ammonia ordinarily takes place with immeasurable rapidity. When the gases are 'completely dry' they are said not to react at all. There is no stage of dryness at which a reaction with measurable velocity occurs. There does not appear to be agreement about the facts themselves: consequently their interpretation is difficult.

Solutions

(a) Reactions in Solution and in the Gaseous State.

The limiting case of foreign additions is the provision of a complete atmosphere of solvent. The decomposition of nitrogen pentoxide* has approximately the same rate and the same energy of activation in carbon tetrachloride, chloroform, and a series of similar solvents as in the gaseous phase at an equivalent concentration. But in certain solvents, nitric acid, for example, the rate and activation energies are different from the normal. The isomerization of pinene† takes place at the same rate in the gaseous and the pure liquid states. In the decomposition of chlorine monoxide‡ the activation energy for the gas

* Eyring and Daniels, *J. Amer. Chem. Soc.*, 1930, **52**, 1473.
† D. F. Smith, ibid., 1927, **49**, 43.
‡ Moelwyn-Hughes and Hinshelwood, *Proc. Roy. Soc.*, A, 1931, **131**, 177.

is 21,000 and for the solution in carbon tetrachloride 20,300, the rates being identical within the limits of experimental error. The ratio of rates for the interaction of ozone and chlorine* in carbon tetrachloride solution and the gas phase is about 1·5, the activation energy for the gas reaction being a little doubtful. The ortho-para hydrogen conversion† and the addition reactions of quinones and dienes‡ also have speeds of the same order both in the gas and in solution.

This rather varied series of reactions shows that there is nothing absolutely essential about the geometry or the mechanics of the liquid state which changes the order of magnitude of the reaction rate of substances dissolved. This result can be foreseen theoretically in a general way (page 17).§

Nevertheless the fact that reaction rates for a given set of reactants may vary a thousandfold with change of solvent shows that highly specific influences can also be at work. These should indeed be in evidence with the majority of reactions in solution, for, in general, a really inert solvent will refuse to dissolve any but the simplest molecules, solubility itself normally depending upon specific interactions of solvent and solute; and since we can only investigate reactions in media which will dissolve the reactants, we should expect to find these influences affecting the reaction rate.

A number of attempts have been made to investigate the kinetics in the gaseous phase of reactions which had previously been studied in solution. Examples of these are: the formation of quaternary ammonium salts,‖ the interaction of acetic anhydride and ethyl alcohol, the interaction of methyl alcohol and hydrogen chloride, the interaction of methyl alcohol and acetic acid,** and the acid-catalysed decompositions of certain organic compounds.††

In all of them the reaction proved to take place predominantly in an adsorbed layer on the wall of the vessel, that is to say, virtually in a two-dimensional solution.

Similarly the combination of ethylene and bromine in glass vessels takes place almost entirely on the walls:‡‡ when the walls are covered

* Bowen, Moelwyn-Hughes, and Hinshelwood, ibid., A, 1931, **134**, 211.
† Farkas and Sachsse, *Z. physikal. Chem.*, B, 1933, **23**, 1, 19.
‡ Wassermann, Benford, and Khambata, *Nature*, 1937, **139**, 669; Benford and Wassermann, *J. Chem. Soc.*, 1939, 362.
§ See also R. P. Bell, *Trans. Faraday Soc.*, 1939, **35**, 324.
‖ Moelwyn-Hughes and Hinshelwood, *J. Chem. Soc.*, 1932, 230.
** Winkler and Hinshelwood, *Trans. Faraday Soc.*, 1935, **31**, 1739.
†† Bell and Burnett, ibid., 1939, **35**, 474.
‡‡ Stewart and Edlund, *J. Amer. Chem. Soc.*, 1923, **45**, 1014.

with paraffin wax the reaction is very slow, but when stearic acid and other polar substances are used much more rapid.*

(b) The Influence of Solvents.

The phenomenon of solubility shows that, in general, molecules are likely to exert influences on one another. Indeed, whenever two molecules approach to within a molecular diameter of one another there must be an appreciable modification of the potential-energy curves of each. Thus we should expect catalytic influences to be very general. For the change in the potential-energy curves must reflect itself in some change in the activation energies of reactions which the disturbed molecule might be undergoing. In gases, however, these effects are not commonly perceptible, because the disturbances are only exercised during the very short period for which the foreign molecule is within a distance of the order of a molecular diameter of the reacting molecule. Thus for the catalytic effect to be appreciable the lowering of the activation energy must be great enough to outweigh the improbability of the necessary encounter. In solutions the state of affairs is quite different: there are nearly always molecules of the solvent within reach of the reacting molecules. The first effect one might expect is, therefore, that appropriate solvents should change the activation energy considerably. This is certainly found. Fig. 31 shows an example: the variation of E for the reaction between pyridine and methyl iodide in a series of mixed solvents.

When E changes as a result of changing the solvent, PZ of the reaction velocity equation usually changes concurrently (page 257). The total change in PZ can be analysed into two parts, one bearing a close functional relation to the change in E itself, the other independent of E.

Superimposed on the correlation with the change of E itself there is a general tendency for P to be greater in more polar solvents. This factor seems itself to be composite and probably depends partly on an actual increase in Z in the more polar solvents, and partly on an action of the latter in stabilizing the products of certain reactions. The increase in Z would be due to the kind of extrusion of solute molecules from the structural pattern of the solvent, an effect which was mentioned on page 19. The stabilization effect will only be in evidence in reactions, such as the formation of quaternary ammonium salts, where the product is a highly polar substance, and where the transition complex

* Norrish, J. Chem. Soc., 1923, **123**, 3006.

will have a great tendency to relapse into its original components unless a polar environment is provided to fix it. If much reversion occurs, P will be small. Hence the increase of P with polarity of solvent.

The interactions of solvent and solute are often spoken of as solvation: in the light of modern views on liquids, it is probably best to

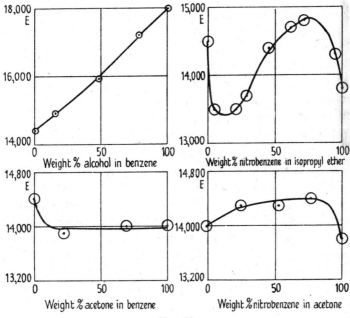

FIG. 31.

regard solvation as a fitting of solvent and solute molecules into a common structural pattern. The adaptation of the reactants to this pattern may be better than that of the products or vice versa; in the first case one would say that the reaction was contingent upon desolvation, and in the latter that it involved an increase in solvation.

Another way in which the solvent may be concerned is in modifying the time during which two reacting molecules in a bimolecular reaction are held more or less in contact, that is, modifying the collision time. In all but rather simple reactions internal redistributions of energy must occur before the chemical transformation can complete itself. If the molecules part company again too quickly, the reaction will not occur.

In this connexion reference may be made to the influence of hydrostatic pressure on the rate of reactions in solution.* It appears that

* Gibson, Fawcett, and Perrin, *Proc. Roy. Soc.*, A, 1935, **150**, 223; Williams, Perrin, and Gibson, ibid., A, 1936, **154**, 684; Perrin and Williams, ibid., A, 1937, **159**, 162.

pressures of several thousand atmospheres produce very great increases in P in bimolecular reactions, such as the formation of quaternary ammonium salts, where the value of P is initially small: much smaller increases in reactions which initially have larger values of P, and no increase, or even decreases, with unimolecular reactions.

Reactions of Solids.*

The interaction of two solids is determined by the mechanisms available for bringing the different kinds of molecule into contact, and is hardly a problem of chemical kinetics at all. The decomposition of a single solid is, however, a phenomenon with well-defined kinetic characteristics.

It is not usual for the reaction product to form solid solutions to an appreciable extent with the reactant: this means that the molecules or ions of the product are more stable when placed in their own space lattice than when uniformly disseminated among the molecules or ions of the initial substance. Consequently, the chemical reaction can take place more easily, that is, with a lower activation energy, if there is ready formed some of the lattice of the product to which fresh elements can attach themselves. The result of this is that solid reactions usually spread from nuclei. The formation of the initial nuclei is an independent process requiring a higher activation energy than the subsequent growth. The reaction proceeds by the advance of the newly formed crystal face through the unchanged material. The nuclei can be poisoned and prevented from growing by the action of foreign substances: for example, the silver nuclei from which the reaction†

$$Ag_2C_2O_4 = 2Ag + 2CO_2$$

spreads are poisoned by oxygen. As the chemical change proceeds, the extent of the interface between the original substance and the reaction product changes and the rate of reaction thus varies in a complex fashion. The shape of the curve representing the extent of reaction as a function of time depends upon the rate at which fresh nuclei are formed relative to the rate of growth of existing nuclei. When the change spreads from a limited number of nuclei for each particle of the solid, the rate increases with time and then passes through a maximum

* See e.g. Smith and Topley, *Proc. Roy. Soc.*, A, 1931, **134**, 224; Spencer and Topley, *J. Chem. Soc.*, 1929, 2633; Topley and Hume, *Proc. Roy. Soc.*, A, 1928, **120**, 211; Bradley, Colvin, and Hume, ibid., A, 1932, **137**, 531; Topley, ibid., A, 1932, **136**, 413; and also the papers in *Trans. Faraday Soc.*, 1938, **34**, 822–1084, where references will be found to the numerous papers of Garner and others on the subject.

† Macdonald, *J. Chem. Soc.*, 1936, 832, 839.

giving rise to a typical S-shaped curve for the amount of reaction against time. By careful analysis of these curves conclusions can be drawn about the rate of advance of the crystal face, and also about the kind of nucleation processes which occur.

The Temperature-independent Factor of the Reaction Velocity Equation

(a) Bimolecular Reactions.

To a high degree of approximation the rate of reaction, as we have seen, is represented by the equation

$$\text{number of molecules reacting} = PZe^{-E/RT},$$

Z being the collision number and P a factor independent of temperature except for second-order differences.

At an early stage the study of gas reactions revealed the existence of a considerable number of cases where P approached unity, thus defining a sort of standard of behaviour where activation is not only a necessary but also a sufficient condition for reaction. But this simple type of behaviour is by no means general, a fact which early became evident in the investigation of the first-order decompositions of organic molecules.

Even with bimolecular reactions Christiansen* pointed out that in solution there are a number of reactions for which P is much less than unity. At first there was some disposition to regard this state of affairs as characteristic of the liquid as distinct from the gaseous state. But this idea was dispelled in two ways: first, by comparison of gas reactions with the corresponding reactions in solution to which reference has already been made; and secondly, by the fact that there are many reactions in solution where P may approach unity.† These latter are usually reactions in which one of the reactants is a simple ion such as hydroxyl.‡

For a time it then seemed possible that reactions might fall into two classes, roughly describable as 'slow' and 'fast', and determined by the presence or absence of some special factor, such as a quantum-mechanically forbidden electronic transition. But further experiments have not supported this idea: and it now appears that there is a continuous range with P varying from 10^{-8} to unity, and, in rather rare examples, rising above unity.

Fig. 32§ gives an idea of the distribution of P values. The median

* Z. physikal. Chem., 1924, 113, 35.
† Moelwyn-Hughes, Kinetics of Reactions in Solution, Oxford, 1933.
‡ Grant and Hinshelwood, J. Chem. Soc., 1933, 258.
§ Winkler and Hinshelwood, ibid., 1936, 371.

line of each of the Gauss curves gives the mean value of P for the series of reactions indicated by the lettering, and the curves themselves give an idea of the distributions about the mean of the values for different reactions in each series, the ordinates being proportional to the relative numbers with P in various ranges. The distributions indicated are very

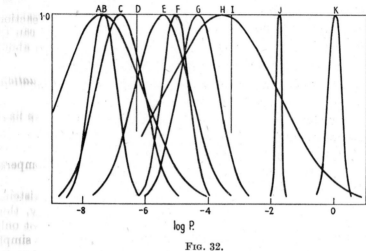

Fig. 32.

rough, since there are not enough results for a real statistical analysis: but the mean values are reliable, and the diagram as a whole illustrates the essential fact that there is a fairly even distribution over the whole spectrum of possible P values.

The series represented are: A, esterification in alcoholic solution, the catalyst being the undissociated molecule of acid; B, benzoylation of aromatic amines; C, quaternary ammonium salt formation in benzene solution; D, interaction of acetic anhydride and alcohol; E, esterification with hydrion as catalyst; F, halogenation of phenolic ethers; G, reaction between trinitroanisol and substituted dimethylanilines; H, oxidation of cyclic compounds by potassium permanganate; I, addition to dienes; J, alkaline hydrolysis of substituted benzoic esters; K, interaction of alkyl halides and negative ions.

Other examples might be added without changing the general effect.

The impression one receives from the study of a large number of bimolecular reactions is that $P = 1$ is a limit reached with certain reactions of a specially simple character, and that, in other reactions, the necessity for the fulfilment of more exacting internal conditions reduces the probability of reaction to a greater or smaller extent. This impression, however, is only partly correct. For one thing, a few reactions, apparently bimolecular, are known where P is greater than 1, for example, the hydrolysis of arylsulphuric acids.* And for another, the following considerations also throw doubt upon the propriety of regarding the limit $P = 1$ as of absolute significance. When a given reaction occurs in a series of different media there is often a functional relation between the various values of P and the corresponding values of E (see page 257). In a number of examples the relation between $\log P$ and $1/E^{\frac{1}{2}}$ is approximately linear: the extrapolation of the lines to $1/E^{\frac{1}{2}} = 0$ gives values of P several powers of 10 greater than unity. Even if values approaching this have not been actually observed, the continuity of the curves suggests that there is no reason in principle why they should not be. The interpretation of these facts will be discussed in a later section.

(b) Unimolecular Reactions.

Since the actual rate of a unimolecular reaction is often quite independent of the collision number, we write $k = \chi e^{-E/RT}$, bearing in mind that, unless there is a chain reaction—to which none of the observations which follow apply—*the collision number must be at least as great as* χ, because the molecules cannot react more rapidly, and indeed for a first-order reaction must react much less rapidly than they are activated by collision. The constant χ can hardly have a unique meaning for all unimolecular reactions, but its order of magnitude is a matter of interest. The problem has been discussed by Polanyi and Wigner† who give the diagram shown in Fig. 33. In spite of such disturbances by chain reactions as may alter the numerical values somewhat, the result is probably a reasonably representative one. It is evident that the value 10^{13} to 10^{14} occurs much more often than any of the others. Polanyi and Wigner in their treatment do not consider how the energy is communicated, but assume a large molecule already containing the necessary energy of activation, and fix their attention on the period between activation and transformation.

They assume the energy to fluctuate in the molecule in elastic waves, and the transformation to occur when, by interference of these waves, the amplitude at one of the linkings between the atoms reaches a critical value. Taking the velocity of propagation of a disturbance across the molecule as of the same order as the velocity of sound, they find that

* Burkhardt, Horrex, and Jenkins, *J. Chem. Soc.*, 1936, 1649.
† *Z. physikal. Chem.*, A, Haberband, 1928, 439.

the order of magnitude of the factor χ should be that of the atomic frequency, which is the order of magnitude required. With regard to what in the last section was called PZ, it is clear that for these unimolecular reactions the collision number must be greater than χ, i.e. greater, on the average, than 10^{13} to 10^{14}. For the bimolecular reactions referred to in the last section, the value $P = 1$ corresponded to

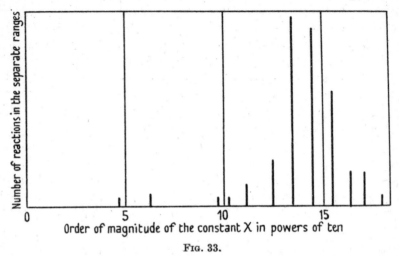

Number of reactions in the separate ranges

Order of magnitude of the constant X in powers of ten

FIG. 33.

$PZ = 10^{11}$ or 10^{12}. Evidently activation rates in unimolecular reactions are, on the average, very much greater—a matter which has already been dealt with in connexion with the reactions of complex molecules (page 78).

(c) The Range of Values of P.

The first important distinction is between bimolecular and unimolecular reactions. In the former, with a few exceptions, PZ varies from 10^{12} downwards, i.e. P from unity downwards; in the latter, χ, which is less than the possible activation rate, is usually greater than 10^{12} and may be considerably greater. To account for the activation rate in unimolecular reactions which are not chain reactions it has been necessary to invoke the internal degrees of freedom. The number of collisions in which the necessary energy can be communicated becomes much greater than $Ze^{-E/RT}$ in this case: and hence χ may be—though it is not absolutely necessary for it to be—large. Once a complex molecule has the necessary energy inside it, there is an interval corresponding to the time between collisions for the flow of this energy to the appropriate part of the molecule. Consequently the energy in the large number of internal degrees of freedom becomes available, and χ may be large. If, formally, we write $\chi = PZ$, then, in this sense, P is large also, though this does not mean that the actual probability is large. It only means that there is a large proportion of the molecules compared with $e^{-E/RT}$ which count as active.

In bimolecular reactions, on the other hand, *any complex conditions which have to be fulfilled must in general be satisfied at the moment of encounter, since the molecules part again in a time very short indeed compared with that available in a unimolecular reaction. Hence we find that, as a rule, P is unity or less.*

We come now to those bimolecular reactions where P is actually greater than unity (or where there are indications that under appropriate conditions P might become greater than unity).

The natural course is to interpret them on the same lines as unimolecular reactions by supposing that in special cases the duration of the collisions is long enough for quite complicated internal redistributions of energy to occur: in these circumstances the internal degrees of freedom may contribute to the activation rate. There may be an actual complex formation between the two reactants: or merely a mutual influence which leads to a collision of abnormal duration. According to either view we are virtually dealing no longer with a bimolecular reaction, but with a unimolecular reaction of a substance whose concentration happens to be proportional to the product of the concentrations of two other substances. Therefore, what we measure is not so much PZ as χ.

From the point of view of the transition state theory one must suppose that in these reactions the activated state is a more probable one than normally because, as Polanyi expresses it, the mobility of some parts of the molecule is greater in the transition complex than it is in the initial state. This means that there are more factors than normally in the numerator of the expression for K (page 235) and a correspondingly increased reaction rate. Here we are dealing direct with χ. PZ must be at least great enough to render possible the occurrences thus envisaged. Hence the need for the extra degrees of freedom. In a solution these are always available, even if only when the aid of adjacent solvent molecules is enlisted.

Functional Relation between the Constants of the Arrhenius Equation.

In the reaction-velocity equations $k = PZe^{-E/RT}$ and $k = \chi e^{-E/RT}$ the constants PZ or χ and E, instead of being independent, have sometimes been found to exhibit a correlation, PZ or χ increasing with E through a series of reactions. In the discussion it will be enough to refer to PZ.

The correlation of P and E would, of course, have no significance if the data examined related only to reactions selected for study because they proceed at conveniently measurable rates in a given temperature interval. Even if any value of P could occur with any value of E, only those reactions would have been chosen for experiment in which the values of P and E so compensated one another as to give what was considered the convenient rate.

There is also doubt about the reality of the correlations when data of unspecified accuracy are used: $\log PZ$ is calculated by adding $\log k$ to E/RT; E is less accurately measurable than $\log k$. If E has been overestimated, then the value of $\log PZ$ will be correspondingly too large. But numerous studies are now available where there is no question of selection of the data, and little doubt that their accuracy is quite sufficient to establish the reality of the correlation.

It is usually expressed as a linear relation between the *logarithm* of PZ and the activation energy itself. The logarithmic form is essential, but any simple *algebraic* function of the activation energy will usually do as well, over a limited range, as E itself.

Some good examples of this correlation appear when we pass through a series of mixed or pure solvents of approximately the same polarity. Such examples are found with ester hydrolysis or with quaternary ammonium salt formation in various mixtures of water, acetone, and alcohol, where large changes in E are correlated simply with the changes in $\log PZ$.

Examples of the following kinds have from time to time been noted: heterogeneous reactions;[*] unimolecular reactions in different solvents, e.g. decomposition of acetonedicarboxylic acid,[†] and the rearrangement of triazoles;[‡] unimolecular reactions of series of related compounds such as substituted malonic acids[§] and other carboxylic acids;[||] bimolecular reactions such as the formation of allylpyridinium bromide in different solvents,[**] esterification of acids in different alcohols,[††] formation of sulphonium salts in different solvents;[‡‡] hydrolysis of different aryl-

[*] See Storch, *J. Amer. Chem. Soc.*, 1935, **57**, 1395.
[†] Wiig, *J. Physical Chem.*, 1928, **32**, 961.   [‡] Dimroth, *Annalen*, 1910, **373**, 367.
[§] Bernoulli and Wege, *Helv. Chim. Acta*, 1919, **2**, 511.
[||] Fairclough, *J. Chem. Soc.*, 1938, 1186.   [**] Hawkins, ibid., 1922, **121**, 1170.
[††] Hinshelwood and Legard, ibid., 1935, 587.
[‡‡] Syrkin and Gladischev, *Acta Physicochim. U.R.S.S.*, 1935, **2**, 291.

sulphuric acids in water.* The most conspicuous examples are, however, perhaps those in which for a given reaction the medium is subjected to a continuous variation (see Fig. 34).

On the whole, variation of the reactants, by substituent groups for
example, more often leaves PZ constant. It seems clear that the basis

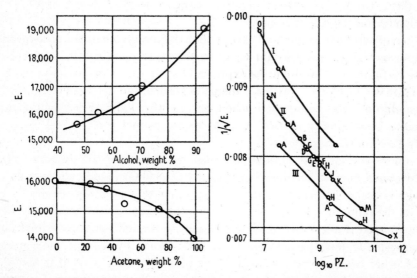

FIG. 34. I, Alkaline hydrolysis of methyl acetate. II, Alkaline hydrolysis of éthyl
benzoate. III, Formation of methylpyridinium iodide. IV, Hydrolysis of ethyl bromide.
Relation between log PZ and a simple algebraic function of E. If log PZ were plotted
against E itself the degree of approximation to a linear relation over the range shown
would be about the same. The curves on the left are given to show the actual range
of variation in E itself for various alcohol-water and alcohol-acetone-water mixtures.
The letters refer to solvents: A to H contain a constant proportion of water with a
varying ratio of alcohol to acetone (all have approximately the same dielectric constant); G to M are alcohol-water mixtures; N is a dioxan-water mixture and O is water.

of the correlation must be a very general one, but involve factors of
a kind which, in a given example, may or may not be operative.

With regard to the interpretation of this relation, perhaps the most
general form of argument which can be used is as follows.

We imagine a reaction to take place under some ideal standard
conditions where the activation energy is E and the probability factor
is P. Now let the conditions be changed so that the value of E is
lowered. The lowering of E is due either to the effect of one single
factor or to the simultaneous co-operation of a number of factors. It
is in the latter case that the correlation is to be expected. For each

* Burkhardt, Horrex, and Jenkins, *J. Chem. Soc.*, 1936, 1649.

factor can be thought of as reducing E by an amount e, and if n factors co-operate the change is given by $\Delta E = ne$. But the chance that each of these factors is favourable at the moment of activation is less than unity, so that for n of them to be favourable at once the probability of reaction will be reduced in the ratio $P'/P = p^n$, where p is less than unity. Taking logarithms and eliminating n, we find that E and $\log P$ change in a parallel manner.

In general one might well expect that the more violent the activation process the less need would there be for other more subtle conditions to be fulfilled. This might be expressed by the following analogy: when a safe is opened by a key little energy is needed, but precise geometrical conditions must be satisfied: when, on the other hand, it is blown open, much more energy is used, but the exact geometry of its lock ceases to be of much importance.

More special explanations can also be suggested. In unimolecular reactions, such as the decarboxylation of the ions of acids, the mechanism is probably such that the activation energy is mainly required for the breaking of a bond. And it is possible that reaction may only be completed if a number of factors ensure to the activated molecules an abnormally long period free from disturbance by solvent molecules. In other cases also the activated complex may only react if it has an abnormally long life which allows time for appropriate internal energy redistributions to follow the activating collision.*

Suppose the average time which elapses between the formation of the activated complex and the reversal of this process be θ. In the majority of cases the attainment of the right phase for reaction may demand a longer time than this, which we call t, and no reaction occurs. The chance that the activated complex survives for this time is, according to well-established principles,

$$W = e^{-t/\theta}. \qquad (1)$$

t is the time required for the completion of a certain fraction of the complete period of a complex internal motion, which in general will involve a considerable number, n, of cycles of vibration of one of the reacting bonds. If the frequency of the latter is ν, $t = n/\nu$. Thus the probability of reaction is proportional to $e^{-n/\nu\theta}$.

If the structure of the molecules remains constant but the bond strengths are changed by substitution, or by the influence of the medium, ν will vary, and E, the activation energy, will vary also. On

---

* Fairclough and Hinshelwood, *J. Chem. Soc.*, 1937, 538.

the whole, if bond strengths increase, both ν and E will increase together. If we write $\nu = f(E)$, then the rate of reaction becomes

$$k = A\,e^{-n/\theta f(E)}e^{-E/RT},$$

whence

$$\log k = \log A - n/\theta f(E) - E/RT = \log PZ - E/RT,$$

whence

$$\log PZ = \text{constant} - n/\theta f(E).$$

When changes in E are small compared with $f(E)$, this approximates to

$$\Delta \log PZ = B\,\Delta E,$$

where B is a constant.

Only when t is appreciably greater than θ in equation (1) should the correlation between PZ and E be observable. When t is much less than θ, equation (1) approximates to $W = 1$, and PZ is no longer dependent upon E. Thus two main types of behaviour are to be expected. The factors making for a large value of θ, and therefore for a constant P, are the formation of a fairly stable collision complex, infrequency of collisions which might deactivate the complex, and poor energy transfer in such potentially deactivating collisions. On the other hand, simplicity of the reacting system tends to diminish t, which has the same result as increasing θ.

The exact relation between E and the frequency is difficult to determine and is of no great importance. If E is set proportional to the force constant of the link it works out that $\log PZ$ should vary as $1/E^{\frac{1}{2}}$, but no great significance can be attached to this precise form. Usually the changes in E are not great enough to decide empirically between different simple algebraic forms. The essential part is the *logarithmic* nature of the relation: and the ultimate statistical basis of this is the same in the present special as in the more general discussion above: it arises from the assumption that reaction depends upon a number of rarely fulfilled conditions—in the present example an abnormally long life of the active complex which in turn has to be ensured by the co-operation of a number of favourable factors in the solution.

In a reversible reaction, the influence of the life of the activated complex would act equally on the two opposing changes. On the other hand, influences depending upon solvation, or the pattern formed by' the solvent molecules in the transition state, could act preferentially on the forward or on the reverse reaction. Long ago, van 't Hoff pointed out that the effect of solvents on reaction velocity should be analysed into two parts, one which changes the velocity of both opposing reactions in the same ratio and another which, by changing one velocity more than the other, leads to the well-known shift of equilibrium, expressed in the van 't Hoff-Dimroth solubility relation.*

The Logarithmic Relation between the Velocity Constants of Related Series of Reactions.

If we have two series of reactions with velocity constants k_1^a, k_1^b,... and k_2^a, k_2^b,..., all members of series 1 and all members of series 2 respectively being chemically analogous among themselves, and the members a, b,... of a given series differing in the structure of one or other of the reactants or in the substituents present, then there is often found a relation of the following form:†

$$\log k_1 = \alpha \log k_2 + \text{const.,} \tag{1}$$

where α is the same for all the members of the series a, b,.... For example, such a relation may be found by plotting the logarithm of the velocity constant for the hydrolysis of benzoic esters with a series of nuclear substituents against $\log k$ for the benzoylation of aromatic amines with the same series of substituents.

Another form which the relation may take is

$$\log k = \alpha \log K + \text{const.,}$$

where $\log k$ refers to the velocity constant of a reaction and $\log K$ to the equilibrium constant of another reaction in which one of the reactants can participate. The best known example of this kind is the Brønsted relation between the catalytic coefficient for the action of a series of acids on a given substrate and the dissociation constants in water of the same series of acids.

Writing the reaction rate in the form

$$\log k = \log PZ - E/RT,$$

for variations among members of a given series, we have

$$\Delta \log k = \Delta \log PZ - \Delta E/RT.$$

Two cases arise. In the simplest, PZ is constant for a given series, and equation (1) only requires $\Delta E_1 = \alpha \Delta E_2$. Since PZ often remains nearly constant through a series, this case is of some importance. Suppose we are studying the effect of the same series of substituents on two reactions. Let us suppose schematically that one particular bond in each type of molecule is principally influenced by the substituents, their effect on the rest of the molecule being in the first approximation

---

* van 't Hoff, *Lectures.*
† See Hammett, *Chem. Reviews*, 1935, **17**, 125.

negligible for the purpose of the reaction. If in one case the bond in question is a strong one requiring considerable activation while in the other case it is very weak or requires no activation, we may evidently have ΔE_2 finite but ΔE_1 nearly equal to zero, i.e. $\alpha = 0$. At the other extreme we shall have the bond of approximately equal strength and requiring the same amount of activation in each reaction and $\Delta E_1 = \Delta E_2$ with $\alpha = 1$. In between we shall have fractional values of α. The condition that the fractional value shall be a constant for the series is that the effect of the substituent on the bond strength shall not be an absolute magnitude but one proportional to the original strength of the bond. Alternatively, we may suppose that ΔE_1 is much smaller than ΔE_2 because the effect of the substituent is not wholly transmitted to the part of the molecule where it will influence the activation energy; in this case we must assume, in order to arrive at a constant α, that a constant fraction of the maximum effect is transmitted for all members of the series.

Substituent	Alkaline hydrolysis of benzoic esters in 85% alcohol	Benzoylation of nuclear-substituted anilines	Benzoylation of aniline with substituted benzoyl chlorides
Me . .	18,200	6,800	7,800
H . . .	17,700	7,350	7,350
NO_2 . .	14,500	11,800	5,900
Cl . .	16,800	7,600	7,000

The above table gives the activation energies for three reactions influenced by para-substituents in the benzene nucleus. Fig. 35 shows that the variations in activation energy may well be nearly proportional to one another, and that the values of ΔE decrease in the order: substituted amines, esters, substituted acid chlorides. This may well be due to the fact that the transmission of the effect of the substituent is less efficient in the case of the amines than with the esters, while with the acid chlorides the effect is produced in a molecule which does not in any case need much activation, most being required in the other reaction partner.

When PZ varies considerably in the series of reactions, the matter is more complicated. In order to preserve relation (1) we most simply assume that $\Delta \log P_1 Z_1 = \alpha \Delta \log P_2 Z_2$. There are examples where, in a series of reactions, $\log PZ$ increases linearly with E, so that

$$\Delta \log P_1 Z_1 = \rho_1 \Delta E_1 \quad \text{and} \quad \Delta \log P_2 Z_2 = \rho_2 \Delta E_2,$$

and we now have $\rho_1 = \rho_2$. In other words, the factor which makes PZ increase with E must be one operating equally in the case of both series of reactions. In many cases ρ tends to zero, and it must of course be remembered that the smaller ρ, the less accurately need $\rho_1 = \rho_2$ for relation (1) to be fairly well obeyed. An interesting special case must be mentioned here. At least one example is known in which there are rather irregular, though not very marked, variations in PZ in a series of basic catalyses, while the Brønsted relation is obeyed with great

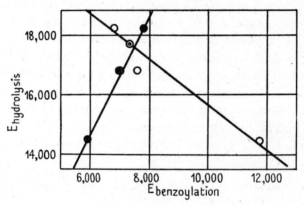

FIG. 35.

accuracy. The deviations of PZ from constancy seem, therefore, to be due to a factor which has equal effects on the dissociation of an acid and on its catalytic power. An abnormally great PZ for a given acid of the series means that the reaction goes more easily than we should expect from the activation energy. Since the Brønsted relation is obeyed, we infer that that same acid also has an abnormally great tendency to give up a proton to water. If we attribute any anomalous behaviour to that part of the reaction mechanism connected with the giving up of the proton, rather than to any other kind of activation of the reaction partner, then we can see how the anomaly may show itself in the (P, E) relation while not appearing in the Brønsted relation.

From the point of view of the transition state theory, the matter may be looked at as follows.* If K is an equilibrium constant, $\log K$ is proportional to the free energy of the reaction, and analogously $\log k$ can be regarded as proportional to the free energy of the reaction by which the reactants pass to the transition state. By introducing the thermodynamic equation $d \log k/d\chi = (\beta_1 - \beta_2)/RT$, where β is the differential coefficient of the free energy with respect to some variable χ, the experimental relations referred to above can be connected with the

* See Evans, *Trans. Faraday Soc.*, 1938, **34**, 49.

thermodynamic properties of the transition state by a simple algebraical elimination.

To account for the linear logarithmic relations one has to assume first, that all the various β's are constants, and secondly, that if the influence of change in structure or substituents is represented by a parameter χ, then the ratio (χ for reaction 1)/(χ for reaction 2) is a constant for all the members a, b,... of the series. In other words, we can translate the experimental relationship into a statement of the kind that certain quantities, formally similar to ordinary thermo-dynamic quantities, maintain a constant ratio throughout a series.

In this way it may prove possible to build up a useful body of empirical information about transition states.

Quantum-mechanical Theories of the Probability of Spontaneous Molecular Transformation.

According to one view developed in the foregoing pages, in a uni-molecular reaction there is a supply of activated molecules, maintained by collision, and there is a definite probability that a molecule will undergo transition before losing its energy. This probability may or may not be a continuous function of the excess of energy possessed by the molecule over and above the minimum required for 'activation'. According to quantum-mechanical theories the probability might be a continuous function of the energy content over the whole range of values, with no sharp threshold of activation. But according to all theories the vast *majority* of the molecules which are transformed possess energies in a narrow range in the neighbourhood of the energy of activation. The probability of transition of these molecules is found experimentally to be such that the time elapsing between activation, 'classically' regarded, and transformation is of the same order of magnitude as the 'period of revolution of an electron in its orbit'. Polanyi and Wigner arrived at this same numerical value by a theory based upon the interference of elastic waves in the molecule, leading to a concentration of energy at a particular point. Attempts have been made to treat the problem by the application of quantum-mechanical considerations. The results are not very definite, but the principles involved are interesting.

All the attempts are adaptations of the Gamow theory* of radio-active disintegration, or of the wave-mechanical theory of 'radiationless transfers' of electrons.† It is first necessary to explain these theories

* Gamow, *Z. Physik*, 1928, **51**, 204.
† Wentzel, *Physikal. Z.*, 1928, **29**, 321; *Z. Physik*, 1927, **43**, 524.

sufficiently to show the chemical analogies. First, with regard to the question of nuclear disintegration: inside an atomic nucleus an α-particle must be under the influence of an attractive force, since nuclei in general are in fact stable. Outside the nucleus it suffers a repulsion, which is in accordance with Coulomb's law when the distance from the centre of the nucleus is greater than about 10^{-12} cm. Yet, after escaping from a nucleus, the α-particle is found not to possess the kinetic energy which it should if the repulsive forces had acted on it from the point where they begin to be effective. This is expressed by saying that the α-particles 'leak through' the potential barrier surrounding the nucleus. In the wave-mechanical treatment of the matter, we take a rather idealized form of potential barrier, and write down the equations expressing the amplitude of the wave function (the square of whose absolute magnitude gives the relative number of α-particles in an element of volume) for three regions: viz. inside the nucleus, in the barrier itself, and outside the nucleus. These equations involve the potential energy of the particle in the various regions. Then in a way somewhat analogous to Fresnel's treatment of reflection and refraction of light, the condition is written down that the wave function and its differential coefficient shall be continuous at the two boundaries. In this way we find the amplitude of the wave outside the nucleus, which determines the probability of escape of the α-particle. It must be remarked that the wave-mechanical treatment does not explain *why* an α-particle can escape from a region which it could not possibly leave in a 'classical' manner: being a statistical method of calculation using continuous equations, it automatically provides for a certain concentration of α-particles outside the nucleus and then determines a value for this concentration. The important success of the theory is that it gives the Geiger-Nuttall law for the relation between the energy of the particle and its rate of escape, and moreover, with the numerical coefficients approximately correct.

If we are prepared to admit that the transformation of an activated molecule is analogous to the disintegration of a nucleus, an analogous treatment becomes possible.* The actual probability of transformation cannot be satisfactorily estimated, but the interesting possibility arises that, just as those radioactive changes occur most rapidly which give α-particles of the greatest energy, so those unimolecular reactions which

    * Roginsky and Rosenkewitsch, *Z. physikal. Chem.*, B, 1930, **10**, 47, where references to the work of Bourgin, Oppenheimer, and Langer are also given. Compare also remarks by O. K. Rice, *Phys. Rev.*, II, 1929, **34**, 1451.

are most exothermic should have the greatest values of the constant χ in the equation $k = \chi e^{-E/RT}$.

But there is no particularly good ground for assuming that the chemical changes of an activated molecule are really at all similar to a radioactive decay. The analogy of a 'radiationless transfer' of an electronic system to a state of equal energy is perhaps closer. To understand the wave mechanics of this we must again rid our minds of the idea that we are giving individual attention to any member of an assemblage: the equations refer to the assemblage itself. Suppose, for simplicity, that we have a molecule AB capable of splitting up into A and B. Before and after the transformation the parts A and B can be thought of as possessing definite total energies. If letters with dashes refer to the final state, $E_A + E_B = E_{A'} + E_{B'}$. Now consider an assemblage of AB molecules. Its behaviour is described by a wave function with a frequency obtained by dividing $E_A + E_B$ by h. The assemblage of transformed molecules has a wave function with the same frequency (by the conservation of energy). Thus, even if the amplitude of its wave function is initially zero, it will grow by *resonance*. The rate of change of amplitude determines the probability of the individual transformations. Such a treatment has been successfully applied to the Auger effect (transfer of an electron to a new orbit with simultaneous ejection from the atom of a second electron). In their application of the method to a chemical reaction, Roginsky and Rosenkewitsch deduce as a positive consequence that, in the equation $k = \chi e^{-E/RT}$, the logarithm of the constant χ should be proportional to $(Q-E)/\sqrt{E}$, where Q is the heat of reaction. (The signs are such that the absolute values of Q and E are added for exothermic reactions.) This result is similar to that inferred from the assumed applicability of some analogue of the Geiger-Nuttall law to chemical reactions.

The experimental evidence is very doubtful. Unimolecular reactions of sufficiently varied heat of reaction are scarcely known. Roginsky and Rosenkewitsch consider the general balance of evidence in favour of such a relation, but this evidence is not at all convincing.*

While quantum mechanics opens up the possibility that changes may occur in which passage over an energy barrier can in principle be avoided, it also turns out that the probability of such transitions is

---

* For example, in Fig. 5 of their paper, referring to unimolecular gas reactions, there are 8 points, through which two straight lines are drawn. The point relating to Dienger's reaction should not be included, since the reaction is almost certainly not a homogeneous change at all. When this is omitted the remaining points appear almost randomly grouped about a mean.

very small when the energy barrier is high, and that the classical idea of passage over the energy barrier is for all practical purposes quite valid. It very definitely appears that in most reactions the molecules do not react unless they have the requisite energy of activation. And indeed the whole of the coherent body of chemical evidence showing the dependence of rate on heat of activation, the possibility in many cases of calculating the rate correctly, and the success of the recent calculations of the energy of activation itself go to show that the quantum-mechanical leakage effect need not generally be invoked in explaining rates of reaction. Indeed, it appears theoretically that in the case of a bimolecular reaction in the gas phase the probability of the leakage is negligible during the time of a collision.

In general, quantum-mechanical formulae for the rate of 'penetration of potential barriers' contain an exponential term involving the mass of the particle. (The mass comes in from the original Schrödinger equation: or, what amounts to the same thing, from the expression $\lambda = h/mv$ for the 'wave-length' of the particle.) The result is that 'non-classical transitions' are much easier for particles of small mass than for particles of large mass. For transitions of *electrons* they become of predominating importance. With atoms and molecules behaviour approximates more to the classical. In the case of chemical reactions involving the transfer of particles not heavier than a proton or hydrogen atom, Bell has shown that the deviation from classical behaviour may possibly be considerable at low temperatures, while with heavier particles it is almost negligible.

Conclusion.

The impression produced by the foregoing chapters is probably one of diversity rather than of unity: and this impression would only have been greater had it been possible to follow up the ramifications of fact and theory which almost every detail of the subject now presents.

The real unities underlying the interpretation of chemical changes are seldom open and apparent but tangled in a confusion which here and there might well appear inextricable, did not a broader view reveal that through the tangle run certain threads bright enough to show a plan.

The strongest and brightest of these threads is the idea of the activation energy. All molecules are at least relatively stable entities: and before they can be rearranged to yield other atomic patterns they must suffer to a greater or lesser extent some kind of preliminary dislocation.

For this they require energy which, in general, they have no means of acquiring save by the hazards of molecular collisions. Only when the chance of acquiring it becomes appreciable does a chemical reaction attain an observable rate. This chance is an exponential function of E/RT, the form depending, first, upon the fact that exceptional molecules arise by the fortuitous concurrence of many favourable factors, and, secondly, upon the very definition of the quantity e as the limiting value of a function which enters materially into calculations of chance.

The exponential relation makes the activation energy the most important single factor determining reaction velocity: it defines the law of temperature variation, and largely governs the way in which changes of structure or the presence of substituents or of foreign molecules modify reaction velocity. An early optimism almost led to the belief that the presence of the activation energy in molecules was a sufficient as well as a necessary condition for reaction.

Molecular encounters, however, are but fleeting: and therefore we find that where two molecules, or more, associate or interact, even when they are activated, the chance that the right conditions are fulfilled in other ways is, in general, small and variable, though for quite simple systems it may be high. When, on the other hand, a single molecule decomposes, it is left free for a relatively long time after activation and may mobilize energy scattered in its different parts, an advantage of which dissociation reactions make full use but in varying degrees.

The domination of the activation energy is opposed by other potent influences. Often the initial dislocation of one of the molecules concerned in a reaction goes to the limit of complete resolution into atoms or free radicals, which, once produced, propagate long chains; and this means that the reaction velocity may be a good deal greater than would have been expected from energy considerations alone. Not infrequently it seems that a chain reaction and a non-chain reaction may compete on more or less equal terms: in the one there is an easy primary process without any catastrophic consequences; in the other, a much more difficult primary process, the effect of which is magnified by numerous secondary processes following inevitably in its train. These secondary processes can be of complex and varied nature, and this fact is responsible for whole chapters of complicated chemistry.

Another factor which tends to limit the influence of the activation energy is the following: to achieve a given end a lot of energy may be employed in a simple way—for example, by splitting one of the reacting molecules into atoms; or a smaller amount of energy may be used in a more subtly planned manner, as where suitable conditions are fulfilled simultaneously at several points of the pattern of reacting molecules. Here the energy conditions require a more or less complex co-operation of others. One of the results of this is that mechanisms of which one alone, from the purely energetic point of view, might have predominated, compete on more nearly equal terms. Sometimes, in consequence, we find series of chemically similar reactions following what appear to be strangely contrasted kinetic laws. And sometimes we find, for a given reaction, simultaneous mechanisms, the relative preponderance of which changes with comparatively small variations in the conditions. A somewhat similar blurring of the clear-cut energy relationships occurs when there is a different probability of decomposition for molecules in different energy states, and we may find a whole spectrum, as it were, of activation energies contributing to an observed reaction.

Alternative and competing mechanisms play a great part in chemical kinetics generally and give rise to great complexity. If the spontaneous processes of nature be described in terms of the thermodynamic idea of a descent of energy to lower levels of availability, then we must agree that it does not flow in one placid stream, but rather resembles the water of a mountain lake lashed by the wind to overflow its rocky margin in many tortuous rivulets. The true unity and simplicity is only to be found in the statistical principles according to which the whole intricate system evolves.

INDEX

PRINTED IN
GREAT BRITAIN
AT THE
UNIVERSITY PRESS
OXFORD
BY
CHARLES BATEY
PRINTER
TO THE
UNIVERSITY